TEST ITEMS
AND
INTERACTIVE ELECTRONIC STUDY GUIDE QUESTIONS

FOR STARR'S

B I O L O G Y
Concepts and Applications

SECOND EDITION

LARRY G. SELLERS
Louisiana Tech University

DAVID J. COTTER
Georgia College

KENDALL CORBIN
University of Minnesota

JOHN D. JACKSON
North Hennepin Community College

ALLEN REICH
Harvard University

JANE B. TAYLOR
Northern Virginia Community College

TOMMY E. WYNN
North Carolina State University

Wadsworth Publishing Company
Belmont, California
A Division of Wadsworth, Inc.

D1294388

SUPPLEMENTS PACKAGE

This information appears only in instructors' examination copies.

FOR LECTURES

Instructor's Resource Manual—hundreds of lecture and lab enrichment ideas and other aids

Lecture Outlines on Electronic Disk—IBM, Mac

HyperCard Stacks and Toolbook that correlate the text to all videodiscs

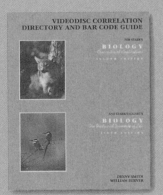

Videodisc Correlation Directory and Bar Code Guide for three general biology videodiscs

Text-specific videodisc with drawings from text in step-by-step format, with some fully animated; new films, interviews; photographic stills

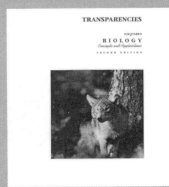

Transparencies—500 illustrations

Slides—250 illustrations

Photo CD—all text drawings on CD-ROM

FOR TESTING

Test Items and Interactive Electronic Study Guide Questions—5000 test items, many conceptual

Test Items on Electronic Disk—IBM, Mac. Also on WordPerfect for DOS, Microsoft Word for Mac

Learning Objectives on Electronic Disk—IBM, Mac

FOR THE LABORATORY

Four-color Laboratory Manual with 600 full-color drawings and photographs

Instructor's Manual for the Laboratory Manual—detailed suggestions for lab preps and other aids

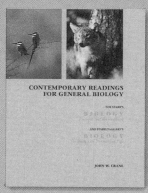

**Study Guide and Workbook:
An Interactive Approach**

**Electronic Study Guide with
on-screen explanations for
right and wrong answers—
IBM, Mac**

**Contemporary Readings for
General Biology**

**Science and the Human Spirit:
Contexts for Writing and
Learning**

**Critical Thinking Software
Tools and Workbook**

**A Beginner's Guide to
Scientific Method**

The Game of Science

**Answers to End-of-Chapter
Review Questions**

**Environment: Problems
and Solutions**

**Green Lives, Green
Campuses**

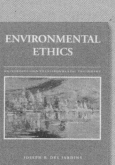

**Flash Cards for 1000
Glossary Terms**

**Environmental
Ethics**

**Watersheds: Classic Cases
in Environmental Ethics**

Cover photo: © Jim Brandenburg—Minden Pictures

International Thomson Publishing
The trademark ITP is used under license.

Printer: Malloy Lithographing, Inc.

Printed in the United States of America

1 2 3 4 5 6 7 8 9 10—98 97 96 95 94

ISBN 0-534-17625-9

CONTENTS

PREFACE

The test items and interactive electronic study guide questions in this book accompany Starr's *Biology: Concepts and Applications,* Second Edition.

TEST ITEMS

Several instructors contributed to the test bank, including three who have extensive experience writing questions for the Educational Testing Service. Eight reviewers also contributed valuable suggestions to help eliminate inadvertent ambiguity and to check for possible errors. The test bank represents a consensus of the kind of questions that are most suitable for students.

All questions are ranked according to level of difficulty (E = easy, M = moderate, and D = difficult). Each rank is represented by about a third of the total questions. This book contains more than 3,200 test items, including the following categories:

1. Multiple-choice questions.
2. Matching questions.
3. Classification questions, which use the same group of answers for a series of questions. (On the disk version of the test bank, because of the requirements of the test-generator program, the first question in the set contains the answers for the entire set. In choosing questions, if you choose not to use the first question of a set, you must take care to transfer the list of potential answers to the beginning of the new set.)
4. Select the Exception questions, which require the student to select the exception from four or five given answers.
5. Problems, which appear only in two of the genetics chapters.

Answers are indicated with an asterisk in the margin. We hope you find these questions useful, and we welcome any comments that will help improve them.

INTERACTIVE ELECTRONIC STUDY GUIDE QUESTIONS

When students take multiple-choice exams, they are often not told why a particular answer is correct and are almost never told why a choice is wrong. The Interactive Electronic Study Guide includes this feedback, thus improving the ability of students to learn the material.

This Electronic Study Guide is interactive because students choosing the wrong answer are told the answer is incorrect and why. Students choosing the correct answer are told they are right and information is given to justify the correct choice. On the electronic disk the answers also identify the text reference and topic so that students can refer back to the text for review. The level of understanding necessary to answer the questions varies as does the level of detail being covered. This approach encourages students to completely cover the text and to read the tables, figure legends, and commentaries.

We hope you find this new type of test bank useful and welcome any comments for improvement.

CHAPTER 1
METHODS AND CONCEPTS
IN BIOLOGY

Multiple-Choice Questions

SHARED CHARACTERISTICS OF LIFE

E   1. Which is the smallest unit of life that can exist as a separate entity?
* a. a cell
    b. a molecule
    c. an organ
    d. a population
    e. an ecosystem

E   2. The chemical processes in the living cell are collectively called
    a. adaptation.
    b. homeostasis.
    c. evolution.
    d. respiration.
* e. metabolism.

E   3. During metabolism, ATP (adenosine triphosphate) is an energy source for the following processes:
    a. reproduction and growth
    b. reproduction and maintenance
    c. growth
    d. growth and maintenance
* e. reproduction, growth, and maintenance

E   4. The ability to acquire, store, transfer, or utilize energy is called
    a. biochemistry.
    b. photosynthesis.
* c. metabolism.
    d. respiration.
    e. phosphorylation.

M   5. A fertilized moth egg passes through which stages of development before becoming an adult?
    a. larval
    b. pupal
* c. larval and pupal
    d. larval and reproductive
    e. pupal and reproductive

E   6. The ability to maintain a constant internal environment is
    a. metabolism.
* b. homeostasis.
    c. development.
    d. physiology.
    e. thermoregulation.

E   7. Homeostasis provides what kind of environment?
- a. positive
- * b. constant
- c. limiting
- d. changing
- e. chemical and physical

M   8. The adjective that best describes homeostasis in living organisms is
- a. rigid.
- b. biological.
- * c. dynamic.
- d. chemical.
- e. physical.

E   9. Each cell is able to maintain a constant internal environment. This is called
- a. metabolism.
- * b. homeostasis.
- c. physiology.
- d. adaptation.
- e. evolution.

M   10. About 12 to 24 hours after the last meal, a person's blood sugar level normally varies from 60 to 90 milligrams per 100 milliliters of blood, although it may rise to 130 mg/100 ml after meals high in carbohydrates. That the blood sugar level is maintained within a fairly narrow range despite uneven intake of sugar is due to the body's ability to carry out
- a. adaptation.
- b. inheritance.
- c. metabolism.
- * d. homeostasis.
- e. all of the above

E   11. Hereditary instructions must
- a. be unchanging most of the time.
- b. pass from one generation to the next.
- c. control a large number of different characteristics.
- d. provide for the rare change in instructions.
- * e. all of the above

E   12. A mutation is a change in
- a. homeostasis.
- b. the developmental pattern in an organism.
- c. metabolism.
- * d. hereditary instructions.
- e. the life cycle of an organism.

M   13. All organisms are alike in
- a. their requirements for energy.
- b. their participation in one or more nutrient cycles.
- c. their ultimate dependence on the sun.
- d. their interaction with other forms of life.
- * e. all of the above

LIFE'S DIVERSITY

E   14.   The genus portion of a scientific name when written by hand is
            a.   never capitalized; never underlined.
     *   b.   always underlined; always capitalized.
            c.   always capitalized; never underlined.
            d.   never capitalized; always underlined.
            e.   connected with the species names to form one word.

E   15.   The plural for genus is
            a.   genus.
            b.   geni.
     *   c.   genera.
            d.   genuses.
            e.   genae.

E   16.   Which group includes all of the other groups?
     *   a.   phylum
            b.   order
            c.   family
            d.   genus
            e.   species

E   17.   A scientific name consists of which of the following?
            a.   family name
            b.   genus name
            c.   species
            d.   both a and b
     *   e.   both b and c

M   18.   The least inclusive of the taxonomic categories listed here is
            a.   family.
            b.   phylum.
            c.   class.
            d.   order.
     *   e.   genus.

E   19.   The animals used by Darwin to show variation in domesticated forms were
     *   a.   pigeons.
            b.   chickens.
            c.   pigs.
            d.   dogs.
            e.   cats.

M   20.   The principal point of the Darwin theory of evolution by natural selection was that
            a.   long-term heritable changes in organisms are caused by use and disuse.
            b.   those mutations that adapt an organism to a given environment somehow always arise in the greatest frequency in the organisms that occupy that environment.
            c.   mutations are caused by all sorts of environmental influences.
     *   d.   survival of characteristics in a population depends on competition between organisms, especially between members of the same species.
            e.   all of the above

M 21. Which premise used by Darwin in his theory is incorrectly stated?
   a. More offspring are produced than can survive to reproduce.
   b. Members of populations show heritable variation.
   c. Some varieties have a better chance to survive and reproduce.
 * d. Organisms that possess advantageous traits have a decreased chance of producing offspring.
   e. Some traits become more common because their bearers contribute more offspring to the next generation.

E 22. Members of what kingdom are single cells of considerable internal complexity?
   a. Animalia
 * b. Protista
   c. Fungi
   d. Plantae
   e. Monera

E 23. Members of what kingdom are multicellular producers?
   a. Animalia
   b. Protista
   c. Fungi
 * d. Plantae
   e. Monera

THE NATURE OF BIOLOGICAL INQUIRY

M 24. A scientific principle is a(n)
   a. observable fact of nature.
 * b. synthesis of several explanations of many observations.
   c. scientific statement.
   d. testable hypothesis.
   e. experimental procedure.

M 25. Of the following, which is the first explanation of a problem? It is sometimes called an "educated guess."
   a. principle
   b. law
   c. theory
   d. fact
 * e. hypothesis

E 26. Hypotheses are
   a. often in the form of a statement.
   b. often expressed negatively.
   c. sometimes crude attempts to offer a possible explanation for observations.
   d. testable predictions.
 * e. all of the above

E 27. Which statement is true about observations in the scientific process?
   a. They are made directly.
   b. They are made indirectly.
   c. Special equipment may be necessary.
   d. They may be made with an instrument such as a microscope.
 * e. all of the above

E   28. Who first stated that the earth circled the sun?
   a. Galileo Galilei
 * b. Nicolaus Copernicus
   c. Sir Isaac Newton
   d. Cecie Starr
   e. Johannes Kepler

E   29. In a scientific experiment, conditions that could affect the outcome of the experiment, but do not because they are held constant, are called
   a. independent variables.
   b. dependent variables.
 * c. controlled variables.
   d. statistical variables.
   e. data set.

M   30. To eliminate the influence of uncontrolled variables during experimentation, one should
   a. increase the sampling error as much as possible and suspend judgment.
 * b. establish a control group identical to the experimental group except for the variable being tested.
   c. use inductive reasoning to construct a hypothesis.
   d. make sure the experiments are repeatable.
   e. all of the above

E   31. Which represents the lowest degree of certainty?
 * a. hypothesis
   b. conclusion
   c. fact
   d. principle
   e. theory

E   32. In order to arrive at a solution to a problem, a scientist usually proposes and tests
   a. laws.
   b. theories.
 * c. hypotheses.
   d. principles.
   e. facts.

D   33. Which statement could be considered a scientific principle?
   a. The proportions of the Miss America contestants have been increasing over the last three decades.
   b. Chemistry and physics are more exact sciences than biology.
 * c. Radioactive isotopes can be used as tracers because radioactive isotopes behave the same as other isotopes.
   d. The growth of a plant is faster in a growth chamber than in a greenhouse.
   e. Leaves bend toward the light because they know light is needed to grow.

M   34. The control in an experiment
   a. makes the experiment valid.
   b. is an additional replicate for statistical purposes.
   c. reduces the experimental errors.
   d. minimizes experimental inaccuracy.
 * e. allows a standard of comparison for the experimental group.

D   35. Which statement is false?
         a. It is easier to prove something false than true.
         b. Scientific experiments have limited applications.
         c. Experimental data are valid if they can be repeatedly obtained by the same experiment.
      * d. Scientific conclusions are invalid if any step in the scientific method is omitted.
         e. Good science often uses experimentation.

M   36. An experimenter does all but which of the following?
         a. revises a hypothesis as a result of data collected
      * b. manipulates dependent variables
         c. reviews other research results obtained by other scientists
         d. examines the effects of independent variables
         e. draws conclusions based only on appropriate experimental data

M   37. As a result of experimentation
         a. more hypotheses may be developed.
         b. more questions may be asked.
         c. a new biological principle could emerge.
         d. entire theories may be modified or discarded.
      * e. all of the above

M   38. In an experiment, the control group
         a. is not subjected to experimental error.
         b. is exposed to experimental treatments.
      * c. is maintained under strict laboratory conditions.
         d. is treated exactly the same as the experimental group, except for the one independent variable.
         e. is statistically the most important part of the experiment.

E   39. The choice of whether a particular organism belongs to the experimental group or the control group should be based on
         a. age.
         b. size.
      * c. chance.
         d. designation by the experimenter.
         e. sex.

E   40. The validity of scientific discoveries should be based on
         a. morality.
         b. aesthetics.
         c. philosophy.
         d. economics.
      * e. none of the above

E   41. Science is based on
         a. faith.
         b. authority.
      * c. evidence.
         d. force.
         e. consensus.

M   42. After an experiment is completed and the results are collected, the next step is to
         a. resample the data.
         b. generalize from the conclusion.
         c. randomize the results.
      * d. organize the data.
         e. manipulate the results.

Classification Questions

Answer questions 43–46 by matching the statement to the most appropriate function, process, or trait listed below.

     a. metabolism
     b. reproduction
     c. photosynthesis
     d. growth
     e. homeostasis

M   43. A process found only in plants and some bacteria

E   44. Most organisms exhibit this characteristic that tends to buffer the effects of environmental change

M   45. The capacity to acquire, store, and use energy

E   46. Process in which one generation replaces another

Answers: 43. c   44. e   45. a   46. b

Answer questions 47–54 by matching the statement with the most appropriate kingdom listed below.

     a. Monera
     b. Protista
     c. Plantae
     d. Fungi
     e. Animalia

E   47. Multicellular producers

E   48. Bacteria

M   49. Unicellular organisms of considerable internal complexity

M   50. Multicellular consumers

E   51. First living organisms

M   52. One-celled producers

D   53. Multicelled producers

M   54. Multicelled decomposers

Answers: 47. c   48. a   49. b   50. e   51. a   52. b
               53. c   54. d

Selecting the Exception

E   55. Four of the five answers listed below are necessary characteristics to the life of an individual. Select the exception.
    a. metabolism
    b. homeostasis
    c. development
    d. heredity
 *   e. diversity

E   56. Four of the five answers listed below are aspects of the scientific method. Select the exception.
          a. observation
          b. hypothesis
          c. experimentation
     *   d. philosophy
          e. conclusion

M   57. Four of the five answers listed below are terms associated with the scientific method. Select the exception.
     *   a. fact
          b. theory
          c. principle
          d. law
          e. hypothesis

M   58. Four of the five answers listed below are taxonomic categories. Select the exception.
          a. family
     *   b. kind
          c. species
          d. order
          e. genus

D   59. Four of the five statements listed below are deductions made by Charles Darwin. Select the exception.
          a. Natural selection is a result of differential reproduction.
          b. Much of biological variation is heritable.
          c. More offspring are produced than can survive.
     *   d. Mutations produce changes in inheritance.
          e. Some variations of heritable traits improve chances of survival.

M   60. Four of the five answers listed below are characteristics of life. Select the exception.
     *   a. ionization
          b. metabolism
          c. reproduction
          d. growth
          e. cellular organization

M   61. Four of the five answers listed below are names of kingdoms. Select the exception.
          a. Animalia
          b. Protista
     *   c. Bacteria
          d. Fungi
          e. Plantae

CHAPTER 2
CHEMICAL FOUNDATIONS FOR CELLS

Multiple-Choice Questions

ORGANIZATION OF MATTER

E   1. Water is an example of a(n)
      a. atom.
      b. ion.
 * c. compound.
      d. mixture.
      e. element.

M   2. Which includes the other four?
      a. atoms
 * b. molecules
      c. electrons
      d. elements
      e. protons

M   3. Which is NOT an element?
 * a. water
      b. oxygen
      c. carbon
      d. chlorine
      e. hydrogen

M   4. Which is the smallest portion of a substance that retains the properties of an element?
 * a. atom
      b. compound
      c. ion
      d. molecule
      e. mixture

E   5. The atom that represents the greatest weight in the human body is
      a. hydrogen.
      b. carbon.
      c. nitrogen.
 * d. oxygen.
      e. phosphorus.

E   6. The atomic number refers to the
      a. mass of an atom.
 * b. number of protons in an atom.
      c. number of both protons and neutrons in an atom.
      d. number of neutrons in an atom.
      e. number of electrons in an atom.

M   7. Radioactive isotopes
      a. are electrically unbalanced.
      b. behave the same chemically and physically but differ biologically from other isotopes.
      c. are the same physically and biologically but differ from other isotopes chemically.
 * d. have an excess number of neutrons.
      e. are produced when substances are exposed to radiation.

E   8.   Which is NOT a compound?
- a. salt
- b. a carbohydrate
- * c. carbon
- d. a nucleotide
- e. methane

E   9.   The negative subatomic particle is the
- a. neutron.
- b. proton.
- * c. electron.
- d. both a and b
- e. b and c

E   10.   The positive subatomic particle is the
- a. neutron.
- * b. proton.
- c. electron.
- d. both a and b
- e. b and c

E   11.   The neutral subatomic particle is the
- * a. neutron.
- b. proton.
- c. electron.
- d. both a and b
- e. none of the above

E   12.   The nucleus of an atom contains
- * a. neutrons and protons.
- b. neutrons and electrons.
- c. protons and electrons.
- d. protons only.
- e. neutrons only.

E   13.   Which components of an atom are negatively charged?
- * a. electrons
- b. protons
- c. neutrons
- d. both a and b
- e. both b and c

E   14.   Which components of an atom do not have a charge?
- a. electrons
- b. protons
- * c. neutrons
- d. both a and b
- e. both b and c

M   15.   The atomic weight (or mass) of an atom is determined by the weight of
- * a. neutrons and protons.
- b. neutrons and electrons.
- c. protons and electrons.
- d. protons only.
- e. neutrons only.

M   16. The atomic number is determined by the number of
        a. neutrons and protons.
        b. neutrons and electrons.
        c. protons and electrons.
    * d. protons only.
        e. neutrons only.

E   17. All atoms of an element have the same number of
        a. ions.
    * b. protons.
        c. neutrons.
        d. electrons.
        e. protons and neutrons.

M   18. Radioactive isotopes have
        a. excess electrons.
        b. excess protons.
    * c. excess neutrons.
        d. insufficient neutrons.
        e. insufficient protons.

M   19. A molecule is
    * a. a combination of two or more atoms.
        b. less stable than its constituent atoms separated.
        c. electrically charged.
        d. a carrier of one or more extra neutrons.
        e. none of the above

M   20. Radioactive iodine tends to concentrate in the
        a. heart.
        b. lungs.
        c. gonads.
        d. bones.
    * e. thyroid glands.

M   21. Magnesium has 12 protons. How many electrons are in its third energy level?
    * a. 2
        b. 4
        c. 6
        d. 8
        e. 10

M   22. Magnesium has 12 protons. How many electrons are in its first energy level?
    * a. 2
        b. 4
        c. 6
        d. 8
        e. 10

M   23. Magnesium has 12 protons. How many electrons are in its second energy level?
        a. 2
        b. 4
        c. 6
    * d. 8
        e. 10

M   24. Which statement is NOT true?
         a. Electrons closest to the nucleus are at the lowest energy level.
         b. No more than two electrons can occupy a single orbital.
      * c. Electrons are unable to move out of the assigned orbital space.
         d. The innermost orbital holds two electrons.
         e. At the second energy level there are four possible orbitals with a total of eight electrons.

D   25. When a molecule is excited by heat or light,
         a. it may lose an electron.
         b. it may gain an electron.
      * c. an electron from an inner energy level may move to another level.
         d. an electron from an outer energy level may move to an inner level.
         e. an electron may be ejected from the nucleus of the atom.

D   26. If the atomic weight of carbon is 12 and the atomic weight of oxygen is 16, the molecular weight of glucose $C_6H_{12}O_6$ expressed in grams is
         a. 24 grams.
         b. 28 grams.
         c. 52 grams.
         d. 168 grams.
      * e. 180 grams.

BONDS BETWEEN ATOMS

E   27. What is formed when an atom loses or gains an electron?
         a. mole
      * b. ion
         c. molecule
         d. bond
         e. reaction

E   28. The bond in table salt (NaCl) is
         a. polar.
      * b. ionic.
         c. covalent.
         d. double.
         e. nonpolar.

M   29. How do hydrophobic molecules react with water?
         a. attracted to
         b. absorbed by
      * c. repelled by
         d. mixed with
         e. polarized by

D   30. The shape (or tertiary form) of large molecules is often controlled by what kind of bonds?
      * a. hydrogen
         b. ionic
         c. covalent
         d. inert
         e. single

D   31.   A hydrogen bond is
         a.   a sharing of a pair of electrons between a hydrogen and an oxygen nucleus.
         b.   a sharing of a pair of electrons between a hydrogen nucleus and either an oxygen or a nitrogen nucleus.
    *   c.   an attractive force that involves a hydrogen atom and an oxygen or a nitrogen atom that are either in two different molecules or within the same molecule.
         d.   none of the above
         e.   all of the above

D   32.   Water is an excellent solvent because
         a.   it forms spheres of hydration around charged substances and can form hydrogen bonds with many nonpolar substances.
         b.   it has a high heat of fusion.
         c.   of its cohesive properties.
         d.   it is a liquid at room temperature.
    *   e.   all of the above

D   33.   In a lipid bilayer, _____ tails point inward and form a region that excludes water.
         a.   acidic
         b.   basic
         c.   hydrophilic
    *   d.   hydrophobic
         e.   none of the above

D   34.   Glucose dissolves in water because it
         a.   ionizes.
         b.   is a polysaccharide.
    *   c.   is polar and forms many hydrogen bonds with the water molecules.
         d.   has a very reactive primary structure.
         e.   none of the above

ACIDS, BASES, AND SALTS

M   35.   Which of the following is a naked proton?
    *   a.   hydrogen ion
         b.   acid
         c.   base
         d.   hydroxyl ion
         e.   acceptor

M   36.   A pH of 10 is how many times as basic as a pH of 7?
         a.   2
         b.   3
         c.   10
         d.   100
    *   e.   1,000

M   37.   A solution with a pH of 8 has how many times fewer hydrogen ions than a solution with a pH of 6?
         a.   2
         b.   4
         c.   10
    *   d.   100
         e.   1,000

D   38. Sodium chloride (NaCl) in water could be described by any of the following EXCEPT:
        a. Na$^+$ and Cl$^-$ form
        b. a solute
        c. ionized
     * d. forms spheres of hydration
        e. dissolved

M   39. A salt will dissolve in water to form
        a. acids.
        b. gases.
     * c. ions.
        d. bases.
        e. polar solvents.

M   40. A reaction of an acid and a base will produce water and
        a. a buffer.
     * b. a salt.
        c. gas.
        d. solid precipitate.
        e. solute.

M   41. Which of the following would NOT be used in connection with the word *acid*?
        a. excess hydrogen ions
        b. contents of the stomach
     * c. magnesium hydroxide
        d. HCl
        e. pH less than 7

M   42. Cellular pH is kept near a value of 7 because of
        a. salts.
     * b. buffers.
        c. acids.
        d. bases.
        e. water.

CARBON COMPOUNDS

E   43. The three most common atoms in your body are
     * a. hydrogen, oxygen, and carbon.
        b. carbon, hydrogen, and nitrogen.
        c. carbon, nitrogen, and oxygen.
        d. nitrogen, hydrogen, and oxygen.
        e. carbon, oxygen, and sulfur.

E   44. Carbon usually forms how many bonds with other atoms?
        a. 2
        b. 3
     * c. 4
        d. 5
        e. 6

E   45. The atom diagnostically associated with organic compounds is
     * a. carbon.
        b. oxygen
        c. nitrogen.
        d. sulfur.
        e. hydrogen.

M   46. Which are NOT macromolecules?
       a. proteins
       b. starches
   * c. nucleotides
       d. lipids
       e. nucleic acids

D   47. Which compound is hydrophobic?
       a. ethyl alcohol
       b. simple sugar
   * c. hydrocarbon
       d. glycerol
       e. amino acid

M   48. An —OH group is a(n) _____ group.
       a. carboxyl
   * b. hydroxyl
       c. amino
       d. methyl
       e. ketone

M   49. A —CH_3 group is a(n) _____ group.
       a. carboxyl
       b. hydroxyl
       c. amino
   * d. methyl
       e. ketone

M   50. An —NH_2 group is a(n) _____ group.
       a. carboxyl
       b. hydroxyl
   * c. amino
       d. methyl
       e. ketone

M   51. A —COOH group is a(n) _____ group.
   * a. carboxyl
       b. hydroxyl
       c. amino
       d. methyl
       e. ketone

E   52. Amino acids are the building blocks for
   * a. proteins.
       b. steroids.
       c. lipids.
       d. nucleic acids.
       e. carbohydrates.

M   53. Nucleotides are the building blocks for
       a. proteins.
       b. steroids.
       c. lipids.
   * d. ATP, NAD^+, and FAD.
       e. carbohydrates.

M   54. The formation of large molecules from small repeating units is known as what kind of reaction?
   a. oxidation
   b. reduction
 * c. condensation
   d. hydrolysis
   e. decarboxylation

M   55. The breakdown of large molecules by the enzymatic addition of water is an example of what kind of reaction?
   a. oxidation
   b. reduction
   c. condensation
 * d. hydrolysis
   e. decarboxylation

M   56. Which reaction results in the breakdown of a chemical into simpler substances?
   a. synthesis
 * b. hydrolysis
   c. condensation
   d. polymerization
   e. both b and c, but not a or d

E   57. Which is a "building block" of carbohydrates?
   a. glycerol
   b. nucleotide
   c. simple sugar
   d. monosaccharide
 * e. c and d

E   58. Which substance is the most common in cells?
   a. carbohydrates
   b. salts and minerals
   c. proteins
   d. fats
 * e. water

M   59. Which of the following includes all the others?
   a. sucrose
   b. glucose
   c. cellulose
   d. glycogen
 * e. carbohydrate

M   60. Which of the following is composed of a 1:2:1 ratio of carbon to hydrogen to oxygen?
 * a. carbohydrate
   b. protein
   c. lipid
   d. nucleic acid
   e. steroid

M   61. Which is NOT a monosaccharide?
   a. glucose
   b. fructose
   c. deoxyribose
 * d. starch
   e. ribose

M 62. Cellulose is
* a. a material found in cell walls.
  b. a component of cell membranes.
  c. a plant protein.
  d. formed by photosynthesis.
  e. the most complex of the organic compounds.

D 63. Monosaccharides are characterized by all EXCEPT which of the following?
  a. a carboxyl group
  b. carbon, hydrogen, and oxygen in a 1:2:1 ratio
  c. a molecule of three to seven carbon atoms
  d. possession of one or more hydroxyl groups
* e. the presence of glycerol and fatty acids

M 64. Fructose and glucose are
  a. isotopes.
  b. monosaccharides.
  c. disaccharides.
  d. six-carbon sugars.
* e. both b and d, but not a or c

M 65. Fructose and glucose are
  a. hexoses.
  b. structurally different.
  c. monosaccharides.
  d. simple sugars.
* e. all of the above

M 66. Glucose and ribose
  a. have the same number of carbon atoms.
  b. have the same structural formulas.
  c. are the two components of sucrose.
* d. are monosaccharides.
  e. are molecules whose atoms are arranged the same way.

M 67. Sucrose is composed of
  a. two molecules of fructose.
  b. two molecules of glucose.
* c. a molecule of fructose and a molecule of glucose.
  d. a molecule of fructose and a molecule of galactose.
  e. two molecules of fructose.

M 68. The combination of glucose and galactose forms
  a. fructose.
  b. maltose.
* c. lactose.
  d. sucrose.
  e. mannose.

E 69. Plants store their excess carbohydrates in the form of
* a. starch.
  b. glycogen.
  c. glucose.
  d. cellulose.
  e. fats.

M   70.   Glycogen is a polysaccharide used for energy storage by
*   a.   animals.
     b.   plants.
     c.   protistans.
     d.   monera.
     e.   both a and c, but not b or d

M   71.   Triglycerides are
     a.   carbohydrates.
     b.   nucleotides.
     c.   proteins.
*   d.   fats.
     e.   amino acids.

M   72.   Oils are
     a.   liquid at room temperatures.
     b.   unsaturated fats.
     c.   found only in animals.
     d.   complex carbohydrates.
*   e.   both a and b, but not c or d

E   73.   Which of the following are lipids?
     a.   steroids
     b.   triglycerides
     c.   oils
     d.   waxes
*   e.   all of the above

M   74.   An example of a saturated fat is
     a.   olive oil.
     b.   corn oil.
*   c.   butter.
     d.   oleo.
     e.   soybean oil.

M   75.   Lipids
*   a.   serve as food reserves in many organisms.
     b.   include cartilage and chitin.
     c.   include fats that are broken down into one fatty acid molecule and three glycerol molecules.
     d.   are composed of monosaccharides.
     e.   none of the above

M   76.   Plasma membranes are characterized by the presence of
     a.   triglycerides.
*   b.   phospholipids.
     c.   unsaturated fats.
     d.   steroid hormones.
     e.   fatty acids.

M   77.   All steroids have
     a.   the same number of double bonds.
     b.   the same position of double bonds.
*   c.   four rings of carbon to which are attached other atoms.
     d.   the same functional groups.
     e.   both a and b, but not c or d

M 78. Steroids are
  a. compounds that are related to lipids.
  b. sex hormones.
  c. components of membranes.
  d. troublesome on walls of arteries.
  * e. all of the above

D 79. Which element is NOT characteristic of the primary structure of proteins?
  a. sulfur
  b. carbon
  * c. phosphorus
  d. oxygen
  e. nitrogen

M 80. Proteins may function as
  a. structural units.
  b. hormones.
  c. storage molecules.
  d. transport molecules.
  * e. all of the above

E 81. What kind of bond exists between two amino acids in a protein?
  * a. peptide
  b. ionic
  c. hydrogen
  d. amino
  e. sulfhydroxyl

E 82. The sequence of amino acids is the _____ structure of proteins.
  * a. primary
  b. secondary
  c. tertiary
  d. quaternary
  e. stereo

E 83. Amino acids are linked by what kind of bonds to form the primary structure of a protein?
  a. disulfide
  b. hydrogen
  c. ionic
  * d. peptide
  e. none of the above

M 84. The secondary structure of proteins is
  a. helical.
  b. sheetlike.
  c. globular.
  d. the sequence of amino acids.
  * e. both a and b

M 85. Which of the following is NOT found in every nucleic acid?
  * a. ribose
  b. phosphate group
  c. purine
  d. pyrimidine
  e. All of the above are characteristic of every nucleotide.

M   86.   The nucleotide most closely associated with energy is
          a. cyclic AMP.
          b. FAD.
          c. NAD.
       * d. ATP.
          e. all of the above

M   87.   Nucleotides contain what kind of sugars?
          a. three-carbon
          b. four-carbon
       * c. five-carbon
          d. six-carbon
          e. seven-carbon

M   88.   DNA
          a. is one of the adenosine phosphates.
          b. is one of the nucleotide coenzymes.
       * c. contains protein-building instructions.
          d. all of the above
          e. none of the above

Matching Questions

M   89.   Choose the one most appropriate answer for each.

1	_____	enzymes	A.	a six-carbon sugar
2	_____	glucose	B.	energy carrier such as NAD and FAD
3	_____	nucleotide coenzymes	C.	principal components of cell membranes
4	_____	phospholipids	D.	speed up metabolic reactions
			E.	DNA and RNA

Answers: 1. D   2. A   3. B   4. C

Classification Questions

The various energy levels in an atom of magnesium have different numbers of electrons. Use the following numbers to answer questions 90–92.

          a. 1
          b. 2
          c. 3
          d. 6
          e. 8

D   90.   Number of electrons in the first energy level

D   91.   Number of electrons in the second energy level

D   92.   Number of electrons in the third energy level

Answers: 90. b   91. e   92. b

The following are types of chemical bonds. Answer questions 93–97 by matching the statement with the most appropriate bond type.

a. hydrogen
b. ionic
c. covalent
d. disulfide
e. peptide

M   93.   The bond between the atoms of table salt

M   94.   The bond type holding several molecules of water together

M   95.   The bond between the oxygen atoms of gaseous oxygen

M   96.   The bond that breaks when salts dissolve in water

M   97.   Atoms connected by this kind of bond share electrons

Answers: 93. b   94. a   95. c   96. b   97. c

The following are chemical functional groups that may be part of a biologically active molecule. Answer questions 98–108 by matching the statement with the most appropriate group.

a. —COOH
b. —CH$_3$
c. —NH$_2$
d. —OH
e. $>$C$=$O
f.
$$\begin{matrix} & O \\ & \| \\ - & P—O \\ & | \\ & O \end{matrix}$$
g. —CHO

E   98.   The amino group

E   99.   The carboxyl group

M   100.   The group that is acidic

M   101.   The group that occurs repeatedly in sugars; composed of two elements

E   102.   The methyl group

E   103.   The hydroxyl group

E   104.   The ketone group

M   105.   The group on the amino-terminal end of proteins

M   106.   The group on the carboxy-terminal end of proteins

D   107.   A group composed of three different elements; found in sugars

M   108.   The group typical of energy carriers such as ATP

Answers: 98. c   99. a   100. a   101. d   102. b   103. d
            104. e   105. c   106. a   107. g   108. f

The following are basic building blocks of biopolymers. Answer questions 109–116 by matching the statement with the most appropriate building block.

    a. amino acids
    b. glucose
    c. glycerol
    d. fatty acids
    e. nucleotides

E   109. The basic unit of proteins

E   110. The basic unit of DNA

E   111. The basic unit of messenger RNA

E   112. The basic unit of cellulose

E   113. The basic unit of glycogen

E   114. The basic unit of starch

M   115. The "building block" unit of a polypeptide chain

M   116. Which two units combine in various ways to form lipids?
    a. amino acids and glucose
    b. amino acids and glycerol
    c. glucose and glycerol
    d. glucose and fatty acids
    e. glycerol and fatty acids

Answers: 109. a   110. e   111. e   112. b   113. b   114. b
              115. a   116. e

Selecting the Exception

D   117. Four of the five answers listed below possess electrons in the third energy level. Select the exception.
    a. sodium
    b. magnesium
    c. chlorine
    * d. nitrogen
    e. sulfur

D   118. Four of the five answers listed below are related by a unifying characteristic. Select the exception.
    a. ionic bond
    b. covalent bond
    c. polar bond
    d. hydrogen bond
    * e. cluster of nonpolar groups

D   119. Four of the five answers listed below are alkaline (pH above 7). Select the exception.
    a. milk of magnesia
    b. household ammonia
    c. Tums
    d. phosphate detergent
    * e. wine

D   120. Four of the five answers listed below are acidic (pH below 7). Select the exception.
        a. vinegar
        b. soft drink
    *   c. soap
        d. lemon juice
        e. beer

M   121. Four of the five answers listed below are positively charged ions. Select the exception.
        a. potassium ion
        b. hydrogen ion
        c. calcium ion
        d. magnesium ion
    *   e. chlorine ion

M   122. Four of the five answers listed below are characteristics of water. Select the exception.
        a. stabilizes temperature
        b. common solvent
        c. cohesion and surface tension
    *   d. produces salts
        e. changes shape of hydrophilic and hydrophobic substances

D   123. Four of the five answers listed below are related by a common chemical similarity. Select the exception.
        a. cellulose
    *   b. hydrochloric acid
        c. amino acid
        d. protein
        e. nucleic acid

M   124. Four of the five answers listed below are related as members of the same group. Select the exception.
        a. glucose
        b. fructose
    *   c. cellulose
        d. ribose
        e. deoxyribose

D   125. Four of the five answers listed below are related as members of the same group. Select the exception.
        a. lactose
        b. sucrose
        c. maltose
        d. table sugar
    *   e. fructose

D   126. Four of the five answers listed below are carbohydrates. Select the exception.
    *   a. glycerol
        b. cellulose
        c. starch
        d. sucrose
        e. glycogen

D   127.   Four of the five answers listed below are lipids. Select the exception.
- a. triglyceride
- b. wax
- c. cutin
- * d. insulin
- e. steroid

M   128.   Three of the four answers listed below are saturated fats. Select the exception.
- a. butter
- b. bacon
- * c. peanut oil
- d. animal fat

D   129.   Four of the five answers listed below are amino acids. Select the exception.
- a. glycine
- * b. adenine
- c. phenylalanine
- d. valine
- e. tyrosine

D   130.   Four of the five answers listed below are functional groups. Select the exception.
- * a. R group
- b. amino group
- c. carboxyl group
- d. hydroxyl group
- e. aldehyde group

CHAPTER 3
CELL STRUCTURE AND FUNCTION

Multiple-Choice Questions

THE NATURE OF CELLS

E 1. The first cell that was seen under a microscope was a
*   a. cork cell.
     b. blood cell.
     c. sperm cell.
     d. skin cell.
     e. root tip cell.

E 2. One portion of the cell theory states that
     a. all cells have a nucleus.
     b. all cells divide by meiosis.
*   c. all living organisms are made up of cells.
     d. cells arise through spontaneous generation.
     e. growth is solely the result of cell division.

E 3. The cell theory was proposed by
     a. Robert Hooke.
     b. Robert Brown.
*   c. Theodor Schwann and Matthias Schleiden.
     d. Rudolf Virchow.
     e. Antony van Leeuwenhoek.

M 4. There are how many nanometers in a meter?
     a. 1,000
     b. 100,000
     c. 1,000,000
*   d. 1,000,000,000
     e. 1,000,000,000,000

E 5. The idea that all living cells come from preexisting living cells was proposed by
     a. Robert Hooke.
     b. Robert Brown.
     c. Theodor Schwann.
*   d. Rudolf Virchow.
     e. Antony van Leeuwenhoek.

E 6. The maximum power of magnification of a light microscope is
     a. 500.
     b. 1,000.
*   c. 2,000.
     d. 4,000.
     e. 10,000.

E 7. The highest magnification generally used to study cells is provided by the
*   a. transmission electron microscope.
     b. compound light microscope.
     c. phase contrast microscope.
     d. scanning electron microscope.
     e. binocular dissecting microscope.

M   8. Which microscope has the highest magnification?
          a. compound light
     *   b. transmission electron
          c. scanning electron
          d. phase contrast
          e. dissecting

CELL MEMBRANES

M   9. The phospholipid molecules of most membranes have
          a. a hydrophobic head and a hydrophilic tail.
          b. a hydrophobic head and a hydrophobic tail.
          c. a hydrophobic head and two hydrophobic tails.
     *   d. a hydrophilic head and two hydrophobic tails.
          e. none of the above

E   10. Hydrophobic reactions of phospholipids may produce clusters of their fatty acid tails,
          which form
     *   a. a lipid bilayer.
          b. hydrolysis of the fatty acids.
          c. a protein membrane.
          d. a cytoskeleton.
          e. a nonpolar membrane.

M   11. Unsaturated tails of lipids
          a. are hydrophilic.
          b. are unstable and tend to break apart.
     *   c. have kinks in them and lessen the interaction between adjacent fat
          d. will break whenever exposed to phosphate ions.
          e. all of the above

M   12. The relative impermeability of membranes to water-soluble molecules is a result of the
          a. nonpolar nature of water molecules.
          b. presence of large proteins that extend through both sides of membranes.
          c. presence of inorganic salt crystals scattered through some membranes.
          d. presence of cellulose and chemicals such as cutin, lignin, pectin, and suberin in the
             membranes.
     *   e. presence of phospholipids in the lipid bilayer.

D   13. Which statement is NOT true?
          a. Membranes are often perforated by proteins that extend through both sides of the
             membrane.
          b. Some membranes have proteins with channels or pores that allow for the passage of
             hydrophilic substances.
     *   c. Hydrophilic substances have an easier time passing through membranes than
             hydrophobic substances do.
          d. The current concept of a membrane can be best summarized by the fluid mosaic model.
          e. The lipid bilayer serves as a hydrophobic barrier between two fluid regions.

D   14. Which affects the rate of diffusion through a semipermeable membrane?

          **I. steeper concentration   II. higher temperatures   III. membrane pore
              gradients   size**

          a. I only
          b. II only
          c. I and II
          d. II and III
     *   e. I, II, and III

D 15. The rate of diffusion through a semipermeable membrane will be lowest when which of the following are true?

| I. **Concentration gradients are steep.** | II. **Temperatures are low.** | III. **Solutes are small molecules.** |

    a. I only
*   b. II only
    c. I and III
    d. II and III
    e. I, II, and III

M 16. In simple diffusion
    a. the rate of movement of molecules is controlled by temperature and pressure.
    b. the movement of individual molecules is random.
    c. the movement of molecules of one substance is independent of the movement of any other substance.
    d. the net movement is away from the region of highest concentration.
*   e. all of the above

M 17. Which of the following is NOT a form of active transport?
    a. sodium–potassium pump
    b. endocytosis
    c. exocytosis
*   d. diffusion
    e. none of the above

M 18. A single-celled freshwater organism, such as a protistan, is transferred to salt water. Which of the following is likely to happen?
    a. The cell bursts.
    b. Salt is pumped out of the cell.
*   c. The cell shrinks.
    d. Enzymes flow out of the cell.
    e. all of the above

M 19. Which statement is true?
    a. A cell placed in an isotonic solution will swell.
*   b. A cell placed in a hypotonic solution will swell.
    c. A cell placed in a hypotonic solution will shrink.
    d. A cell placed in a hypertonic solution will remain the same size.
    e. A cell placed in a hypotonic solution will remain the same size.

M 20. A red blood cell will swell and burst when placed in which of the following kinds of solution?
*   a. hypotonic
    b. hypertonic
    c. isotonic
    d. any of the above
    e. none of the above

M 21. If a plant cell is placed in a hypotonic solution,
    a. the entire cell will not swell or shrink.
    b. the entire cell will shrink.
    c. the turgor pressure will increase.
    d. the cell wall prevents the cell from exploding.
*   e. c and d

M 22. Wilting of a plant occurs
    a. if the plant is placed in an isotonic solution.
    b. if there is a rise in turgor pressure.
    c. as a result of facilitated diffusion.
*   d. when a plant with flexible cell walls is placed in a hypertonic solution.
    e. any of the above

E 23. Movement of a molecule against a concentration gradient is
    a. simple diffusion.
    b. facilitated diffusion.
    c. osmosis.
*   d. active transport.
    e. passive transport.

M 24. The method of movement that requires the expenditure of ATP molecules is
    a. simple diffusion.
    b. facilitated diffusion.
    c. osmosis.
*   d. active transport.
    e. passive transport.

M 25. White blood cells use _____ to get rid of foreign particles in the blood.
    a. simple diffusion
    b. bulk flow
    c. osmosis
*   d. phagocytosis
    e. facilitated diffusion

E 26. The sodium-potassium pump is an example of
    a. simple diffusion.
    b. facilitated diffusion.
    c. osmosis.
*   d. active transport.
    e. passive transport.

M 27. The carrier molecules used in active transport are
    a. calcium ions in the calcium pump.
*   b. proteins.
    c. ATP molecules.
    d. carbohydrates.
    e. lipids.

PROKARYOTIC CELLS—THE BACTERIA

E 28. Which are examples of prokaryotes?
    a. Protozoa
*   b. Bacteria
    c. Algae
    d. Fungi
    e. Mosses

M 29. Prokaryotic cells do NOT have
    a. nucleoid regions.
*   b. membrane bound nuclei.
    c. cytoplasm.
    d. plasma membrane.
    e. a and b

E   30. Prokaryotes
             a. have DNA regions.
             b. are unicellular.
             c. have cell walls.
             d. are monera.
    *   e. all of the above

EUKARYOTIC CELLS

M   31. Which of the following are made of two subunits and are composed of RNA and protein?
             a. Golgi
             b. mitochondria
             c. chloroplasts
    *   d. ribosomes
             e. endoplasmic reticula

E   32. An organelle found in the nucleus is a
             a. plastid.
             b. vacuole.
             c. microvillus.
    *   d. nucleolus.
             e. basal body.

E   33. Organelles composed of a system of canals, tubes, and sacs that transport molecules inside the cytoplasm are
             a. Golgi bodies.
             b. ribosomes.
             c. mitochondria.
             d. lysosomes.
    *   e. endoplasmic reticula.

E   34. These are sometimes referred to as rough or smooth, depending on the structure.
             a. Golgi bodies
             b. ribosomes
             c. mitochondria
             d. lysosomes
    *   e. endoplasmic reticula

M   35. These are the primary cellular sites for the production of proteins.
             a. Golgi bodies
    *   b. ribosomes
             c. mitochondria
             d. lysosomes
             e. smooth endoplasmic reticula

M   36. These are the primary cellular sites for the recapture of energy from carbohydrates.
             a. Golgi bodies
             b. ribosomes
    *   c. mitochondria
             d. lysosomes
             e. endoplasmic reticula

M   37. These are the primary structures for the packaging of cellular secretions for export from the cell.
   *   a. Golgi bodies
       b. ribosomes
       c. mitochondria
       d. lysosomes
       e. endoplasmic reticula

M   38. These contain enzymes and are the main organelles of intracellular digestion.
       a. Golgi bodies
       b. ribosomes
       c. mitochondria
   *   d. lysosomes
       e. endoplasmic reticula

M   39. These contain enzymes used in the breakdown of glucose and generation of ATP.
       a. Golgi bodies
       b. ribosomes
   *   c. mitochondria
       d. lysosomes
       e. endoplasmic reticula

D   40. Energy stored in which of the following molecules is converted by mitochondria to a form usable by the cell?
       a. water
   *   b. carbon compounds
       c. NAD
       d. ATP
       e. carbon dioxide

D   41. Animal cells dismantle and dispose of waste materials by
       a. using centrally located vacuoles.
   *   b. several lysosomes fusing with a sac that encloses the wastes.
       c. microvilli packaging and exporting the wastes.
       d. mitochondrial breakdown of the wastes.
       e. all of the above

M   42. Fluid-filled sacs that may store food or water in cells are called
       a. plastids.
   *   b. vacuoles.
       c. microvilli.
       d. nucleoli.
       e. Golgi.

M   43. Structural features that contain the protein actin and help to control the shapes of cells are
       a. plastids.
       b. vacuoles.
       c. microvilli.
       d. nucleoli.
   *   e. microfilaments.

M   44. Organelles used to move chromosomes are the
       a. cilia.
       b. flagella.
   *   c. microtubules.
       d. microfilaments.
       e. Golgi apparatuses.

M   45. Organelles that dramatically increase the cell size and surface area are
   a. plastids.
   * b. vacuoles.
   c. chloroplasts.
   d. nucleoli.
   e. microfilaments.

E   46. The organelle that is compared to a whip is a
   a. microfilament.
   b. cilium.
   c. microvillus.
   * d. flagellum.
   e. microtubule.

E   47. A 9+2 array refers to
   a. microtubules.
   b. Golgi bodies.
   c. ribosomes.
   d. cilia.
   * e. both a and d, but not b or c

M   48. Which is NOT found as a part of all cells?
   a. cell membrane
   * b. cell wall
   c. ribosomes
   d. DNA
   e. RNA

Matching Questions

M   49. Choose the one most appropriate answer for each.

1 _____ microtubules

2 _____ chloroplasts

3 _____ Golgi bodies

4 _____ DNA molecules

5 _____ RNA molecules

6 _____ central vacuoles

7 _____ lysosomes

8 _____ mitochondria

9 _____ nucleoli

10 _____ ribosomes

A. contain enzymes for intracellular digestion

B. primary cellular organelles where proteins are assembled

C. package cellular secretions for export

D. extract energy stored in carbohydrates; synthesize ATP; produce water and CO_2

E. synthesize subunits that will be assembled into two-part ribosomes in the cytoplasm

F. transcription, translation of hereditary instructions into specific proteins

G. increase cell surface area; store substances

H. encoding hereditary information

I. help distribute chromosomes to the new cells during cell division

J. convert light energy to chemical energy stored in the chemical bonds of glucose or starch

Answers: 1. I   2. J   3. C   4. H   5. F   6. G
                  7. A   8. D   9. E   10. B

Classification Questions

The following items a–e are organelles found in animal cells. Answer questions 50–58 with reference to these organelles.

a. ribosomes
b. mitochondria
c. lysosomes
d. Golgi bodies
e. endoplasmic reticula

E 50. The structures upon which proteins are assembled

M 51. The cellular digestion and disposal of biological molecules occurs inside of which organelle?

M 52. Aerobic respiration occurs in which organelle?

M 53. RNA carries out the genetic code translation process in association with ribosomes on which organelle?

M 54. The packaging of secretory proteins occurs in association with which structure?

M 55. Which organelle is involved in lipid production and protein transport?

D 56. The hemoglobin of mammals and birds is synthesized on which tiny, two-part organelles?

E 57. Sugar metabolism occurs in association with which organelle?

D 58. DNA synthesis occurs in the nucleus. Its breakdown can occur in which organelle?

Answers: 50. a 51. c 52. b 53. e 54. d 55. e
56. a 57. b 58. c

Questions 59–63 ask about membrane permeability. Answer them in reference to the five processes below:

a. simple diffusion
b. facilitated diffusion
c. osmosis
d. active transport
e. endocytosis

E 59. Which process would be used by white blood cells to ingest bacteria?

E 60. What process specifically moves water molecules across a differentially permeable membrane?

E 61. Which explains the movement of any kind of molecule from areas of higher concentration to ones of lower concentration?

E 62. What is the process whereby a protein assists in simple diffusion?

M 63. What explains the movement of molecules against a concentration gradient?

Answers: 59. e 60. c 61. a 62. b 63. d

Selecting the Exception

D   64. Four of the five answers listed below are related by a common observation. Select the exception.
- a. Hooke
- * b. Galileo
- c. Schwann
- d. Schleiden
- e. Virchow

M   65. Four of the five answers listed below are portions of a well-known theory. Select the exception.
- a. Cells are the structural and functional components of living things.
- b. Cells arise from preexisting cells.
- c. All organisms are composed of cells.
- d. Cells are the basic living unit or organization of living things.
- * e. All cells have a nucleus.

M   66. Four of the five answers listed below are familiar organelles in the cytoplasm. Select the exception.
- * a. nucleolus
- b. mitochondria
- c. ribosome
- d. Golgi apparatus
- e. chloroplast

M   67. Four of the five answers listed below are features of plasma membrane extensions. Select the exception.
- * a. amyoplast
- b. centriole
- c. microtubule
- d. basal body
- e. 9+2 array

M   68. Four of the five answers listed below are bound by membranes. Select the exception.
- a. mitochondria
- * b. ribosome
- c. chloroplast
- d. vacuole
- e. lysosome

M   69. Four of the five answers listed below are characteristics of the plasma membrane. Select the exception.
- a. phospholipid
- b. fluid mosaic
- c. lipid bilayer
- * d. inert and impermeable
- e. hydrophobic tails

M   70. Four of the five answers listed below result when a cell is placed in a hypertonic solution. Select the exception.
- a. wilting
- b. plasmolysis
- * c. turgid
- d. limp
- e. shriveled

D   71. Four of the five answers listed below are related by energy requirements. Select the exception.
      a. active transport
      b. endocytosis
*   c. facilitated diffusion
      d. exocytosis
      e. sodium–potassium pump

CHAPTER 4
GROUND RULES OF METABOLISM

Multiple-Choice Questions

ENERGY AND LIFE

D　　1.　According to the first law of thermodynamics,
　　　　a. although energy in the universe is constant, energy in an earthly system may accumulate.
　　　　b. the amount of energy in the universe is constant.
　　　　c. chemical reactions do not create or destroy energy.
　　　　d. energy can change from one form to another.
　*　　e. all of the above

D　　2.　The second law of thermodynamics holds that
　　　　a. matter can neither be created nor destroyed.
　　　　b. energy can neither be created nor destroyed.
　*　　c. energy of one form is converted to a less concentrated form whenever energy is transformed or transferred.
　　　　d. entropy decreases with time.
　　　　e. none of the above

M　　3.　The second law of thermodynamics states that
　　　　a. energy can be transformed into matter and, because of this, we can get something for nothing.
　　　　b. energy can only be destroyed during nuclear reactions, such as those that occur inside the sun.
　　　　c. if energy is gained by one region of the universe, another place in the universe also must gain energy in order to maintain the balance of nature.
　*　　d. energy tends to become increasingly more disorganized.
　　　　e. none of the above

E　　4.　Essentially, the first law of thermodynamics says that
　　　　a. one form of energy cannot be converted into another.
　　　　b. entropy is increasing in the universe.
　*　　c. energy can be neither created nor destroyed.
　　　　d. energy cannot be converted into matter or matter into energy.
　　　　e. all of the above

THE NATURE OF METABOLISM

M　　5.　The lock-and-key concept refers to the
　　　　a. inhibition of enzymes by small molecules.
　　　　b. fit of coenzymes to enzymes.
　*　　c. matching of enzyme with substrate.
　　　　d. regeneration of ATP from ADP.
　　　　e. stepwise cascade of electrons in the oxidation–reduction reactions.

M　　6.　Which reaction is NOT an exergonic reaction?
　*　　a. protein synthesis
　　　　b. digestion
　　　　c. fire
　　　　d. respiration
　　　　e. movement

M 7. Chemical reactions will reach a dynamic equilibrium under which of the following conditions?
   a. There is enough time.
   b. The reactions are reversible.
   c. A product remains after it is formed.
   d. There are sufficient reactants.
 * e. all of the above

M 8. A dynamic equilibrium
   a. means the concentration of reactants and products is the same.
 * b. means the rate of opposing reactions is equal.
   c. means highly spontaneous reactions are less likely to occur than when the system is not at equilibrium.
   d. means that both reactions are typically proceeding against concentration gradients.
   e. occurs only in endergonic reactions.

ENZYMES

M 9. During enzyme-catalyzed reactions, *substrate* is a synonym for
   a. end products.
   b. byproducts.
   c. enzymes.
 * d. reactants.
   e. none of the above

D 10. Which of the following may show enzymatic activity?
   a. lipids
 * b. proteins
   c. DNA
   d. a and b
   e. b and c

M 11. Which of the following is NOT true of enzyme behavior?
   a. Enzyme shape may change during catalysis.
   b. The active site of an enzyme orients its substrate molecules, thereby promoting interaction of their reactive parts.
   c. All enzymes have an active site where substrates are temporarily bound.
 * d. Each enzyme can catalyze a wide variety of different reactions.
   e. none of the above

E 12. Enzymes
   a. are very specific.
   b. act as catalysts.
   c. are organic molecules.
   d. have special shapes that control their activities.
 * e. all of the above

M 13. Enzymes
   a. control the speed of a reaction.
   b. change shapes to facilitate certain reactions.
   c. may place physical stress on the bonds of the substrate.
   d. may require cofactors.
 * e. all of the above

M   14. The active site of an enzyme
          a. is where the coenzyme is located.
          b. is a specific bulge or protuberance on an enzyme.
   *   c. is a groove or crevice in the structure of the enzyme.
          d. will react with only one substrate no matter how many molecules may resemble the shape of the substrate.
          e. rigidly resists any alteration of its shape.

D   15. Which of the following substances would be unlikely to function as a coenzyme?
          a. a water-soluble vitamin
          b. an iron ion
   *   c. glucose
          d. NAD^+
          e. a magnesium ion

M   16. Enzymes increase the rate of a given reaction by lowering what kind of energy?
          a. combination
   *   b. activation
          c. thermal
          d. electrical
          e. solar

M   17. Enzymatic reactions can be controlled by
          a. the amount of substrates available.
          b. the concentration of products.
          c. temperature.
          d. modification of reactive sites by substances that fit into the enzyme and, later, their reactive site.
   *   e. all of the above

M   18. Allosteric inhibition is generally a result of
          a. excess substrates.
   *   b. binding regulatory molecules at another site.
          c. a change in the temperature of the system.
          d. a lack of coenzymes.
          e. pH inhibition.

ELECTRON TRANSFERS IN METABOLIC PATHWAYS

D   19. An allosteric enzyme
   *   a. has an active site where substrate molecules bind and another site that binds with intermediate or end-product molecules.
          b. is an important energy-carrying nucleotide.
          c. carries out either oxidation reactions or reduction reactions but not both.
          d. raises the activation energy of the chemical reaction it catalyzes.
          e. all of the above

M   20. A molecule that gives up an electron becomes
          a. ionized
          b. oxidized
          c. reduced
   *   d. a and b
          e. b and c

M   21. The removal of electrons from a compound is known as
          a. dehydration.
     *   b. oxidation.
          c. reduction.
          d. phosphorylation.
          e. a nonreversible chemical reaction.

M   22. When NAD^+ combines with hydrogen, the NAD^+ becomes
     *   a. reduced.
          b. oxidized.
          c. phosphorylated.
          d. denatured.
          e. none of the above

ATP—THE MAIN ENERGY CARRIER

M   23. ATP acts as what type of agent in almost all metabolic pathways?
     *   a. transfer
          b. feedback
          c. catalytic
          d. allosteric
          e. enzymatic

E   24. ATP contains
          a. alanine.
          b. arginine.
     *   c. ribose.
          d. tyrosine.
          e. glucose.

E   25. ATP contains
     *   a. adenine.
          b. cytosine.
          c. uracil.
          d. thymine.
          e. guanine.

Matching Questions

M   26. Choose the one most appropriate answer for each.

          1 _____ active site
          2 _____ allosteric enzyme
          3 _____ adenosine triphosphate
          4 _____ catalyst
          5 _____ denaturation
          6 _____ equilibrium
          7 _____ feedback inhibition
          8 _____ phosphorylation

          A. rate of forward reaction equals rate of reverse reaction

          B. attaching a phosphate group by a high-energy bond

          C. an excess of end-product molecules alters the shape of the first enzyme in the pathway and shuts off that metabolic pathway

          D. part of an enzyme that binds to the substrate

          E. by binding a regulatory molecule, it changes the activity of a metabolic pathway

          F. lowers the activation energy of a reaction

          G. universal energy currency

          H. a permanent loss of protein structure

Answers: 1. D   2. E   3. G   4. F   5. H   6. A
              7. C   8. B

Classification Questions

Items a–c below are processes that occur during different stages of photosynthesis. Answer questions 27–30 by selecting one of these three processes.

    a. oxidation
    b. reduction
    c. phosphorylation

E   27. Which process leads to the formation of ATP from ADP plus inorganic phosphate?

M   28. When an electron is passed to an electron acceptor molecule, such as NADP, which process occurs to the NADP?

D   29. When a photon of light energy causes an electron to leave the chlorophyll molecule, this involves which process?

M   30. When an electron transport molecule, such as ferrodoxin, gives up an electron, which process occurs to the ferrodoxin?

Answers: 27. c   28. b   29. a   30. a

Selecting the Exception

E   31. Four of the five answers listed below are related to the second law of thermodynamics. Select the exception.
      a. entropy
*   b. Energy can neither be created nor destroyed.
      c. The amount of available energy in a closed system declines with time.
      d. Energy is lost as it is transferred or transformed to another form.
      e. Energy flows spontaneously from high- to low-quality forms.

M   32. Four of the five answers listed below apply to conditions where energy is released. Select the exception.
*   a. endergonic reaction
      b. respiration
      c. entropy
      d. second law of thermodynamics
      e. exergonic reaction

M   33. Four of the five answers listed below are related by their description of enzyme properties. Select the exception.
      a. cofactors
      b. active sites
      c. activation energy
*   d. substrate
      e. catalyst

D   34. Four of the five answers listed below are cofactors or coenzymes. Select the exception.
      a. mineral
      b. water-soluble vitamin
      c. metallic ions
      d. NAD^+
*   e. protein

D   35. Four of the five answers listed below affect the rate of an enzymatic reaction. Select the exception.
- a. pH
- b. temperature
- c. concentration
- d. built-up product
- * e. presence of hormones

D   36. Three of the four answers listed below are parts of a common molecule. Select the exception.
- a. phosphate group
- b. adenine
- * c. deoxyribose
- d. ribose

CHAPTER 5
ENERGY-ACQUIRING PATHWAYS

Multiple-Choice Questions

SUN, RAIN, AND SURVIVAL

E 1. Plants need which of the following to carry on photosynthesis?
  a. H_2O
  b. CO_2
  c. O_2
  d. lipid
 * e. a and b

D 2. Chemosynthetic bacteria may use which element as a hydrogen donor instead of water?
  a. potassium dihydrogen phosphate
 * b. sulfur
  c. hydrogen sulfate
  d. hydrogen chloride
  e. hydrogen peroxide

E 3. Organisms that derive their chemical energy either from the process of chemosynthesis or photosynthesis are classified as
 * a. autotrophs.
  b. parasites.
  c. heterotrophs.
  d. saprophytes.
  e. mutualists.

PHOTOSYNTHESIS: AN OVERVIEW

E 4. The carbon source for organisms that derive their energy from photosynthesis is
  a. carbon monoxide.
 * b. carbon dioxide.
  c. hydrocarbons.
  d. methane.
  e. glucose.

M 5. Most carbon enters the web of life through
  a. chemosynthesis.
  b. aerobic respiration.
  c. anaerobic respiration.
 * d. photosynthesis.
  e. both a and b, but not c or d

M 6. The oxygen released in photosynthesis comes from
  a. carbon dioxide.
  b. glucose.
  c. ribulose bisphosphate.
 * d. water.
  e. atmospheric oxygen.

M   7. The internal membrane system of the chloroplast is called a
*   a. thylakoid.
     b. stroma.
     c. lamella.
     d. mitochondrion.
     e. tracheid.

LIGHT-DEPENDENT REACTIONS

M   8. All of the following statements are true EXCEPT:
     a. Photons are packages of solar energy.
*   b. The longer the wavelength of light, the more energy it has.
     c. Chlorophyll absorbs energy from light.
     d. Photons with different energy levels produce different colors.
     e. Visible light is a very small portion of the electromagnetic spectrum.

M   9. Chlorophyll reflects (does not absorb) which color of light?
     a. red
     b. yellow
     c. orange
*   d. green
     e. blue

M   10. Carotenoid pigments reflect (do not absorb) which color of light?
     a. red
*   b. yellow
     c. orange
     d. green
     e. blue

E   11. Thylakoid disks are stacked in groups called
*   a. grana.
     b. stroma.
     c. lamellae.
     d. cristae.
     e. none of the above

M   12. When light excites chlorophyll, the chlorophyll molecule
     a. changes to carotene.
     b. becomes agitated and moves rapidly.
     c. becomes radioactive.
*   d. absorbs the energy and moves an electron to a higher energy state.
     e. becomes ionized.

M   13. The first event in photosynthesis is the
     a. formation of phosphoglyceric acid.
*   b. donation of an electron from the photosystem to an acceptor.
     c. fixation of carbon dioxide.
     d. breakdown of the thylakoid membrane.
     e. formation of phosphoglyceraldehyde.

M   14. Where in a plant cell is chlorophyll found?
     a. on the outer chloroplast membrane
     b. inside the mitochondria
     c. in the stroma
*   d. in the thylakoids
     e. none of the above

E   15. The final hydrogen acceptor in the noncyclic pathway of ATP formation is
   - a. FAD.
   - b. PGA.
   - * c. $NADP^+$.
   - d. FMN.
   - e. PEP.

E   16. The cyclic pathway of ATP formation functions mainly to
   - a. fix CO_2.
   - b. produce O_2.
   - * c. make ATP.
   - d. reduce NADP.
   - e. split H_2O.

M   17. Photolysis involves
   - a. the cyclic pathway of ATP formation.
   - b. photosystem I.
   - c. carotenoid pigments.
   - * d. the noncyclic pathway of ATP formation.
   - e. both a and b, but not c or d

M   18. The concept that concentration differences in H^+ and electric gradients across a membrane are responsible for ATP formation is known as the
   - * a. chemiosmotic theory.
   - b. photosystem mechanism.
   - c. process of photolysis.
   - d. electron transfer system.
   - e. cyclic pathway.

M   19. The electrons that are passed to $NADP^+$ during noncyclic pathways were obtained from
   - * a. chlorophyll.
   - b. CO_2.
   - c. glucose.
   - d. sunlight.
   - e. ATP.

M   20. Plant cells produce one molecule of O_2
   - a. by splitting carbon dioxide.
   - b. during respiration.
   - c. by splitting ribulose bisphosphate.
   - * d. by splitting two molecules of water.
   - e. by breaking down glucose.

E   21. An important electron and hydrogen acceptor in noncyclic pathways of ATP formation is
   - * a. $NADP^+$.
   - b. ADP.
   - c. O_2.
   - d. H_2O.
   - e. none of the above

D   22. Hydrogen ion flow in the thylakoid compartments
   - a. occurs between photosystems I and II.
   - b. is called the hydrogen transfer system.
   - * c. provides energy to produce ATP molecules.
   - d. causes excitation of chlorophyll molecules.
   - e. requires the intermediary action of acceptor molecules.

D   23. In the noncyclic pathways
- a. there is a one-way flow of electrons from photosystem I to photosystem II.
- b. ATP alone is produced.
- *   c. hydrogen ions accumulate in the thylakoid compartments.
- d. only electrons are transferred to hydrogen acceptors.
- e. water is not involved in any of the reactions.

LIGHT-INDEPENDENT REACTIONS

E   24. All but which condition must be present for light-independent reactions to occur?
- a. Carbon dioxide is present.
- *   b. The plant is exposed to light.
- c. Ribulose bisphosphate is present.
- d. ATP and NADPH are present.
- e. Required enzymes are present.

E   25. The light-independent reactions were discovered by
- a. M. D. Hatch.
- b. Andrew Benson.
- c. Melvin Calvin.
- d. Robert Hill.
- *   e. both b and c

M   26. The first stable compound produced from CO_2 in the light-independent reactions is
- *   a. phosphoglycerate (PGA).
- b. ribulose bisphosphate (RuBP).
- c. phosphoglyceraldehyde (PGAL).
- d. glucose.
- e. oxaloacetate.

M   27. The carbon dioxide acceptor in the Calvin–Benson cycle is
- a. phosphoglycerate (PGA).
- *   b. ribulose bisphosphate (RuBP).
- c. phosphoglyceraldehyde (PGAL).
- d. glucose.
- e. oxaloacetate.

M   28. Which of the following chemicals has five carbon atoms?
- a. phosphoglycerate (PGA)
- *   b. ribulose bisphosphate (RuBP)
- c. phosphoglyceraldehyde (PGAL)
- d. glucose
- e. oxaloacetate

D   29. For each six atoms of carbon dioxide fixed in the light-independent reactions, how many molecules of PGAL (phosphoglyceraldehyde) are produced?
- a. 2
- b. 3
- c. 6
- *   d. 12
- e. 15

D   30. How many molecules of PGAL (phosphoglyceraldehyde) are used to regenerate the six molecules of RuBP (ribulose bisphosphate)?
  - a. 3
  - b. 6
  - * c. 10
  - d. 12
  - e. 18

M   31. The joining of carbon dioxide to RuBP occurs in the
  - a. thylakoids.
  - * b. stroma.
  - c. mitochondria.
  - d. cytoplasm.
  - e. P700.

M   32. Which chemical has six carbon atoms?
  - a. phosphoglycerate (PGA)
  - b. ribulose bisphosphate (RuBP)
  - c. phosphoglyceraldehyde (PGAL)
  - * d. glucose
  - e. oxaloacetate

M   33. Which chemical has the most energy?
  - a. phosphoglycerate (PGA)
  - b. ribulose bisphosphate (RuBP)
  - c. phosphoglyceraldehyde (PGAL)
  - * d. glucose
  - e. oxaloacetate

M   34. Which chemical has four carbon atoms?
  - a. phosphoglycerate (PGA)
  - b. ribulose bisphosphate (RuBP)
  - c. phosphoglyceraldehyde (PGAL)
  - d. glucose
  - * e. oxaloacetate

M   35. Which is a C_4 plant?
  - a. corn
  - b. pine
  - c. sugarcane
  - d. crabgrass
  - * e. all except b

M   36. The C_4 pathway involves
  - a. RuBP.
  - b. FAD.
  - * c. oxaloacetate.
  - d. ATP.
  - e. water.

E   37. Plants need which of the following to carry on photosynthesis?
  - * a. carbon dioxide and water
  - b. nitrogen and hydrogen
  - c. oxygen and carbon dioxide
  - d. water and oxygen
  - e. ribose and carbon dioxide

CHEMOSYNTHESIS

M   38. Chemosynthetic bacteria (autotrophs) obtain energy from
- a. sunlight.
- b. sugar.
- c. water.
- * d. inorganic ions.
- e. chlorophyll.

Matching Questions

M   39. Choose the one most appropriate answer for each.

1 _____ cyclic pathway	A. uses ribulose bisphosphate; produces PGA
2 _____ noncyclic pathway	B. uses ATP and NADPH
3 _____ carbon dioxide fixation	C. detaches two phosphate groups
4 _____ the PGA to PGAL conversion	D. produces ATP and NADPH
5 _____ the formation of glucose	E. uses an electron transport system to produce ATP

Answers: 1. E   2. D   3. A   4. B   5. C

Classification Questions

The processes listed below represent major chemical pathways in the photosynthetic process. Answer questions 40–44 with reference to these five processes.
- a. light-dependent reactions
- b. chemosynthetic reactions
- c. carbon dioxide fixation
- d. Calvin–Benson cycle
- e. C_4 pathway

D   40. The formation of glucose-6-phosphate (sugar phosphate) from two molecules of phosphoglyceraldehyde

M   41. Carbon dioxide is incorporated first into an unstable intermediate compound and then into phosphoglycerate.

E   42. Yields NADPH as well as ATP

M   43. A carbon-fixing system that precedes the Calvin–Benson cycle in some plants

M   44. PGAL molecules are formed from the reaction of PGA molecules with ATP and NADPH.

Answers: 40. d   41. c   42. a   43. e   44. d

The five reactions listed below occur during noncyclic pathways of ATP formation. Use them to answer questions 45–49.

a. reduction of NADP
b. phosphorylation of ADP
c. photolysis of water
d. oxidation of chlorophyll
e. reduction of chlorophyll

D   45. Which process releases electrons to fill "holes" in chlorophyll in noncyclic pathways?

D   46. When light energy is absorbed by a leaf, what will the first result be?

D   47. What is the final step that occurs during noncyclic pathways of ATP formation?

M   48. High-energy phosphate bonds are formed during which process?

D   49. Oxygen is produced by which process?

Answers: 45. c   46. d   47. a   48. b   49. c

Selecting the Exception

E   50. Four of the five answers listed below are heterotrophs. Select the exception.
    a. fungus
*   b. carrot
    c. earthworm
    d. lobster
    e. parasite

M   51. Four of the five answers listed below are autotrophic. Select the exception.
    a. self-nourishing
    b. carbon source is CO_2
    c. chemosynthetic organisms
*   d. most bacteria
    e. sulfur bacteria

D   52. Four of the five answers listed below are part of the light-independent reactions. Select the exception.
*   a. water
    b. carbon dioxide
    c. ribulose bisphosphate
    d. phosphoglyceraldehyde
    e. phosphoglycerate

M   53. Four of the five answers listed below are participants in photosynthesis. Select the exception.
    a. photosystem
    b. grana
*   c. mitochondrion
    d. chloroplast
    e. thylakoid

D   54. Four of the five answers listed below are processes associated with light-dependent reactions. Select the exception.
    a. photolysis
    b. chemiosmosis
*   c. fixing carbon dioxide
    d. photosystem I and II
    e. noncyclic pathways of ATP formation

D   55. Four of the five answers listed below are processes associated with light-independent reactions. Select the exception.
        a. uses ATP and NADPH
        b. involves RuBP
        c. produces PGA
        d. is called the Calvin–Benson pathway
    *   e. requires light

M   56. Three of the four answers listed below are C_4 plants. Select the exception.
        a. corn
    *   b. spinach
        c. sugarcane
        d. crabgrass

M   57. Three of the four answers listed below are sources of energy for chemosynthesis. Select the exception.
        a. ammonium ions
        b. iron compounds
    *   c. sunlight
        d. sulfur compounds

CHAPTER 6
ENERGY-RELEASING PATHWAYS

Multiple-Choice Questions

ATP-PRODUCING PATHWAYS

M   1. When molecules are broken apart in respiration,
      a. the heat produced is used to drive biological reactions.
      b. the oxygen in the compounds that are broken apart is used as an energy source.
*   c. the energy released in respiration is channeled into molecules of ATP.
      d. ATP is converted into ADP.
      e. ADP is released as a waste product.

M   2. Which of the following has the most energy?
      a. cAMP
      b. ADP
      c. ATP
*   d. glucose
      e. NADPH

E   3. The main source of energy for humans is
      a. fats.
*   b. carbohydrates.
      c. proteins.
      d. nucleotides.
      e. steroids.

E   4. ATP is
*   a. the energy currency of a cell.
      b. produced by the destruction of ADP.
      c. expended in the process of photosynthesis.
      d. produced during the phosphorylation of any organic compound.
      e. none of the above

M   5. ATP
      a. can be produced by photosynthesis.
      b. is produced in the degradation of organic compounds such as glucose.
      c. is generated in anaerobic respiration.
      d. is released in aerobic respiration.
*   e. all of the above

AEROBIC RESPIRATION

D   6. Before a glucose molecule can be broken down to release energy
      a. one ATP molecule must be added to glucose.
*   b. two phosphate groups must be attached to glucose.
      c. three ATP molecules must be added to glucose.
      d. one ATP molecule must be taken away from glucose.
      e. two ATP molecules must be taken away from glucose.

D 7. The amount of energy released from a glucose molecule is dependent on what happens to
    a. carbon atoms.
    b. oxygen atoms.
*   c. hydrogen atoms.
    d. phosphorus atoms.
    e. water molecules.

E 8. Which liberates the most energy in the form of ATP?
*   a. aerobic respiration
    b. anaerobic respiration
    c. alcoholic fermentation
    d. lactate fermentation
    e. All liberate the same amount, but through different means.

D 9. Glycolysis depends on a continuous supply of
    a. NADP.
    b. pyruvate.
*   c. NAD^+.
    d. NADH.
    e. H_2O.

E 10. Glycolysis
    a. occurs in the mitochondria.
    b. happens to glucose only.
    c. results in the production of pyruvate.
    d. occurs in the cytoplasm.
*   e. c and d

M 11. The end product of glycolysis is
    a. acetyl CoA.
    b. oxaloacetate.
*   c. pyruvate.
    d. citrate.
    e. a and b

M 12. How many ATP molecules (net yield) are produced per molecule of glucose degraded during glycolysis?
    a. 1
*   b. 2
    c. 4
    d. 36
    e. 38

M 13. Aerobes use _____ as the final electron acceptor in electron transport phosphorylation.
    a. hydrogen
    b. carbon
*   c. oxygen
    d. H_2O
    e. NAD^+

M 14. The correct operational sequence of the three processes listed below is:

I. glycolysis   **II. ETP**   **III. Krebs**
    a. I → II → III
    b. II → I → III
    c. III → I → II
    d. II → III → I
*   e. I → III → II

M 15. The greatest number of ATP molecules is produced in
   a. glycolysis.
   b. alcoholic fermentation.
   c. anaerobic electron transport.
 * d. electron transport phosphorylation.
   e. the Krebs cycle.

D 16. The conversion of PGAL to pyruvate involves
   a. anaerobic respiration.
   b. photophosphorylation.
   c. the electron transport chain.
 * d. substrate-level phosphorylation.
   e. the Krebs cycle.

M 17. In the breakdown of glucose, the compound formed after two phosphorylation reactions is split into two three-carbon compounds. The three-carbon compound is named
 * a. phosphoglyceraldehyde (PGAL).
   b. pyruvate.
   c. acetyl CoA.
   d. lactate.
   e. acetaldehyde.

M 18. Which is capable of being reduced during both glycolysis and the Krebs cycle?
 * a. NAD$^+$
   b. FAD$^+$
   c. ADP
   d. NADH
   e. NADP$^+$

E 19. The Krebs cycle takes place in the
   a. ribosomes.
   b. cytoplasm.
   c. nucleus.
 * d. mitochondria.
   e. chloroplasts.

E 20. Pyruvate can be regarded as the end-product of
 * a. glycolysis.
   b. acetyl CoA formation.
   c. fermentation.
   d. the Krebs cycle.
   e. electron transport.

E 21. When glucose is used as the energy source, the largest amount of ATP is produced in
   a. glycolysis.
   b. acetyl CoA formation.
   c. the Krebs cycle.
   d. substrate-level phosphorylation.
 * e. electron transport phosphorylation.

M 22. What is the name of the process by which reduced NAD$^+$ transfers electrons to oxygen?
   a. glycolysis
   b. acetyl CoA formation
   c. the Krebs cycle
 * d. electron transport phosphorylation
   e. substrate-level phosphorylation

M   23. The breakdown of pyruvate in the Krebs cycle results in the release of
          a. energy.
          b. carbon dioxide.
          c. oxygen.
          d. hydrogen.
     *   e. all except c

D   24. To break down a glucose molecule completely requires how many passes through the
          Krebs cycle?
     *   a. 2
          b. 3
          c. 4
          d. 6
          e. 12

E   25. During electron transport phosphorylation, which ions accumulate in the outer compartment
          of the mitochondria?
          a. calcium
     *   b. hydrogen
          c. oxygen
          d. phosphorus
          e. sodium

M   26. The first intermediate produced in the Krebs cycle is
          a. pyruvate.
          b. acetyl CoA.
          c. fructose bisphosphate.
          d. oxaloacetate.
     *   e. citrate.

M   27. The last intermediate produced in the Krebs cycle is
          a. pyruvate.
          b. acetyl CoA.
          c. fructose bisphosphate.
     *   d. oxaloacetate.
          e. citrate.

D   28. During which phase of aerobic respiration is ATP produced directly by substrate-level
          phosphorylation?
          a. glucose formation
          b. ethanol production
          c. acetyl CoA formation
     *   d. the Krebs cycle
          e. all of the above

M   29. Which is a transition from glycolysis to the Krebs cycle?
     *   a. acetyl CoA formation
          b. conversion of PGAL to PGA
          c. regeneration of reduced NAD^+
          d. oxidative phosphorylation
          e. substrate-level phosphorylation

M   30. The ultimate electron acceptor in aerobic respiration is
          a. NAD^+
          b. CO_2
          c. ADP
          d. $NADP^+$
     *   e. O_2

D   31.   Which is NOT ordinarily capable of being reduced at any time?
   a. NAD^+
   b. FAD
   c. oxygen, O_2
 * d. water
   e. all of the above

M   32.   The energy used to generate most of the ATP formed in aerobic respiration is released when electrons ultimately are passed from NADH to which of the following?
 * a. oxygen
   b. acetyl CoA
   c. FADH
   d. CO_2
   e. NADPH

M   33.   The generation of concentration gradients across the membranes of mitochondria is known as which theory of ATP production?
   a. glycolytic
   b. negative ion generator
   c. phosphate pump
 * d. chemiosmotic
   e. none of the above

D   34.   Which statement is false?
   a. High concentrations of ATP inhibit the formation of more ATP.
   b. When cells need large supplies of energy, the ATP concentration in these cells actually decreases at first.
 * c. When ATP concentration declines, enzymatic activity that produces ATP declines.
   d. Cells constantly adjust their metabolic reactions to provide energy whenever it is needed.
   e. The activity of many different enzymes influences the supply of ATP in cells.

M   35.   The first forms of life that produced ATP probably used pathways similar to
   a. photosynthesis.
   b. photophosphorylation.
 * c. glycolysis and fermentation.
   d. the Krebs cycle.
   e. aerobic respiration.

E   36.   The ultimate source of energy for living things is the
   a. Krebs cycle.
   b. fossil fuels.
 * c. sun.
   d. glycolysis.
   e. aerobic respiration.

ANAEROBIC ROUTES

E   37.   Under anaerobic conditions muscle cells produce
   a. ethyl alcohol.
   b. acetaldehyde.
   c. pyruvate.
 * d. lactate.
   e. citrate.

E   38.   Sour cream and sour milk are produced by bacteria that form
         a.   ethyl alcohol.
         b.   acetaldehyde.
         c.   pyruvate.
      *   d.   lactate.
         e.   citrate.

D   39.   If fermentation follows glycolysis,
         a. CO_2 will be one of the products as pyruvate is converted to lactate.
      *   b.   the two NADH molecules produced during glycolysis will (depending on the organism) be used to reduce pyruvate to either lactate or ethanol and CO_2.
         c.   ATP will be required to convert pyruvate to either lactate or ethanol and CO_2.
         d.   oxidative phosphorylation occurs either on the plasma membrane or on derivatives of the plasma membrane.

D   40.   Fermentation
      *   a.   may occur in a muscle under anaerobic conditions.
         b.   produces more ATP than is liberated in the hydrogen transfer series.
         c.   breaks down glucose in reaction with oxygen.
         d.   is restricted to yeasts.
         e.   none of the above

D   41.   If you were searching for anaerobic bacteria, you would NOT look for them in
         a.   the guts of farm animals.
         b.   swamps.
      *   c.   mountain streams.
         d.   sediments of lakes and oceans.
         e.   sealed canned goods.

M   42.   Lactate production in muscle cells is
         a.   temporary.
         b.   due to oxygen deficiency.
         c.   an NAD regenerator.
         d.   a and b only
      *   e.   a, b, and c

D   43.   The bacteria that live in hot springs use _____ as their final hydrogen acceptor.
         a.   oxygen
      *   b.   sulfate
         c.   nitrogen
         d.   magnesium
         e.   phosphorus

ALTERNATIVE ENERGY SOURCES IN THE HUMAN BODY

D   44.   In glycolysis, approximately what percent of the total energy in glucose is released?
      *   a.   2
         b.   6
         c.   10
         d.   15
         e.   20

M   45.   Molecules associated with glycolysis and the Krebs cycle provide
         a.   sources of energy for ATP formation.
         b.   intermediates in the formation of carbohydrates.
         c.   intermediates in the formation of lipids.
         d.   intermediates in the formation of proteins.
      *   e.   all of the above

M 46. When blood glucose levels decrease (as between meals), what reserves are tapped?
  * a. glycogen
    b. fats
    c. proteins
    d. steroids
    e. amino acids

M 47. When proteins and fats are used as energy sources, their breakdown subunits enter
    a. glycolysis.
    b. electron transport.
  * c. Krebs cycle.
    d. chemiosmosis.
    e. fermentation.

Matching Questions

M 48. Matching. Choose the one most appropriate answer for each.

1 _____ glycolysis   A. produces NADH and CO_2; changes pyruvate

2 _____ fermentation   B. produces ATP, NADH, and CO_2

3 _____ acetyl-CoA formation   C. splits glucose into two pyruvate molecules

4 _____ the Krebs cycle   D. regenerates NAD^+ as pyruvate is converted to ethanol or lactate

5 _____ electron transport phosphorylation   E. uses a membrane-bound system that contains cytochromes to produce ATP

Answers: 1. C   2. D   3. A   4. B   5. E

Classification Questions

Use the five processes listed below to answer questions 49–53.
    a. glycolysis
    b. aerobic respiration
    c. anaerobic electron transport
    d. alcoholic fermentation
    e. lactate fermentation

E 49. In which process is the energy yield equal to two molecules of ATP and the final product is ethanol?

E 50. In which process is the final product lactate?

M 51. Which process yields the most energy?

D 52. Which process involves electron transport phosphorylation?

E 53. Which process precedes the Krebs cycle?

Answers: 49. d   50. e   51. b   52. b   53. a

Use the five compounds listed below to answer questions 54–58.

    a. ethanol
    b. pyruvate
    c. lactate
    d. citrate
    e. acetaldehyde

M   54. Which compound is utilized in alcoholic fermentation and lactate fermentation?

M   55. Which compound is the most likely end-product of a human runner experiencing an oxygen debt?

D   56. Which compound is an intermediate product of alcoholic fermentation, but not lactate fermentation?

M   57. Which compound is the end-product of glycolysis?

E   58. Which compound is an end-product of anaerobic respiration in exercising muscle?

Answers: 54. b   55. c   56. e   57. b   58. c

Selecting the Exception

D   59. Four of the five answers listed below are hydrogen acceptors. Select the exception.
    a. oxygen
    b. cytochrome
  * c. ATP
    d. NAD^+
    e. FAD

D   60. Four of the five answers listed below are compounds associated with anaerobic respiration. Select the exception.
    a. pyruvate
    b. lactic acid
    c. ethanol
  * d. oxaloacetic acid
    e. phosphoglyceraldehyde

D   61. Four of the five answers listed below are compounds in the glycolysis reactions. Select the exception.
    a. fructose-1,6-bisphosphate
    b. 3-phosphoglycerate (3 = PGA)
    c. pyruvate
    d. phosphoenol pyruvate (PEP)
  * e. isocitrate

D   62. Four of the five answers listed below are intermediates in the Krebs cycle. Select the exception.
    a. succinate
    b. citrate
    c. malate
    d. fumarate
  * e. acetyl CoA

D   63. Four of the five answers listed below are compounds in the Krebs reactions. Select the exception.
   a. oxaloacetate
   b. isocitrate
   c. alpha-ketoglutarate
 * d. pyruvate
   e. succinyl CoA

D   64. Four of the five answers listed below are molecules that donate hydrogens to NAD^+. Select the exception.
   a. pyruvate
   b. alpha-ketoglutarate
   c. isocitrate
 * d. succinate
   e. malate

D   65. Four of the five answers listed below are degradation processes for carbon compounds. Select the exception.
 * a. Calvin–Benson cycle
   b. Krebs cycle
   c. fermentation
   d. respiration
   e. glycolysis

CHAPTER 7
CELL DIVISION AND MITOSIS

Multiple-Choice Questions

DIVIDING CELLS: THE BRIDGE BETWEEN GENERATIONS

M 1. When a cell undergoes mitosis,
   a. the daughter cells have identical genes.
   b. the daughter cell has genes identical to those of the mother cell that produced it.
   c. the amount of cytoplasm in the mother cell and in each of the daughter cells is equal.
   d. there is an exact duplication and division of all of the organelles between daughter cells.
   * e. both a and b, but not c or d

D 2. When a eukaryotic cell divides, the daughter cells
   a. manufacture all the organelles from material in the cytoplasm.
   * b. receive enough of the organelles to start up the new cells and produce additional organelles as needed.
   c. produce individual organelles that attach to the spindle fibers and are distributed just like chromosomes.
   d. produce an equal number of organelles distributed to each cell.
   e. get cellular organelles by an unknown process.

E 3. In mitosis, if a parent cell has 16 chromosomes, each daughter cell will have how many chromosomes?
   a. 64
   b. 32
   * c. 16
   d. 8
   e. 4

E 4. Chromatids that are attached at the centromere are called what kind of chromatids?
   a. mother
   b. daughter
   * c. sister
   d. programmed
   e. either a or b, but not c or d

E 5. The spindle apparatus is made of
   a. Golgi bodies.
   * b. microtubules.
   c. endoplasmic reticulum.
   d. nucleoprotein.
   e. chromatids.

E 6. Cells with one genome or set of genetic information are described by the term
   a. polyploid.
   b. diploid.
   c. triploid.
   * d. haploid.
   e. tetraploid.

MITOSIS AND THE CELL CYCLE

M   7.   DNA replication occurs
   *   a. between the gap phases of interphase.
         b. immediately before prophase of mitosis.
         c. during prophase of mitosis.
         d. during prophase of meiosis.
         e. at any time during cell division.

E   8.   Chromosomes are duplicated during which period?
         a. M
         b. D
         c. G_1
         d. G_2
   *   e. S

STAGES OF MITOSIS

M   9.   Mitosis comes from the Greek word *mitos*, which means
         a. divide.
         b. grow.
         c. swell.
   *   d. thread.
         e. shrink.

M   10.   In eukaryotic cells, which can occur during mitosis?
         a. the duplication of chromatids
         b. the replication of DNA
         c. pairing of homologous chromosomes
   *   d. fragmentation and disappearance of nuclear envelope and nucleolus
         e. all of the above

E   11.   The chromosomes are aligned at the spindle equator during
         a. anaphase.
   *   b. metaphase.
         c. interphase.
         d. prophase.
         e. telophase.

E   12.   The chromosomes and genes are actually replicated during
         a. anaphase.
         b. metaphase.
   *   c. interphase.
         d. prophase.
         e. telophase.

E   13.   The spindle apparatus becomes visible during
         a. anaphase.
         b. metaphase.
         c. interphase.
   *   d. prophase.
         e. telophase.

M 14. The chromosomes detach from one another and become visibly separated during
* a. anaphase.
b. metaphase.
c. interphase.
d. prophase.
e. telophase.

E 15. The chromosomes are moving to opposite poles during
* a. anaphase.
b. metaphase.
c. interphase.
d. prophase.
e. telophase.

E 16. The chromosomes have arrived at opposite poles during
a. anaphase.
b. metaphase.
c. interphase.
d. prophase.
* e. telophase.

E 17. The nuclear membrane reforms during
a. anaphase.
b. metaphase.
c. interphase.
d. prophase.
* e. telophase.

M 18. Strictly speaking, mitosis and meiosis are divisions of the
a. nucleus.
b. cytoplasm.
c. chromosomes.
* d. only a and c
e. a, b, and c

D 19. Which of the following is the proper sequence for mitosis?

I. metaphase   II. telophase   III. prophase   IV. anaphase
a. I, III, IV, II
b. I, II, III, IV
* c. III, I, IV, II
d. IV, I, III, II
e. III, IV, I, II

D 20. In which of the stages below does the chromosome consist of two DNA molecules?

I. metaphase   II. telophase   III. prophase   IV. anaphase
a. III and IV
b. I, III, and IV
* c. I and III
d. I, II, and III
e. I, II, III, and IV

DIVISION OF THE CYTOPLASM

M 21. Cytokinesis (cytoplasmic division)
  a. in animal cells begins with various deposits of material associated with groups of microtubules at each pole of the nucleus.
  b. in animal cells occurs when the plasma membrane is pulled inward by a ring of microtubules that has become attached to the cell plate.
  * c. usually accompanies nuclear division.
  d. in plant cells begins with the deposition of a very rigid lipid bilayer, which is the major constituent of the cell wall.
  e. all of the above

M 22. The distribution of cytoplasm to daughter cells is accomplished during
  a. prokaryotic fission.
  b. mitosis.
  c. meiosis.
  * d. cytokinesis (cytoplasmic division).
  e. karyokinesis.

Matching Questions

E 23. Matching. Each item in the left-hand column may be matched with one, more than one, or no items from the right-hand column. Each letter may be used once or not at all.

1 _____ centriole
2 _____ centromere
3 _____ chromatid
4 _____ cytokinesis
5 _____ metaphase
6 _____ microtubules
7 _____ prophase
8 _____ telophase

A. cytoplasm apportioned between the two daughter cells

B. final phase of mitosis; daughter nuclei re-form

C. two sister chromatids are joined here

D. chromosomes condense and mitotic spindle begins to form

E. chromosomes line up at spindle equator

F. sister chromatids separate; move to opposite spindle poles now

G. about 25 mm in diameter; form mitotic spindle

H. half of a chromosome in prophase

I. in pairs in some eukaryotic cells; move to poles during spindle formation

Answers: 1. I   2. C   3. H   4. A   5. E   6. G
             7. D   8. B

Classification Questions

Answer questions 24–33 in reference to the eukaryotic cell cycle. Each question has only one BEST answer.

  a. G_2
  b. mitosis
  c. S
  d. G_1
  e. cytokinesis

E   24. Period when DNA is duplicated

E   25. Period when interphase ends in the parent cell

M   26. Event that forms two daughter cytoplasmic masses

M   27. Period of cell growth before DNA duplication

M   28. Period after DNA is duplicated

E   29. Period of nuclear division

M   30. Period when interphase begins in a daughter cell

E   31. Period commonly followed by cytokinesis

E   32. Period in which metaphase occurs

D   33. Period prior to mitosis

Answers: 24. c   25. a   26. e   27. d   28. a   29. b
                 30. d   31. b   32. b   33. a

The stages of mitosis plus interphase are listed in a–e below. Answer questions 34–44 with reference to these phases.

    a. interphase
    b. prophase
    c. metaphase
    d. anaphase
    e. telophase

E   34. During which stage are homologous pairs of chromosomes lined up on the equatorial plate?

M   35. Chromosomes replicate during which phase?

M   36. Genes replicate during which phase?

E   37. DNA replicates during which phase?

E   38. Condensation and shortening of chromosomes occurs during which phase?

E   39. Spindle fibers first appear during which stage?

M   40. During which phase do the centromeres break apart as the separated sister chromatids begin to move to opposite poles?

E   41. The microtubular spindle develops during which phase?

E   42. Sister chromatids joined at their centromeres are attached to spindle fibers during this phase.

M   43. Cytokinesis occurs as this phase of mitosis proceeds.

E   44. New daughter nuclear membranes form during this phase.

Answers: 34. c   35. a   36. a   37. a   38. b   39. b
                 40. d   41. b   42. c   43. e   44. e

Selecting the Exception

E   45. Four of the five answers listed below are stages of actual nuclear division. Select the exception.
- a. anaphase
- b. prophase
- *c. interphase
- d. telophase
- e. metaphase

D   46. Four of the five answers listed below are related by a common phase of mitosis. Select the exception.
- a. microtubules start to assemble outside the nucleus
- *b. division of centromere
- c. disappearance of nucleolus
- d. disappearance of nuclear membrane
- e. shortening and condensation of a visible chromosome

M   47. Four of the five answers listed below are periods of the same cycle. Select the exception.
- a. G_1
- b. M
- *c. R
- d. S
- e. G_2

D   48. Four of the five answers listed below are related by a common phase of mitosis. Select the exception.
- a. chromosomes decondense
- b. spindle microtubules disappear
- c. nucleolus reappears
- *d. chromosomes separate
- e. nuclear envelope reforms

M   49. Four of the five answers listed below are events occurring during mitosis. Select the exception.
- *a. chromosome replication
- b. division of centromere
- c. lining chromosomes up at the cellular equator
- d. spindle microtubules attach to centromeres
- e. chromosomes migrate to opposite ends of the cell

D   50. Four of the five answers listed below assist in chromosome movement. Select the exception.
- a. microtubule
- b. spindle microtubules
- c. centromeres
- d. centriole
- *e. nuclear envelope

D   51. Four of the five answers listed below are related by a common phase of mitosis. Select the exception.
- *a. chromosomes align at the spindle equator
- b. sister chromatids become individual chromosomes
- c. centromeres divide
- d. the chromosomes move apart
- e. spindle microtubules shorten, pulling chromosomes toward the poles

D   52. Four of the five answers listed below are related by a common division association. Select
         the exception.
         a. mitochondria
    *   b. chromosomes
         c. ribosomes
         d. plastids
         e. microbodies

CHAPTER 8
MEIOSIS

Multiple-Choice Questions

ON ASEXUAL AND SEXUAL REPRODUCTION

M   1. The essence of meiosis is that
     a. gametes are formed that receive one copy of *each* member of *each* pair of homologous chromosomes.
     b. gametes are formed that are diploid.
     c. each gamete receives one member of *each* pair of homologous chromosomes.
     d. gametes are formed that are haploid.
     *   e. c and d are correct

M   2. Through meiosis
     a. alternate forms of genes are shuffled.
     b. parental DNA is divided and distributed to forming gametes.
     c. the diploid chromosome number is reduced to haploid.
     d. offspring are provided with new gene combinations.
     *   e. all of the above

M   3. Asexually produced daughter cells are
     a. identical to each other.
     b. identical to mother cell.
     c. different from mother cell.
     d. different from each other.
     *   e. a and b

M   4. Sexual reproduction
     a. leads to uniform characteristics in a population.
     *   b. results in new combinations of genetic traits.
     c. produces genetic clones.
     d. requires less tissue differentiation than asexual reproduction.
     e. c and d

D   5. Which process is absolutely necessary for sexual reproduction to occur in a life cycle, but is not necessarily required for organisms that only reproduce asexually?
     a. prokaryotic fission
     b. mitosis
     *   c. meiosis
     d. cytokinesis
     e. karyokinesis

E   6. If a parent cell has 16 chromosomes and undergoes meiosis, the resulting cells will have how many chromosomes?
     a. 64
     b. 32
     c. 16
     *   d. 8
     e. 4

M   7. The number of chromosomes found in a eukaryotic cell
         a. indicates the phylogenetic position of the organism.
         b. is constant during the life cycle.
         c. is haploid among asexually reproducing forms and diploid if they reproduce sexually.
    *   d. is doubled by fertilization and cut in half by meiosis.
         e. is dependent on the age of the tissue.

OVERVIEW OF MEIOSIS

E   8. Chromatids are
         a. attached at the centriole.
         b. a pair of chromosomes, one from the mother and one from the father.
         c. attached at their centromeres.
         d. identical until crossing over occurs.
    *   e. both c and d, but not a or b

M   9. Homologous chromosomes
         a. may exchange parts during meiosis.
         b. have alleles for the same characteristics even though the gene expression may not be
             the same.
         c. are in pairs, one chromosome of each pair from the father and one from the mother.
         d. pair up during meiosis.
    *   e. all of the above

E   10. Copies of chromosomes linked together at their centromeres at the beginning of meiosis are
         appropriately called what kind of chromatids?
         a. mother
         b. daughter
    *   c. sister
         d. homologous
         e. none of the above

M   11. Chromosomes of a pair of homologous chromosomes may differ from other chromosomes in
         terms of
         a. size.
         b. shape.
         c. alleles they carry.
         d. position of the centromere.
    *   e. all of the above

STAGES OF MEIOSIS

D   12. Crossing over
         a. generally results in binary fission.
         b. involves nucleoli.
         c. involves breakages and exchanges being made between sister chromatids.
    *   d. alters the composition of chromosomes and results in new combinations of alleles being
             channeled into the daughter cells.
         e. all of the above

E   13. Pairing of homologues and crossing over occur during
         a. anaphase I.
         b. metaphase II.
    *   c. prophase I.
         d. prophase II.
         e. telophase II.

M   14. Meiosis typically results in the production of
          a. 2 diploid cells.
          b. 4 diploid cells.
     *   c. 4 haploid cells.
          d. 2 haploid cells.
          e. 1 triploid cell.

E   15. Under favorable conditions, during which phase of meiosis will the chromosomes appear as packets of four chromatids?
          a. anaphase I
          b. telophase II
          c. anaphase II
     *   d. prophase I
          e. metaphase II

D   16. During meiosis II
          a. cytokinesis results in the formation of a total of two cells.
     *   b. sister chromatids of each chromosome are separated from each other.
          c. homologous chromosomes pair up.
          d. homologous chromosomes separate.
          e. sister chromatids exchange parts.

M   17. Which does NOT occur in prophase I of meiosis?
     *   a. cytokinesis
          b. formation of groups of four chromatids
          c. homologue pairing
          d. crossing over
          e. condensation of chromatin

M   18. Which is NOT true of human chromosomes?
          a. The haploid number is 23.
          b. The diploid number is 46.
          c. There are 23 pairs of chromosomes.
     *   d. Human gametes end up with two of each type of 23 chromosomes.
          e. Human gametes end up one of each type of 23 chromosomes.

D   19. Crossing over is one of the most important events in meiosis because
     *   a. it produces new arrays of alleles on chromosomes.
          b. homologous chromosomes must be separated into different daughter cells.
          c. the number of chromosomes allotted to each daughter cell must be halved.
          d. homologous chromatids must be separated into different daughter cells.
          e. all of the above

GAMETE FORMATION

M   20. Gamete formation is
          a. the result of the process of mitosis.
          b. the pairing of homologous chromosomes.
     *   c. the formation of sex cells.
          d. the fusion of gametes.
          e. a process that occurs only in asexually reproducing forms.

M   21. Sperm are formed directly from the maturation of
          a. sperm mother cells.
     *   b. spermatids.
          c. spermatagonial cells.
          d. primary spermatocytes.
          e. secondary spermatocytes.

M   22. The mature ovum is produced by maturation of the
            a. oogonium.
            b. primary oocyte.
            c. secondary polar body.
            d. polar body I.
      *   e. none of the above

MORE GENE SHUFFLINGS AT FERTILIZATION

M   23. Which does NOT produce variation?
            a. crossing over
            b. random alignment of chromosomes during meiosis
      *   c. asexual reproduction
            d. genetic recombination of alleles
            e. sexual reproduction

MEIOSIS AND MITOSIS COMPARED

M   24. Maternal and paternal chromosomes are shuffled most during
            a. anaphase II.
      *   b. metaphase I.
            c. prophase I.
            d. telophase II.
            e. interphase.

D   25. In comparing mitosis and meiosis, which of the following statements is true?
            a. Meiosis I is more like mitosis than is meiosis II.
            b. Both processes result in four cells.
            c. Synapsis occurs in both.
            d. Chromatids are present only in mitosis.
      *   e. Meiosis II resembles mitosis.

Classification Questions

With reference to the mammalian reproductive system, answer questions 26–28 by using the five items
listed below.

   I. sperm   **II. mature ova**   **III. primary oocytes**
  IV. primary spermatocytes   **V. zygotes**

E   26. During fertilization, which two items combine to form a fertilized egg?
      *   a. I and II
            b. I and III
            c. I and IV
            d. II and IV
            e. III and IV

M   27. Which item or items are the same as fertilized eggs?
            a. II only
            b. III only
      *   c. V only
            d. II and III
            e. III and V

D   28. Which is a normal sequence of development?
          a. I → II → III
          b. I → IV → V
          c. II → III → V
    * d. III → II + I → V
          e. I → IV + II → V

Answer questions 29–32 by using the five numbers below.
          a. 10
          b. 20
          c. 40
          d. 60
          e. 80

M   29. How many sperm would eventually be produced from 20 spermatids?

M   30. How many sperm would eventually be produced from 20 primary spermatocytes?

M   31. How many ova (eggs) would eventually result from 20 secondary oocytes?

M   32. How many ova (eggs) would eventually result from 20 primary oocytes?

Answers: 29. b   30. e   31. b   32. b

Some of the stages of meiosis are listed in a–e below. Answer questions 33–40 with reference to these phases of meiosis.
          a. prophase I
          b. prophase II
          c. anaphase II
          d. anaphase I
          e. telophase I

E   33. The formation of groups of four chromatids occurs during which stage?

E   34. Recombination via crossing over occurs during which stage?

D   35. By the end of which phase is the number of homologous chromosomes reduced in half?

M   36. During which stage do the sister chromatids separate?

D   37. Following this phase, each individual *cell* is haploid.

M   38. Chiasmata are present during which stage?

D   39. During which phase do the centromeres separate?

D   40. New genetic combinations, upon which natural selection can act, is present after which stage?

Answers: 33. a   34. a   35. d   36. c   37. e   38. a
            39. c   40. a

Selecting the Exception

M   41. Three of the four answers listed below concern cells with two chromosome sets. Select the exception.
 a. zygote
 b. somatic cells
 * c. gamete
 d. diploid

D   42. Four of the five answers listed below are characteristic of meiosis. Select the exception.
 a. involves two divisions
 b. reduces the number of chromosomes
 * c. results in producing genetically identical cells
 d. produces haploid cells
 e. occurs in the gonads

M   43. Four of the five answers listed below are terms describing haploid cells. Select the exception.
 a. ovum
 * b. primary spermatocyte
 c. spermatid
 d. polar body
 e. secondary spermatocyte

CHAPTER 9
OBSERVABLE PATTERNS OF INHERITANCE

Multiple-Choice Questions

MENDEL'S INSIGHTS INTO PATTERNS OF INHERITANCE

E   1.   In Mendel's time, most people believed that
          a.   all genetic traits bred true.
          b.   only certain forms of domesticated plants and animals bred true.
     *   c.   the characteristics of parents were blended in the offspring.
          d.   acquired characteristics were inherited.
          e.   the inheritance of traits was controlled by blood.

M   2.   Which of the following statements is true?
     *   a.   Darwin did not know which mechanisms were responsible for the variation he saw.
          b.   The blending theory of inheritance provides excellent support for evolution.
          c.   Darwin received Mendel's paper but did not understand its significance.
          d.   The explanation for genetics had no implications for evolution.
          e.   both a and b

M   3.   In his experiments with plants, Mendel removed which part of the plant to prevent unwanted
          fertilizations?
          a.   flowers
          b.   petals
          c.   pistils
     *   d.   stamens
          e.   stigmas

E   4.   A locus is
          a.   a recessive gene.
          b.   an unmatched allele.
          c.   a sex chromosome.
     *   d.   the location of an allele on a chromosome.
          e.   a dominant gene.

M   5.   Mendel's study of genetics differed from those of his contemporaries because he
          a.   used only pure-breeding parents.
          b.   examined several different traits at the same time.
     *   c.   kept careful records and analyzed the data statistically.
          d.   worked on plants rather than animals.
          e.   confirmed the blending theory of inheritance.

E   6.   Which of the following descriptions of Mendel is incorrect?
     *   a.   He was simply lucky to work out the laws of genetics.
          b.   He focused on contrasting phenotypic characteristics.
          c.   He demonstrated that the blending theory of inheritance was wrong.
          d.   He kept exact mathematical data and was the first scientist to utilize numerical analysis
               of results.
          e.   He was a monk, a science teacher, and a gardener.

E   7. Which organism did Mendel use to work out the laws of segregation and independent assortment?
    a. the fruit fly
    b. *Neurospora*
  * c. the garden pea
    d. the chicken
    e. *E. coli*

E   8. Various forms of a gene at a given locus are called
    a. chiasmata.
  * b. alleles.
    c. autosomes.
    d. loci.
    e. chromatids.

M   9. Diploid organisms
    a. have corresponding alleles on homologous chromosomes.
    b. are usually the result of the fusion of two haploid gametes.
    c. have two sets of chromosomes.
    d. have pairs of homologous chromosomes.
  * e. all of the above

M   10. If R is dominant to r, the offspring of the cross of RR with rr will
    a. be homozygous.
  * b. display the same phenotype as the RR parent.
    c. display the same phenotype as the rr parent.
    d. have the same genotype as the RR parent.
    e. have the same genotype as the rr parent.

M   11. Mendel found that pea plants expressing a recessive trait
  * a. were pure-breeding.
    b. appeared only in the first generation of a cross between two pure-breeding plants expressing contrasting forms of a trait.
    c. disappeared after the second generation.
    d. could be produced only if one of the parents expressed the recessive trait.
    e. none of the above

E   12. Hybrid organisms produced from a cross between two pure-breeding organisms belong to which generation?
    a. P_1
    b. H_1
    c. A_1
  * d. F_1
    e. F_2

E   13. If short hair (L) is dominant to long hair (l), animals LL and Ll have the same
    a. parents.
    b. genotypes.
  * c. phenotypes.
    d. alleles.
    e. genes.

M   14. According to Mendel, what kind of genes "disappear" in F_1 pea plants?
    a. sex-linked
    b. dominant
  * c. recessive
    d. codominant
    e. lethal

M   15. If tall (*D*) is dominant to dwarf (*d*), and two homozygous varieties *DD* and *dd* are crossed, then what kind of offspring will be produced?
         a. all intermediate forms
    *   b. all tall
         c. all dwarf
         d. 1/2 tall, 1/2 dwarf
         e. 3/4 tall, 1/4 dwarf

E   16. The F_2 phenotypic ratio of a monohybrid cross is
         a. 1:1.
         b. 2:1.
         c. 9:3:3:1.
         d. 1:2:1.
    *   e. 3:1.

M   17. If all offspring of a cross have the genotype *Aa*, the parents of the crosses would most likely be
    *   a. *AA* × *aa*.
         b. *Aa* × *Aa*.
         c. *Aa* × *aa*.
         d. *AA* × *Aa*.
         e. none of the above

D   18. Short hair (*L*) is dominant to long hair (*l*). If a short-haired animal of unknown origin is crossed with a long-haired animal and they produce one long-haired and one short-haired offspring, this would indicate that
         a. the short-haired animal was pure-breeding.
    *   b. the short-haired animal was not pure-breeding.
         c. the long-haired animal was not pure-breeding.
         d. the long-haired animal was pure-breeding.
         e. None of the above can be determined with two offspring.

M   19. For Mendel's explanation of inheritance to be correct,
         a. the genes for the traits he studied had to be located on the same chromosome.
    *   b. which gametes combine at fertilization had to be due to chance.
         c. genes could not be transmitted independently of each other.
         d. only diploid organisms would demonstrate inheritance patterns.
         e. none of the above

M   20. The results of a testcross reveal that all offspring resemble the parent being tested. That parent necessarily is
         a. heterozygous.
         b. polygenic.
    *   c. homozygous.
         d. recessive.

D   21. Some dogs have erect ears; others have drooping ears. Some dogs bark when following a scent; others are silent. Erect ears and barking are due to dominant alleles located on different chromosomes. A dog homozygous for both dominant traits is mated to a droopy-eared, silent follower. The phenotypic ratio expected in the F_1 generation is
         a. 9:3:3:1.
    *   b. 100 percent of one phenotype.
         c. 1:1.
         d. 1:2:1.
         e. none of the above

D   22. Some dogs have erect ears; others have drooping ears. Some dogs bark when following a scent; others are silent. Erect ears and barking are due to dominant alleles located on different chromosomes. If two dihybrids are crossed
   a. the most common phenotype is drooping ears and barking.
 * b. all droopy-eared silent dogs are pure-breeding.
   c. the least common phenotype is drooping ears and barking.
   d. there will be no phenotypes or genotypes that resemble the original parents.
   e. there will be no offspring that resemble the F_1 generation.

D   23. A testcross involves
   a. two F_1 hybrids.
   b. an F_1 hybrid and an F_2 offspring.
   c. two parental organisms.
   d. an F_1 hybrid and the homozygous dominant parent.
 * e. an F_1 hybrid and an organism that is homozygous recessive for that trait.

M   24. For monohybrid experiments, a testcross could result in which of the following ratios?
 * a. 1:1
   b. 2:1
   c. 9:3:3:1
   d. 1:2:1
   e. 3:1

M   25. If all the offspring of a testcross are alike and resemble the organism being tested, then that parent is
 * a. homozygous dominant.
   b. homozygous recessive.
   c. heterozygous.
   d. recessive.
   e. incompletely dominant.

M   26. Mendel's principle of independent assortment states that
   a. one allele is always dominant to another.
   b. hereditary units from the male and female parents are blended in the offspring.
   c. the two hereditary units that influence a certain trait segregate during gamete formation.
 * d. each hereditary unit is inherited separately from other hereditary units.
   e. all of the above

D   27. Individuals with the genotype *Gg Hh Ii Jj* will produce how many different kinds of gametes?
   a. 2
   b. 4
   c. 6
   d. 8
 * e. 16

M   28. An individual with a genotype of *Aa Bb CC* is able to produce how many different kinds of gametes?
   a. 2
   b. 3
 * c. 4
   d. 7
   e. 8

D   29.   In cocker spaniels, black coat color (*B*) is dominant over red (*b*), and solid color (*S*) is dominant over spotted (*s*). If a red male was crossed with a black female to produce a red spotted puppy, the genotypes of the parents (with male genotype first) would be
      a.   *Bb Ss* × *Bb Ss.*
*   b.   *bb Ss* × *Bb Ss.*
      c.   *bb ss* × *Bb Ss.*
      d.   *bb Ss* × *Bb ss.*
      e.   *Bb ss* × *Bb ss.*

D   30.   In cocker spaniels, black coat color (*B*) is dominant over red (*b*), and solid color (*S*) is dominant over spotted (*s*). If a red spotted male was crossed with a black solid female and all the offspring from several crosses expressed only the dominant traits, the genotype of the female would be
*   a.   *BB SS.*
      b.   *Bb SS.*
      c.   *Bb Ss.*
      d.   *BB Ss.*
      e.   none of the above

D   31.   In cocker spaniels, black coat color (*B*) is dominant over red (*b*), and solid color (*S*) is dominant over spotted (*s*). If two black solid dogs were crossed several times and the total offspring were eighteen black solid and five black spotted puppies, the genotypes of the parents would most likely be
      a.   *Bb Ss* × *Bb Ss.*
      b.   *Bb Ss* × *Bb SS.*
      c.   *BB Ss* × *Bb ss.*
*   d.   *BB Ss* × *Bb Ss.*
      e.   *Bb ss* × *Bb SS.*

M   32.   In cocker spaniels, black coat color (*B*) is dominant over red (*b*), and solid color (*S*) is dominant over spotted (*s*). If two dihybrids (*Bb Ss*) were crossed, the most common phenotype would be
*   a.   black and solid.
      b.   black and spotted.
      c.   red and solid.
      d.   red and spotted.
      e.   none of the above

M   33.   In cocker spaniels, black coat color (*B*) is dominant over red (*b*), and solid color (*S*) is dominant over spotted (*s*). If two dihybrids (*Bb Ss*) were crossed, which would be produced?
      a.   black and spotted pure-breeding forms
      b.   black and solid pure-breeding forms
      c.   red and solid pure-breeding forms
      d.   red and spotted pure-breeding forms
*   e.   all of the above

D   34.   In cocker spaniels, black coat color (*B*) is dominant over red (*b*), and solid color (*S*) is dominant over spotted (*s*). If two dihybrids (*Bb Ss*) were crossed, what fraction of the black solid offspring would be homozygous?
      a.   4/16
      b.   9/16
*   c.   1/9
      d.   3/16
      e.   3/4

D 35. In cocker spaniels, black coat color (*B*) is dominant over red (*b*), and solid color (*S*) is dominant over spotted (*s*). In the F_2 generation of a cross between *BB ss* with *bb SS*, what fraction of the offspring would be expected to be black and spotted?
   a. 1/16
   b. 9/16
   c. 1/9
 * d. 3/16
   e. 3/4

M 36. In cocker spaniels, black coat color (*B*) is dominant over red (*b*), and solid color (*S*) is dominant over spotted (*s*). A cross of *Bb Ss* with *bb ss* would produce the phenotypic ratio
   a. 9:3:3:1.
 * b. 1:1:1:1.
   c. 1:2:1.
   d. 3:1.
   e. none of the above

D 37. In cocker spaniels, black coat color (*B*) is dominant over red (*b*), and solid color (*S*) is dominant over spotted (*s*). If *Bb Ss* were crossed with *Bb ss*, the chance that a black solid individual would be produced is
   a. 3/16.
   b. 1/3.
   c. 9/16.
 * d. 3/8.
   e. 1/16.

D 38. Coat color in one breed of mice is controlled by incompletely dominant alleles so that yellow and white are homozygous, while cream is heterozygous. The cross of two cream individuals will produce
   a. all cream offspring.
   b. equal numbers of white and yellow mice, but no cream.
   c. equal numbers of white and cream mice.
   d. equal numbers of yellow and cream mice.
 * e. equal numbers of white and yellow mice, with twice as many creams as the other two colors.

D 39. An incompletely dominant gene controls the color of chickens so that *BB* produces black, *Bb* produces a slate-gray color called blue, and *bb* produces splashed white. A second gene controls comb shape, with the dominant gene *R* producing a rose comb and *r* producing a single comb. If a pure-breeding black chicken with a rose comb is mated to a splashed white chicken with a single comb in the F_2 generation, what fraction of the offspring will be black with rose comb?
   a. 9/16
   b. 3/8
 * c. 3/16
   d. 1/8
   e. 1/16

D   40. An incompletely dominant gene controls the color of chickens so that *BB* produces black, *Bb* produces a slate-gray color called blue, and *bb* produces splashed white. A second gene controls comb shape, with the dominant gene *R* producing a rose comb and *r* producing a single comb. If a pure-breeding black chicken with rose comb is mated to a splashed white chicken with a single comb in the F_2 generation, what fraction of the offspring will be black with a single comb?
       a. 9/16
       b. 3/8
       c. 3/16
       d. 1/8
*   e. 1/16

D   41. An incompletely dominant gene controls the color of chickens so that *BB* produces black, *Bb* produces a slate-gray color called blue, and *bb* produces splashed white. A second gene controls comb shape, with the dominant gene *R* producing a rose comb and *r* producing a single comb. If a pure-breeding black chicken with a rose comb is mated to a splashed white chicken with a single comb in the F_2 generation, what fraction of the offspring will be blue with single comb?
       a. 9/16
       b. 3/8
       c. 3/16
*   d. 1/8
       e. 1/16

D   42. An incompletely dominant gene controls the color of chickens so that *BB* produces black, *Bb* produces a slate-gray color called blue, and *bb* produces splashed white. A second gene controls comb shape, with the dominant gene *R* producing a rose comb and *r* producing a single comb. If a pure-breeding black chicken with a rose comb is mated to a splashed white chicken with a single comb in the F_2 generation, what fraction of the offspring will be blue with rose comb?
       a. 9/16
*   b. 3/8
       c. 3/16
       d. 1/8
       e. 1/16

M   43. Assume short hair (*L*) is dominant to long hair (*l*) and black hair (*B*) is dominant to brown (*b*). If you found a black short-haired animal, you could determine its genotype by crossing it to an animal with a genotype of
       a. *LL BB*.
       b. *ll BB*.
       c. *ll Bb*.
*   d. *ll bb*.
       e. *LL bb*.

D   44. In the second generation of a cross of *DD RR* with *dd rr*, the most common genotype would be
       a. *DD RR*.
       b. *Dd RR*.
*   c. *Dd Rr*.
       d. *dd RR*.
       e. *dd Rr*.

E   45. The usual F_2 phenotypic ratio of a dihybrid cross is
         a. 1:1.
         b. 2:1.
      * c. 9:3:3:1.
         d. 1:2:1.
         e. 3:1.

M   46. The theory of independent assortment
      * a. cannot be demonstrated in a monohybrid cross.
         b. is illustrated by the behavior of linked genes.
         c. indicates that the expression of one gene is independent of the action of another gene.
         d. states that alleles for the same characteristic separate during meiosis.
         e. is negated by the phenomenon of epistasis.

E   47. The theory of segregation
         a. deals with the alleles governing two different traits.
         b. applies only to linked genes.
         c. applies only to sex-linked genes.
      * d. explains the behavior of a pair of alleles during meiosis.
         e. none of the above

M   48. If all the offspring of a cross had the genotype *Aa Bb*, the parents of the cross would most
         likely be
         a. *AA BB* × *aa bb*.
         b. *AA bb* × *aa BB*.
         c. *Aa Bb* × *Aa Bb*.
         d. *Aa bb* × *aa Bb*.
      * e. both a or b, but not c or d

E   49. If short hair (*L*) is dominant to long hair (*l*), then what fraction of the offspring produced by
         a cross of *Ll* × *ll* will be homozygous dominant?
         a. 1/2
         b. 1/4
         c. 1/3
      * d. none (no chance of this offspring)
         e. none of the above is correct

M   50. If short hair (*L*) is dominant to long hair (*l*), then to determine the genotype of a short-haired
         animal it should be crossed with
         a. *LL*.
         b. *Ll*.
      * c. *ll*.
         d. all of the above
         e. none of the above

E   51. What fraction of the time will the cross of *Aa Bb Cc* with *Aa Bb Cc* produce an offspring of
         genotype *aa bb cc*?
      * a. 1/64
         b. 1/32
         c. 3/64
         d. 1/16
         e. 9/64

M 52. What fraction of the time will the cross of *Aa Bb Cc* with *Aa Bb Cc* produce an offspring of genotype *Aa bb CC*?
   a. 1/64
* b. 1/32
   c. 3/64
   d. 1/16
   e. 9/64

D 53. What fraction of the time will the cross of *Aa Bb Cc* with *Aa Bb Cc* produce an offspring that expresses the dominant traits *A* and *B* and *cc* (*A_ B_ cc*)?
   a. 1/32
   b. 3/64
   c. 1/16
* d. 9/64
   e. 27/64

D 54. What fraction of the time will the cross of *Aa Bb Cc* with *Aa Bb Cc* produce an offspring that expresses the phenotype represented by the dominant gene *C* (*aa bb C_*)?
   a. 1/32
* b. 3/64
   c. 1/16
   d. 9/64
   e. 27/64

D 55. What fraction of the time will the cross of *Aa Bb Cc* with *Aa Bb Cc* produce an offspring that expresses all three dominant genes?
   a. 3/64
   b. 1/16
   c. 1/8
   d. 9/64
* e. 27/64

D 56. What fraction of the time will the cross of *Aa Bb Cc* with *Aa Bb Cc* produce an offspring that is pure-breeding?
   a. 3/64
   b. 1/16
* c. 1/8
   d. 9/64
   e. 27/64

D 57. The chance of producing an offspring of genotype *Aa BB cc* from a cross of *Aa Bb Cc* with *Aa Bb Cc* is
   a. 1/64.
* b. 1/32.
   c. 3/64.
   d. 1/16.
   e. 3/32.

D 58. The chance of producing an offspring of genotype *Aa Bb cc* from a cross of *Aa BB Cc* with *Aa BB Cc* is
   a. 1/32.
   b. 1/16.
   c. 3/32.
   d. 1/8.
* e. none (no chance of this offspring)

D   59. What fraction of the time will a cross of *Aa Bb Cc* with *Aa BB cc* produce an offspring of genotype *Aa Bb Cc*?
     a. 1/32
     b. 1/16
     c. 3/32
   * d. 1/8
     e. none (no chance of this offspring)

D   60. What fraction of the time will a cross of *Aa BB cc* with *Aa Bb CC* produce an offspring of genotype *Aa Bb CC*?
     a. 1/32
     b. 1/16
     c. 3/32
     d. 1/8
   * e. none (no chance of this offspring)

M   61. Mendel's dihybrid crosses, but not his monohybrid crosses, showed that
     a. some genes were linked together.
     b. the two alleles controlling a trait were divided equally among the gametes.
   * c. alleles for different traits were inherited independently.
     d. one of the pair of alleles is dominant to the other.
     e. the crossing of two different homozygous forms will not produce any offspring in the first generation that will look like either of the parents.

E   62. An individual with a genetic makeup of *aa BB* is said to be
   * a. pure-breeding.
     b. recessive.
     c. hybrid.
     d. dihybrid.
     e. heterozygous.

M   63. A dihybrid cross of two contrasting pure-breeding organisms
     a. produces homozygous offspring.
     b. must produce a phenotype different from either pure-breeding parent.
   * c. results in the disappearance of the recessive traits for the first generation.
     d. takes place only in the laboratory under precisely controlled conditions.
     e. will result in the immediate formation of another pure-breeding variety.

VARIATIONS ON MENDEL'S THEMES

D   64. Susan, a mother with type B blood, has a child with type O blood. She claims that Craig, who has type A blood, is the father. He claims that he cannot possibly be the father. Further blood tests ordered by the judge reveal that Craig is AA. The judge rules that
     a. Susan is right and Craig must pay child support.
   * b. Craig is right and doesn't have to pay child support.
     c. Susan cannot be the real mother of the child; there must have been an error made at the hospital.
     d. it is impossible to reach a decision based on the limited data available.
     e. none of the above

M   65. If red (*RR*) is crossed with white (*rr*) and produces a pink flower (*Rr*), and tall (*D*) is dominant to dwarf (*d*), the F_2 phenotypic ratio from a cross of *RR dd* with *rr DD* would be
     a. 9:3:3:1.
     b. 1:1:1:1.
     c. 1:2:2:4:1:2:1:2:1.
   * d. 3:6:3:1:2:1.
     e. none of the above

M 66. If a child has an AB blood type, the parents
a. must both have different blood types.
b. must be A and B, but not AB.
c. must both be AB.
d. can be any blood type.
* e. can have different blood types, but neither can be blood type O.

M 67. The F_2 phenotypic ratio of a monohybrid cross involving a gene with incompletely dominant alleles is
a. 1:1.
b. 2:1.
c. 9:3:3:1.
* d. 1:2:1.
e. 3:1.

D 68. If shape and color of radishes are due to incompletely dominant genes, crossing two dihybrid heterozygotes will produce how many different phenotypes?
a. 2
b. 3
c. 4
d. 5
* e. 9

M 69. In radishes, red and white are the pure-breeding colors and long and round are the pure-breeding shapes, while the hybrids are purple and oval. The cross of a red long radish and a white round radish will produce an F_1 generation of what phenotype?
a. all long red radishes
b. all long white radishes
c. all long purple radishes
d. all round purple radishes
* e. none of the above

D 70. In radishes, red and white are the pure-breeding colors and long and round are the pure-breeding shapes, while the hybrids are purple and oval. The cross of a red long radish and a white round radish will produce an F_2 generation in which
a. the most common phenotype will be oval and purple.
b. the purple color will occur with all three shapes of radish.
c. the red color will occur with all three shapes of radish.
d. all white long forms produced will be pure-breeding.
* e. all of the above

D 71. In radishes, red and white are the pure-breeding colors and long and round are the pure-breeding shapes, while the hybrids are purple and oval. The cross of a red oval with a purple oval will produce all but which of the following phenotypes?
* a. white and long
b. purple and oval
c. red and oval
d. purple and long
e. red and long

D   72. In radishes, red and white are the pure-breeding colors and long and round are the pure-breeding shapes, while the hybrids are purple and oval. The cross of a white oval and a purple oval will produce more
   a. red long than white long.
   b. purple round than white long.
 * c. purple oval than purple long.
   d. purple long than purple round.
   e. purple round than white oval.

D   73. In radishes, red and white are the pure-breeding colors and long and round are the pure-breeding shapes, while the hybrids are purple and oval. The cross of a purple oval with a purple oval
   a. is a cross between two pure-breeding forms.
   b. is an example of a testcross.
   c. produces only homozygous pure-breeding forms.
   d. produces only heterozygous offspring.
 * e. none of the above

D   74. In radishes, red and white are the pure-breeding colors and long and round are the pure-breeding shapes, while the hybrids are purple and oval. The F_2 generation of a cross between long and white and red and round will produce
   a. offspring that will all express dominant traits.
   b. offspring that will all be phenotypically identical.
   c. offspring that will all be genotypically identical.
 * d. purple round, purple long, white oval, and red oval offspring in equal numbers, as well as other phenotypes.
   e. both b and c, but not a or d

E   75. In incomplete dominance
   a. one allele is not dominant to another allele.
   b. the genotype can be determined by the phenotype.
   c. the heterozygote is somewhat intermediate to the two homozygotes.
   d. the intermediate phenotype may be the result of enzyme insufficiency.
 * e. all of the above

M   76. If a pure-breeding long-tail cat (*LL*) is crossed with a pure-breeding cat with no tail (rumpy, *ll*), and a cat with a short tail (stumpy) is produced, the simplest explanation is
   a. a mutation.
   b. an X-linked gene.
 * c. an incompletely dominant gene.
   d. a lethal gene.
   e. a chromosomal aberration.

M   77. If a child belonged to blood type O, he or she could not have been produced by which set of parents?
   a. Type A mother and type B father
   b. Type A mother and type O father
 * c. Type AB mother and type O father
   d. Type O mother and type O father
   e. a and c could not, but both b and d could produce a type O child

E 78. Genes at one locus that affect the expression of genes at a different locus are said to be
* a. epistatic.
   b. linked.
   c. codominant.
   d. penetrant.
   e. alleles.

E 79. A gene that produces multiple effects is called
   a. a multiple allele.
   b. an autosome.
   c. an epistatic gene.
* d. a pleiotropic gene.
   e. an incompletely dominant gene.

E 80. Multiple effects of a single gene is known as
   a. expressivity.
   b. penetrance.
   c. codominance.
* d. pleiotropy.
   e. multiple alleles.

D 81. If the cross of two guinea pig hybrids produces 9 black, 3 brown, and 4 white, when the hybrid is testcrossed the results will be
   a. 1 black, 1 brown, 1 white.
* b. 1 black, 1 brown, 2 white.
   c. 2 black, 1 brown, 1 white.
   d. 1 black, 2 brown, 1 white.
   e. none of the above

M 82. An F_2 phenotypic ratio of 13:3 is the result of
   a. single recessive epistasis.
   b. double or duplicate recessive epistasis.
   c. single dominant epistasis.
   d. double or duplicate dominant epistasis.
* e. one dominant and one recessive gene epistasis.

M 83. An F_2 phenotypic ratio of 9:7 is the result of
   a. single recessive epistasis.
* b. double or duplicate recessive epistasis.
   c. single dominant epistasis.
   d. double or duplicate dominant epistasis.
   e. one dominant and one recessive gene epistasis.

D 84. An F_2 phenotypic ratio of 9:3:4 is the result of
* a. single recessive epistasis.
   b. double or duplicate recessive epistasis.
   c. single dominant epistasis.
   d. double or duplicate dominant epistasis.
   e. one dominant and one recessive gene epistasis.

E 85. Pleiotropic genes
   a. act on secondary sexual characteristics.
* b. influence more than one aspect of phenotype.
   c. are additive.
   d. produce lethal effects when homozygous.
   e. none of the above

E 86. Which of the following is not a known factor in the expression of sickle-cell anemia?
    a. loss of shape of red blood cells with insufficient oxygen
    b. rheumatism
    c. overactive bone marrow
*   d. excessive absorption of oxygen causing the cell to swell
    e. enlarged spleen

LESS PREDICTABLE VARIATIONS IN TRAITS

E 87. A bell-shaped curve of phenotypic variation is a representation of
    a. incomplete dominance.
*   b. continuous variation.
    c. multiple alleles.
    d. epistasis.
    e. environmental variables on phenotypes.

E 88. The color of Siamese cats is controlled by
    a. multiple alleles.
    b. quantitative inheritance.
    c. incompletely dominant genes.
    d. nondisjunction.
*   e. variation in temperature, with cold temperature producing dark fur.

E 89. The variation of the color in Siamese cats is due to
    a. incomplete codominance.
    b. inactive X chromosomes.
*   c. environmental effects on phenotypes.
    d. quantitative inheritance.
    e. multiple alleles.

M 90. The reason for the darker fur on the tail, ears, nose, and legs of a Siamese cat is
    a. incomplete dominance.
*   b. the interaction of the environment with gene expression.
    c. quantitative inheritance.
    d. epistasis.
    e. none of the above

Problems

M 91. In a certain plant, when individuals with blue flowers are crossed with individuals with blue flowers, only blue flowers are produced. Plants with red flowers crossed with plants with red flowers sometimes produce only red flowers, while other times they produce either red or blue flowers. When plants with red flowers are crossed with plants with blue flowers, sometimes only red flowers are produced; other times either red or blue flowers are produced. Which gene is dominant?

M 92. Which is easier to establish in a pure-breeding population, a dominant or a recessive gene?

M 93. Tall (D) is dominant to dwarf (d). Give the F_2 genotypic and phenotypic ratios of a cross between a pure-breeding tall plant and a pure-breeding dwarf plant.

M 94. If wire hair (W) is dominant to smooth hair (w) and you find a wire-haired puppy, how would you determine its genotype by a genetic breeding experiment? Give both the genotype and phenotype involved with the cross with the unknown.

M 95. In poultry, rose comb is controlled by a dominant allele and its recessive allele controls single comb.
- (a) Give the genotype and phenotype produced from crossing a pure-breeding rose comb chicken with a pure-breeding single comb chicken.
- (b) Give the results of the backcross of the F_1 hybrid with both pure-breeding parents.

M 96. If black fur color is controlled by a dominant allele (*B*) and brown by its recessive allele (*b*), give the genotypes of the parents and offspring of a cross of a black male with a brown female that produces 1/2 black offspring and 1/2 brown offspring.

D 97. If 2 spot (*S*) is dominant to 4 spot (*s*), give the genotypes for the parents in the following crosses:
- (a) 2 spot × 2 spot yields 2 spot and 4 spot
- (b) 2 spot × 4 spot yields only 2 spot
- (c) 2 spot × 4 spot yields 2 spot and 4 spot
- (d) 2 spot × 2 spot yields only 2 spot
- (e) 4 spot × 4 spot yields only 4 spot

D 98. In humans, normal skin pigmentation is influenced by a dominant gene (*C*), which allows pigmentation to develop. All individuals who are homozygous for the recessive allele (*c*) are unable to produce an enzyme needed for melanin formation and are therefore referred to as albino. Two normal parents produce an albino child. What are the chances that the next child will be an albino?

D 99. The allele for albinism (*c*) is recessive to the allele for normal pigmentation (*C*). A normally pigmented woman whose father is an albino marries an albino man whose parents are normal. They have three children, two normal and one albino. Give the genotypes for each person listed.

D 100. In garden peas, one pair of alleles controls the height of the plant and a second pair of alleles controls flower color. The allele for tall (*D*) is dominant to the allele for dwarf (*d*), and the allele for purple (*P*) is dominant to the allele for white (*p*). A tall plant with purple flowers crossed with a dwarf plant with white flowers produces 1/2 tall with purple flowers and 1/2 tall with white flowers. What is the genotype of the parents?

D 101. In garden peas, one pair of alleles controls the height of the plant and a second pair of alleles controls flower color. The allele for tall (*D*) is dominant to the allele for dwarf (*d*), and the allele for purple (*P*) is dominant to the allele for white (*p*). A tall plant with white flowers crossed with a dwarf plant with purple flowers produces all tall offspring with purple flowers. What is the genotype of the parents?

D 102. In garden peas, one pair of alleles controls the height of the plant and a second pair of alleles controls flower color. The allele for tall (*D*) is dominant to the allele for dwarf (*d*), and the allele for purple (*P*) is dominant to the allele for white (*p*). A tall plant with purple flowers crossed with a dwarf plant with white flowers produces 1/4 tall purple, 1/4 tall white, 1/4 dwarf purple, and 1/4 dwarf white. What is the genotype of the parents?

D 103. In garden peas, one pair of alleles controls the height of the plant and a second pair of alleles controls flower color. The allele for tall (*D*) is dominant to the allele for dwarf (*d*), and the allele for purple (*P*) is dominant to the allele for white (*p*). A tall plant with white flowers crossed with a dwarf plant with purple flowers produces 1/4 tall purple, 1/4 tall white, 1/4 dwarf purple, and 1/4 dwarf white. What is the genotype of the parents?

D 104. In garden peas, one pair of alleles controls the height of the plant and a second pair of alleles controls flower color. The allele for tall (*D*) is dominant to the allele for dwarf (*d*), and the allele for purple (*P*) is dominant to the allele for white (*p*). A tall plant with purple flowers crossed with a tall plant with white flowers produces 3/8 tall purple, 1/8 tall white, 3/8 dwarf purple, and 1/8 dwarf white. What is the genotype of the parents?

D   105. In garden peas, one pair of alleles controls the height of the plant and a second pair of alleles controls flower color. The allele for tall (D) is dominant to the allele for dwarf (d), and the allele for purple (P) is dominant to the allele for white (p). A tall purple crossed with a tall purple produces 3/4 tall purple and 1/4 tall white. What is the genotype of the parents?

D   106. In horses, black coat color is influenced by the dominant allele (B), and chestnut coat color is influenced by the recessive allele (b). Trotting gait is due to a dominant gene (T), pacing gait to the recessive allele (t). If a homozygous black trotter is crossed to a chestnut pacer,
    (a)   what will be the appearance of the F_1 and F_2 generations?
    (b)   which phenotype will be the most common?
    (c)   which genotype will be the most common?
    (d)   which of the potential offspring will be certain to breed true?

D   107. In horses, black coat color is influenced by the dominant allele (B) and chestnut coat color by the recessive allele (b). Trotting gait is due to a dominant gene (T), pacing gait to the recessive allele (t). What color horse would you use to find out the genotype of a black trotter? Give the genotype and phenotype.

D   108. Crosses between a yellow rat and a yellow rat always produce yellow. Crosses between a white rat and a white rat always produce white. The alleles affect the same aspect of coat color. The crosses of a white with a yellow produce a cream. What happens if you cross two creams?

D   109. Assume red plants crossed with white plants give rise to pink plants. Explain how to eliminate red plants if you start with two pinks.

D   110. If long or round are homozygous forms of an incompletely dominant gene and oval is the phenotype of the heterozygote, give the F_2 ratio of the cross between long and round (both genotype and phenotype).

D   111. A breeder of cattle has a herd of white cows and a roan bull. Hair color in this breed is controlled by an incompletely dominant gene. The two homozygous forms are either red or white, and the heterozygous is roan.
    (a)   What color of calves are expected and in what proportions?
    (b)   Outline a procedure to develop an all-red herd.

D   112. In radishes, two incompletely dominant genes control color and shape. Red and white radishes are homozygous, while the hybrid is purple. Long and round are homozygous and, if crossed, will produce an oval hybrid. Give the F_2 genotypic and phenotypic ratio produced by crossing pure-breed red long radishes with white round varieties.

D   113. In a certain breed of chicken an incompletely dominant gene controls color. The homozygous black, when crossed with the homozygous splashed-white, produces an intermediate gray color pattern referred to as blue. A second gene controls the shape of the comb. The dominant allele (R) produces rose, while the recessive allele (r) produces single. Give the F_1 and F_2 genotypic and phenotypic ratios of a cross between a pure-breeding black single and a pure-breeding splashed-white rose.

D 114. There are three alleles controlling the ABO blood types. I^A and I^B are codominant genes so that the combination $I^A I^B$ produces the AB blood type. The third allele I^O is recessive to the other two alleles. Indicate which of these parents could produce the given child:

	Parents	Child	Yes or No
(a)	A × AB	B	
(b)	A × O	A	
(c)	A × B	O	
(d)	A × AB	O	
(e)	A × AB	B	
(f)	B × B	O	
(g)	AB × AB	A	

D 115. In horses there are four alleles at the A locus. Arranged in dominance sequence they are:

A (wild) a^b (bay) a^c (brown) a^d (black)

If you bred several bay mares whose sires were brown to a brown stallion whose sire was black, what type of offspring would be produced and in what proportion?

D 116. In rabbits there are four alleles at the c locus. Arranged in dominance sequence they are:

C (agouti) c^{ch} (chinchilla) c^h (Himalayan) and c (albino)

(a) Is it possible to cross two agouti rabbits and produce both chinchilla and Himalayan offspring?

(b) Is it possible to cross two chinchillas and produce 1/2 chinchilla and 1/2 Himalayan?

D 117. Gray is homozygous while blue is a heterozygous form of a semilethal gene. Give the ratio of the offspring produced in the cross of two blues.

D 118. A cross of two Kerry horses always produces Kerry. A cross of a Kerry with a Dexter produces half and half. Crosses of two Dexters produce two Dexters for every Kerry. Explain.

D 119. In the late 1920s, a mutation occurred in many silver fox farms around the world. The fox farms that sold expensive furs were proud of the quality of their furs, and each advertised that it had the best, most pure breed of all the fox farms. The new mutations produced a "platinum" coat pattern that was commercially desirable, so the farms crossed them to get more. The results of their breeding experiments were as follows: (1) silver × silver → all silver offspring; (2) silver × platinum → equal numbers of silver and platinum; (3) platinum × platinum → 2 platinum for each silver offspring. Explain.

D 120. There is a color pattern inherited in certain mice in which agouti (gray) is homozygous and yellow is heterozygous. A cross of two yellows produces two yellows for each agouti. A second gene, C/c, controls the expression of the color genes: C is the dominant allele that allows color to be expressed, and the recessive gene in the homozygous condition (cc) prevents any color from being expressed.

(a) Give the genotypes of a white parent crossed with a yellow parent that produces 1/2 white, 1/3 yellow, 1/6 agouti offspring.

(b) Give the results of the cross of two forms heterozygous for each gene.

(c) Can you develop a pure-breed population for any of the colors?

D   121.   In poultry, the genes for rose comb (*R*) and pea comb (*P*) produce walnut whenever they occur together (*R_ P_*); single-combed individuals have the homozygous condition for both genes (*rr pp*).
   (a)   Give the F_1 and F_2 phenotypic results of a cross of a pure-breeding rose comb (*RR pp*) with a pure-breeding pea comb (*rr PP*).
   (b)   Give the phenotypic results of a cross of *Rr Pp* × *rr Pp*.
   (c)   Give the phenotypic results of a cross of *RR Pp* × *rr Pp*.
   (d)   Give the phenotypic results of a cross of *Rr pp* × *rr Pp*.
   (e)   Give the phenotypic results of a cross of *Rr Pp* × *rr pp*.

D   122.   Congenital deafness in humans is due to the homozygous condition of either or both of the recessive genes *d* or *e*. Both dominant *D* and *E* are necessary for normal hearing. Gene *D/d* affects the middle ear, while gene *E/e* affects the inner ear. It does not matter how good the normal inner ear (as indicated by *E_*) is; if there is something wrong in the middle ear, the individual is unable to hear. The same applies for the other gene. Give the phenotypic results of the following crosses:
   (a)   *Dd EE* × *Dd EE*
   (b)   *Dd Ee* × *Dd Ee*
   (c)   *dd EE* × *DD ee*
   (d)   *Dd EE* × *Dd ee*
   (e)   *Dd EE* × *DD Ee*

D   123.   White fruit color in summer squash is influenced by a dominant allele *W*, while colored fruit must be *ww*. In the presence of *ww*, a dominant gene *G* results in yellow fruit, and if the individual had both recessive genes in the homozygous condition, it would be green. Give the F_2 phenotypic ratios resulting from a cross of a pure-breeding white of genotype *WW GG* with a green.

D   124.   In cultivated stocks, the cross of a variety of white-flower plants produced all red flowers in the F_1 generation, but the F_2 generation produced 87 red, 31 cream, and 39 white. Explain these results by giving the genotypes possible for each phenotype.

D   125.   In summer squash, spherical-shaped fruit has been shown to be dominant to elongated fruit. On one occasion two different spherical varieties were crossed and produced all disk-shaped fruits. When these hybrid disk-shaped fruits were crossed they produced 75 disk-shaped fruits, 48 spherical fruits, and 9 elongated fruits. Explain these results.

D   126.   In sweet peas, genes *C* and *P* are necessary for colored flowers. In the absence of either (*_ pp* or *cc _*), or both (*cc pp*), the flowers are white. What will be the color of the offspring of the crosses in what proportions for the following?
   (a)   *Cc Pp* × *cc pp*
   (b)   *Cc Pp* × *Cc Pp*
   (c)   *Cc PP* × *Cc pp*
   (d)   *Cc pp* × *cc Pp*

D   127.   In sweet peas, genes *C* and *P* are necessary for colored flowers. In the absence of either (*_ pp* or *cc _*), or both (*cc pp*), the flowers are white. Give the probable genotype of a plant with colored flowers and a plant with white flowers that produced 38 plants with colored flowers and 42 plants with white flowers.

D   128.   In a certain variety of plants, a cross between a red-flowered plant and a white-flowered plant produced an all-red flower F_1. In the F_2 there were 140 red, 50 cream, and 65 white.
   (a)   Offer an explanation for this F_2 ratio.
   (b)   What ratio would be produced in a testcross of the F_1 hybrid?
   (c)   What ratio would be produced if all the white F_2 plants were crossed among themselves?

D 129. In a certain breed of chicken two genes control color. A dominant allele (*I*) inhibits the expression of any color gene (*C*). A second recessive gene (*c*) results in albinism when homozygous (*cc*). Give the F_2 phenotypic ratio of a colored chicken *ii CC* with a white *II cc*.

D 130. In mice the allele for colored fur (*C*) is dominant to the allele for albinism (*c*). The allele (*W*) for normal behavior is dominant to that for waltzing movement (*w*). Give the probable genotypes of the parents if they produced the offspring listed after the following crosses:
 (a) Colored normal *x* white waltzer produced 10 colored normal, 8 colored waltzers, 2 white waltzers, 11 white normal.
 (b) Colored normal *x* white normal produced 35 colored normal, 13 colored waltzers.
 (c) Colored normal *x* colored normal produced 37 colored normal, 14 colored waltzers, 9 white normal, and 5 white waltzers.

D 131. Pure-breeding yellow guinea pigs crossed with pure-breeding white ones produce only cream-colored offspring. This pattern indicates incomplete dominance. Rough hair is found to be dominant to smooth hair. Give the F_1 and F_2 genotypic and phenotypic ratios of a cross of a smooth white guinea pig with a homozygous rough yellow guinea pig.

D 132. There are nine coat colors known in foxes. If a red fox were crossed with a double-black fox, all the hybrids would be red above and black below in a pattern known as blended cross. If two blended crosses were mated, the F_2 ratio would be as follows: 1 red, 2 smokey red, 2 cross red, 4 blended cross, 1 standard silver, 2 substandard silver, 1 Alaskan silver, 2 sub-Alaskan silver, and 1 double black.
 (a) Using the letters *A/a* and *B/b* to serve as the genes for these animals, develop a genotype for each variety listed.
 (b) Two crosses will produce all blended-cross offspring. One is used above (red fox x double black); what is the other?
 (c) List the genotype and phenotype of all the pure-breeding foxes.
 (d) Give the genotypic and phenotypic ratio of a cross between two substandard silvers.
 (e) Give the genotype and phenotype of the offspring produced in a cross of 1 sub-Alaskan silver and a cross red.

D 133. In the garden pea Mendel found that tall (*D*) green pods (*G*) and inflated pods (*C*) were dominant to their alleles, dwarf (*d*) yellow pods (*g*) and constricted pods (*c*). Given the following genotypes, determine the chances of producing the offspring shown.
 (a) *DD Gg Cc* × *Dd Gg cc* → *DD gg Cc*
 (b) *DD Gg Cc* × *Dd Gg Cc* → tall green pod, constricted pod
 (c) *Dd Gg Cc* × *Dd GG cc* → tall green pod, inflated pod
 (d) *Dd Gg Cc* × *Dd Gg Cc* → *D_ G_ cc*
 (e) *Dd Gg Cc* × *Dd gg CC* → *D_ G_ C_*
 (f) *Dd gg cc* × *DD Gg cc* → tall green pod, inflated pod
 (g) *Dd Gg Cc* × *Dd Gg Cc* → *Dd Gg Cc*
 (h) *Dd Gg Cc* × *Dd Gg Cc* → *dd gg cc*

D 134. In tomatoes red (*R*) is dominant to yellow (*r*), tall (*D*) is dominant to dwarf (*d*), and smooth (*H*) is dominant to peach or hairy (*h*).
 (a) How many different genotypes are there in relationship to these three characteristics?
 (b) How many different phenotypes are there in relationship to these three characteristics?
 (c) How many different homozygous pure-breeding forms can be produced?

D 135. If you were following the inheritance patterns of two different sets of multiple alleles located on different chromosomes, how many different possible gametes could be produced if locus 1 had five possible alleles and locus 2 had six alleles?

Classification Questions

Answer questions 136–140 using the group of answers below.

  a. 4
  b. 6
  c. 8
  d. 12
  e. 24

D   136. In a dihybrid cross between a parent that is a double heterozygote (*Aa Bb*) and a parent that is homozygous dominant for one gene and heterozygous for the other (*AA Bb*), how many unique genotypes potentially will be present in their offspring?

D   137. In a dihybrid cross between a parent that is a double heterozygote (*Aa Bb*) and a parent that is homozygous recessive for one gene and heterozygous for the other (*aa Bb*), how many unique phenotypes potentially will be present in their offspring?

D   138. In a dihybrid cross between a parent that is a double heterozygote (*Aa Bb*) and a parent that is a double homozygous recessive (*aa bb*), how many unique phenotypes potentially will be present in their offspring?

D   139. Plant species X is diploid (2*n* = 24) and has a quantitative trait, the expression of which is controlled by gene loci on each of its chromosomes. What is the maximum number of alleles for this trait that any one individual of species X could have?

D   140. Animal species X is tetraploid (4*n* = 12). Following gene duplication and translocation, a given gene is found on each chromosome. How many alleles for this gene can be present in an individual of this species?

Answers: 136. b   137. a   138. a   139. e   140. d

Selecting the Exception

D   141. Four of the five answers listed below are dominant traits. Select the exception.
    a. green pod
    b. purple flower
    c. yellow seed coat
  * d. dwarf plant
    e. axial flower position

E   142. Four of the five answers listed below describe the heterozygous condition. Select the exception.
  * a. homozygous
    b. carrier
    c. heterozygotes
    d. hybrid
    e. *Aa*

M   143. Four of the five answers listed below describe the gene makeup. Select the exception.
    a. pure-breeding
    b. homozygous
    c. heterozygous
    d. carrier
  * e. phenotype

M 144. Four of the five answers listed below are accepted as valid explanations of genetic behavior. Select the exception.
* a. blending
   b. dominance
   c. segregation
   d. independent assortment
   e. probability

E 145. Four of the five answers listed below are pure-breeding. Select the exception.
   a. *AA BB*
* b. *Aa BB*
   c. *AA bb*
   d. *aa BB*
   e. *aa bb*

Answers to problems in Chapter 9

91. Red

92. Recessive

93. 1 *DD*, 2 *Dd*, 1 *dd*; 3 tall, 1 dwarf

94. Smooth hair, *ww*

95. (a) *Rr*, rose
  (b) *Rr* × *RR* → all rose, *Rr* × *rr* →
    1/2 rose, 1/2 single

96. Black male (*Bb*) × brown female (*bb*)
  offspring: black (*Bb*) brown (*bb*)

97. (a) *Ss* × *Ss* → *S_* + *ss*
  (b) *Ss* × *ss* → *Ss*
  (c) *Ss* × *ss* → *Ss* + *ss*
  (d) *SS* × *S _* → *S _*
  (e) *ss* × *ss* → *ss*

98. 1/4 chance

99. Normal pigmented woman, *Cc*; albino father, *cc*; albino man, *cc*; normal parents, *Cc* + *Cc*;
  3 children, 2 normal *Cc*, 1 albino *cc*

100. *DD Pp* × *dd pp*

101. *DD pp* × *dd PP*

102. *Dd Pp* × *dd pp*

103. *Dd pp* × *dd Pp*

104. *Dd Pp* × *Dd pp*

105. *Dd Pp* × *DD Pp*

106. (a) F$_1$: black trotters; F$_2$: 9 black trotters,
    3 black pacers, 3 chestnut trotters, 1 chestnut pacer
  (b) Black pacer
  (c) *Bb Tt*
  (d) *bb tt,* chestnut pacers

107. *bb tt*, chestnut pacer

108. 1 yellow, 2 cream, 2 white

109. Cross until you get white, and use white in crosses until you cross two whites, then all subsequent plants will be white.

110   1 *LL*, 2 *Ll*, 1 *ll*; 1 long, 2 oval, 1 round

111. (a)   1/2 white, 1/2 roan

      (b)   Roan with white → roan, roan × roan → red,
            roan × red → red, red × red → red

112. 1 *LL RR* long red, 2 *LL Rr* long purple, 2 *Ll RR* oval red,
      4 *Ll RR* oval purple, 1 *ll RR* round red, 1 *ll Rr* round oval,
      1 *Ll rr* long white, 2 *Ll rr* oval white, 1 *ll rr* round white

113. F_1: *Bb Rr* blue rose; F_2: 3 *BB R_* black rose,
      6 *Bb R_* blue rose, 3 *bb R_* splashed-white rose,
      1 *BB rr* black single, 2 *Bb rr* blue single,
      1 *bb rr* splashed-white single

114. (a) yes; (b) yes; (c) yes; (d) no; (e) yes; (f) yes; (g) yes

115. $a^b a^c$ x $a^c a^d$; 1/2 bay, 1/2 brown

116. (a) no; (b) not likely but possible—would expect a 3:1

117. 1 gray, 2 blues (1 lethal)

118. Kerry is homozygous (*DD*), Exter is heterozygous (*Dd*), *dd* is lethal .

119. *PP* (silver), *Pp* (platinum), *pp* (lethal)

120. (a)   *Yy Cc* × *Yy cc*

      (b)   *Yy Cc* × *Yy Cc* → 3/12 *YY C_* agouti,
            6/12 *Yy C_* yellow, 3/12 *_cc* albino

      (c)   white and agouti

121. (a) F_1: *Rr Pp* walnut; F_2: 9 *R_ P_* walnut, 3 *R_pp* rose,
            3 *rr P_* pea, 1 *rr pp* single

      (b)   3/8 walnut, 3/8 pea, 1/8 rose, 1/8 single

      (c)   3/4 walnut, 1/4 rose

      (d)   1/4 walnut, 1/4 rose, 1/4 pea, 1/4 single

      (e)   1/4 walnut, 1/4 rose, 1/4 pea, 1/4 single

122. (a)   3/4 normal, 1/4 deaf

      (b)   9/16 normal, 7/16 deaf

      (c)   all normal

      (d)   3/4 normal, 1/4 deaf

      (e)   all normal

123. 12/16 *W_ _ _* white, 3/16 *ww G_* yellow, 1/16 *ww gg* green

124. *R*-red, *r*-cream, *A*-pigment, *a*-albino
      9 *R_ A_* red, 3 *rr A_* cream, 4 *_ aa* white

125. 9 *D_ S_* disk, 3 *D_ ss* spherical, 3 *dd S_* spherical, 1 *dd ss* elongated; presence of both
      dominant genes produces disk, while the presence of either one of the genes as homozygous
      recessive produces spherical, and both recessive produces elongated fruit.

126. (a)   1/4 color, 3/4 white

      (b)   9/16 color, 7/16 white

      (c)   3/4 color, 1/4 white

      (d)   1/4 color, 3/4 white

127. *Cc Pp* × *CC pp*

128. (a)   *R*-red, *r*-cream, *A*-color, *a*-albino; 9 *R_ A_* red, 3 *rr A_* cream, 4 *__ aa* white

      (b)   1/4 red, 1/4 cream, 1/2 white

      (c)   all offspring would be white because all would be *__ aa*

129. $9\ I\_\ C\_ + 3\ I\_\ cc + 1\ ii\ cc = 13$ white $+ 3\ ii\ C\_ = 3$ color

130. (a) *Cc Ww* x *cc ww*

    (b) *CC Ww* x *cc Ww*

    (c) *Cc Ww* x *Cc Ww*

131. F_1: rough cream *Yy Rr*; F_2: 3 *YY R_* yellow rough, 6 *Yy R_* cream rough, 3 *yy R_* white rough, 1 *YY rr* yellow smooth, 2 *Yy rr* cream smooth, 1 *yy rr* white smooth

132. (a) 1 *AA BB* red

       2 *AA Bb* smokey red

       2 *Aa BB* cross red

       4 *Aa Bb* blended cross

       1 *aa BB* standard silver

       2 *aa Bb* substandard silver

       1 *AA bb* Alaskan silver

       2 *Aa bb* sub-Alaskan silver

       1 *aa bb* double black

    (b) *aa BB* standard silver x *AA bb* Alaskan silver

    (c) *AA BB* red, *AA bb* Alaskan silver,

       aa BB standard silver, *aa bb* double black

    (d) 1 standard silver *aa BB*

       2 substandard silver *aa Bb*, 1 double black *aa bb*

    (e) 1 smokey red *AA Bb*, 2 blended cross *Aa Bb*,

       1 substandard silver *aa Bb*

133. (a) $(1/2)\ (1/4)\ (1/2) = 1/16$

    (b) $(1)\ (3/4)\ (1/4) = 3/16$

    (c) $(3/4)\ (1)\ (1/2) = 3/8$

    (d) $(3/4)\ (3/4)\ (1/4) = 9/64$

    (e) $(3/4)\ (1/2)\ (1) = 3/8$

    (f) $(1)\ (1/2)\ 0 = 0$

    (g) $(2/4)\ (2/4)\ (2/4) = 8/64$

    (h) $(1/4)\ (1/4)\ (1/4) = 1/64$

134. (a) 27 (b) 8 (c) 8

135. 30 possibilities

CHAPTER 10
CHROMOSOMES AND HUMAN GENETICS

Multiple-Choice Questions

EARLY STUDIES OF CHROMOSOMES

E   1.   Who discovered chromosomes?
            a. Morgan
            b. Mendel
            c. Sturtevant
            d. Weismann
    *   e. Flemming

E   2.   Who discovered the process of meiosis?
            a. Morgan
            b. Mendel
            c. Sturtevant
    *   d. Weismann
            e. Flemming

E   3.   Who was the first to use fruit flies in genetics experiments?
    *   a. Morgan
            b. Mendel
            c. Sturtevant
            d. Weismann
            e. Flemming

M   4.   Weismann proposed that
            a. the number of chromosomes is cut in half in the sex cells.
            b. the number of chromosomes is doubled by mitosis.
            c. half the chromosomes in a diploid cell come from the father and the other half from the mother.
            d. fertilization restores the number of chromosomes.
    *   e. all except b

E   5.   Genes are
            a. located on chromosomes.
            b. inherited in the same way as chromosomes.
            c. arranged in linear sequence on chromosomes.
            d. assorted independently during meiosis.
    *   e. all of the above

E   6.   Chromosomes other than those involved in sex determination are known as
            a. nucleosomes.
            b. heterosomes.
            c. alleles.
    *   d. autosomes.
            e. liposomes.

M   7. DNA coding regions that affect the same trait are called
           a. homologues.
*   b. alleles.
           c. autosomes.
           d. loci.
           e. gametes.

E   8. The location of a gene on a chromosome is its
           a. centromere.
*   b. locus.
           c. autosome.
           d. allele.
           e. none of the above

D   9. In his experiments with *Drosophila melanogaster*, Morgan demonstrated that
           a. fertilized eggs have two sets of chromosomes, but eggs and sperms have only one set in each gamete.
           b. aneuploidy exists in karyotypes that have undergone deletions and inversions in specific chromosomes.
           c. colchicine is effective in producing polyploidy in F_2 generations.
*   d. certain genes are located only on an X chromosome and have no corresponding alleles on the Y chromosome.
           e. all of the above

M   10. All of the genes located on a given chromosome comprise a
           a. karyotype.
           b. bridging cross.
           c. wild-type allele.
*   d. linkage group.
           e. none of the above

E   11. If two genes are on the same chromosome,
           a. crossing over occurs frequently.
           b. they assort independently.
*   c. they are in the same linkage group.
           d. they are segregated during meiosis.
           e. an inversion will usually occur.

E   12. Who proposed the law of independent assortment?
           a. Morgan
*   b. Mendel
           c. Sturtevant
           d. Weismann
           e. Flemming

E   13. In a pedigree chart a male showing the specific trait being studied is indicated by a
*   a. darkened square.
           b. clear square.
           c. darkened diamond.
           d. clear triangle.
           e. darkened circle.

E   14. In a pedigree chart a female who does not demonstrate the trait being studied is represented by a
       a. darkened square.
       b. clear diamond.
*   c. clear circle.
       d. darkened triangle.
       e. darkened oval.

M   15. If two genes are almost always found in the same gamete,
*   a. they are located close together on the same chromosome.
       b. they are located on nonhomologous chromosomes.
       c. they are located far apart on the same chromosome.
       d. they are found on the sex chromosome.
       e. all except c

M   16. Genes that are located on the same chromosome
       a. tend to be inherited together.
       b. will appear together in the gamete.
       c. are said to be linked.
       d. may be separated during crossing over.
*   e. all of the above

D   17. If alleles L, M, and N are on the maternal chromosome and l, m, and n are on the paternal chromosome, the only way that a gamete from a heterozygote will produce a gamete with alleles l, m, and N is through
       a. nondisjunction.
       b. the laws of segregation.
       c. the law of independent assortment.
*   d. crossing over.
       e. chromosome aberration.

D   18. If the paternal chromosome has alleles L, M, and n and the maternal chromosomes have l, m, and N, then the chromosome that cannot be produced by crossing over is
       a. *LMN*.
*   b. *LMn*.
       c. *LmN*.
       d. *Lmn*.
       e. *lmn*.

M   19. Genetic recombination as a result of crossing over occurs more readily in genes that
       a. are on the sex chromosomes.
       b. are on the autosomes.
       c. are located close together on the same chromosome.
*   d. are located far apart on the same chromosome.
       e. are located on different chromosomes.

E   20. A karyotype
       a. compares one set of chromosomes to another.
*   b. is a visual display of chromosomes arranged according to size.
       c. is a photograph of cells undergoing mitosis during anaphase.
       d. of a normal human cell shows 48 chromosomes.
       e. cannot be used to identify individual chromosomes beyond the fact that two chromosomes are homologues.

E   21. In karyotyping, individual chromosomes may be distinguished from others by
         a. a comparison of chromosome lengths.
         b. bands produced on chromosomes by differential staining.
         c. the position of centromeres.
    *   d. all of the above
         e. none of the above

M   22. Karyotyping is usually done using what kind of cells?
         a. muscle
    *   b. blood
         c. cartilage
         d. sex
         e. epidermal

M   23. Which chemical is used to keep chromosomes from separating during metaphase?
         a. Giemsa stain
         b. acetone
    *   c. colchicine
         d. alcohol
         e. formaldehyde

M   24. Karyotyping involves taking pictures of chromosomes during
         a. prophase.
         b. telophase.
    *   c. metaphase.
         d. interphase.
         e. anaphase.

HUMAN GENETICS

M   25. Which is NOT a chromosomal aberration?
         a. deletion
         b. extra chromosomes
         c. translocation (exchange of parts between nonhomologues)
    *   d. crossing over
         e. inversion

D   26. A colorblind man and a woman with normal vision whose father was colorblind have a son. Colorblindness, in this case, is caused by an X-linked recessive gene. If only the male offspring are considered, the probability that their son is colorblind is
         a. .25 (or 25 percent).
    *   b. .50 (or 50 percent).
         c. .75 (or 75 percent).
         d. 1.00 (or 100 percent).
         e. none of the above

M   27. Red–green colorblindness is an X-linked recessive trait in humans. A colorblind woman and a man with normal vision have a son. What is the probability that the son is colorblind?
    *   a. 100 percent
         b. 75 percent
         c. 50 percent
         d. 25 percent
         e. 0 percent

M   28. Red–green colorblindness is an X-linked recessive trait in humans. What is the probability that a colorblind woman and a man with normal vision will have a colorblind daughter?
    a. 100 percent
    b. 75 percent
    c. 50 percent
    d. 25 percent
*   e. 0 percent

M   29. If a daughter expresses an X-linked recessive gene, she inherited the trait from
    a. her mother.
    b. her father.
*   c. both parents.
    d. neither parent.
    e. her grandmother.

M   30. A human X-linked recessive gene may be
    a. found on the Y chromosome.
    b. passed to daughters from their fathers.
    c. passed to sons from their mothers.
    d. expressed more commonly among females.
*   e. both b and c

M   31. An X-linked carrier is a
    a. homozygous dominant female.
*   b. heterozygous female.
    c. homozygous recessive female.
    d. homozygous male.
    e. heterozygous male.

M   32. A human X-linked gene is
    a. found only in males.
    b. more frequently expressed in females.
    c. found on the Y chromosome.
    d. transmitted from father to son.
*   e. found on the X chromosome.

D   33. Colorblindness is an X-linked trait in humans. If a colorblind woman marries a man with normal vision,
    a. only their daughters will be colorblind.
*   b. their sons will be colorblind; daughters will be carriers.
    c. their sons will have normal vision; their daughters will be carriers.
    d. all their children will be colorblind.
    e. all their children will have normal vision.

E   34. Sex chromosomes
    a. determine sex.
    b. vary from one sex to another.
    c. carry some genes that have nothing to do with sex.
    d. were unknown to Mendel.
*   e. all of the above

M   35. A chromosome's gene sequence that was ABCDEFG before modification and ABCDLMNOP afterward is an example of
    a. inversion.
    b. deletion.
    c. duplication.
*   d. translocation.
    e. crossing over.

M 36. A chromosome's gene sequence that was ABCDEFG before modification and ABCDCDEFG afterward is an example of
   a. inversion.
   b. deletion.
 * c. duplication.
   d. translocation.
   e. crossing over.

E 37. A chromosome that has been broken and rejoined in a reversal sequence has undergone
 * a. inversion.
   b. deletion.
   c. duplication.
   d. translocation.
   e. crossing over.

E 38. A chromosome's gene sequence that was ABCDEFG before damage and ABCFG after is an example of
   a. inversion.
 * b. deletion.
   c. duplication.
   d. translocation.
   e. crossing over.

E 39. A chromosome's gene sequence that was ABCDEFG before damage and ABFEDCG after is an example of
 * a. inversion.
   b. deletion.
   c. duplication.
   d. translocation.
   e. crossing over.

M 40. The condition occurring when an organism has a $2n + 1$ chromosome composition is known as
   a. monosomy.
 * b. trisomy.
   c. diploid.
   d. haploid.
   e. both b and d

M 41. Certain human cancer cells may demonstrate which of the following?
   a. deletion
   b. inversion
 * c. translocation
   d. duplication
   e. none of the above

E 42. Which of the following would be the least satisfactory organism for genetic research?
 * a. humans
   b. bacteria
   c. corn
   d. fruit flies
   e. peas

M 43. Routine treatments for genetic disorders currently involve
    a. substituting normal for defective parents.
    b. substituting normal for defective genes.
    c. supplying a missing gene.
  * d. supplying missing enzymes or gene products.
    e. all of the above

M 44. Phenotypic treatments for genetic disorders include
    a. preventing the disorders in the carriers.
    b. elimination of the defective gene.
    c. preventing a disorder from being passed on.
  * d. preventing a disorder from being expressed.
    e. all of the above

M 45. Phenotypic treatments
  * a. may increase the number of defective genes in a population.
    b. do not affect the number of defective genes in a population.
    c. decrease the number of defective genes in a population.
    d. are the ultimate cures for genetic disorder.
    e. have no biological value for either the individual or the population.

M 46. Galactosemia
    a. is an X-linked recessive trait expressed more commonly in males.
    b. occurs more frequently in some ethnic groups than others.
    c. is an autosomal recessive inheritance.
    d. must be homozygous to be expressed.
  * e. both c and d

E 47. Which of the following designates a normal human female?
    a. XXY
    b. XY
  * c. XX
    d. XYY
    e. XO

E 48. Which of the following designates a normal human male?
    a. YY
    b. XX
  * c. XY
    d. XO
    e. XYY

D 49. Suppose a hemophilic male (X-linked recessive allele) and a female carrier for the hemophilic trait have a nonhemophilic daughter with Turner syndrome. Nondisjunction could have occurred in
    a. both parents.
    b. neither parent.
  * c. the father only.
    d. the mother only.
    e. none of the above

M 50. A woman heterozygous for colorblindness (an X-linked recessive allele) marries a man with normal color vision. What is the probability that their first child will be colorblind?
  * a. 25 percent
    b. 50 percent
    c. 75 percent
    d. 100 percent
    e. none of the above

E   51. Queen Victoria
     *   a. was a carrier of hemophilia.
         b. had a hemophilic parent.
         c. had hemophilia.
         d. married a man with hemophilia.
         e. both b and d

M   52. Hemophilia
         a. is rare in the human population.
         b. is more common among men.
         c. was common in English royalty.
         d. is an X-linked recessive trait.
     *   e. all of the above

E   53. Down syndrome involves trisomy
         a. 3.
         b. 5.
         c. 15.
         d. 19.
     *   e. 21.

E   54. *Syndrome* means
         a. a chromosome disorder.
         b. a simple genetic disease.
     *   c. a set of symptoms that occur together.
         d. an incurable disease.
         e. a rare inborn defect.

M   55. A genetic abnormality that may result in sterile males with mental retardation or breast
         enlargement is
     *   a. XXY.
         b. XYY.
         c. Turner syndrome.
         d. Down syndrome.
         e. none of the above

M   56. Males who tend to be taller than average and show mild mental retardation may be
         designated
         a. XXY.
     *   b. XYY.
         c. Turner syndrome.
         d. Down syndrome.
         e. none of the above

D   57. Nondisjunction involving the X chromosomes may occur during oogenesis and produce two
         kinds of eggs. If normal sperm fertilize these two types, which of the following pairs of
         genotypes are possible?
         a. XX and XY
     *   b. XXY and XO
         c. XYY and XO
         d. XYY and YO
         e. none of the above

M   58. In Down syndrome
    *   a. as the age of the mother increases, the chance of the defect occurring in the unborn child increases.
        b. the father has very little influence on the defect.
        c. most embryos abort before complete term.
        d. a person with the defect cannot have a normal child.
        e. none of the above

E   59. The sex chromosome composition of a person with Turner syndrome is
        a. XXX.
    *   b. XO.
        c. XXY.
        d. XYY.
        e. none of the above

E   60. The sex chromosome composition of a person with Klinefelter syndrome is
        a. XXX.
        b. XO.
    *   c. XXY.
        d. XYY.
        e. none of the above

E   61. Symptoms of phenylketonuria (PKU) may be minimized or suppressed by a diet low in
        a. serine.
        b. glycine.
    *   c. phenylalanine.
        d. proline.
        e. glutamic acid.

E   62. Galactose buildup in galactosemia can be detected by
        a. karyotyping.
        b. urine analysis.
        c. blood tests.
        d. saliva tests.
    *   e. both b and c

M   63. Wilson's disorder is a genetic disorder in which the person is unable to utilize
        a. zinc.
    *   b. copper.
        c. iron.
        d. sulfur.
        e. cobalt.

M   64. Amniocentesis involves sampling
        a. the fetus directly.
    *   b. the fetal cells floating in the amniotic fluid.
        c. sperm.
        d. blood cells.
        e. placental cells.

M   65. Karyotype analysis
        a. is a means of detecting and reducing mutagenic agents.
        b. is a surgical technique that separates chromosomes that have failed to segregate properly during meiosis II.
    *   c. is used in prenatal diagnosis to detect chromosomal mutations and metabolic disorders in embryos.
        d. substitutes defective alleles with normal ones.
        e. all of the above

M   66. Amniocentesis is
a. a surgical means of repairing deformities.
b. a form of chemotherapy that modifies or inhibits gene expression or the function of gene products.
* c. used in prenatal diagnosis to detect chromosomal mutations and metabolic disorders in embryos.
d. a form of gene replacement therapy.
e. all of the above

M   67. The most recent technique for analyzing the genetics of the unborn child involves the sampling of
a. the fetus directly.
b. cells in the amniotic fluid.
c. material from the allantois.
* d. the chorionic villi.
e. yolk sac material.

Matching Questions

M   68. Matching I

1 _____ colchicine

2 _____ deletion

3 _____ duplication

4 _____ inversion

5 _____ monosomy

6 _____ translocation

7 _____ trisomy

A. a chromosome segment is permanently transferred to a nonhomologous chromosome

B. $(2n - 1)$; a gamete deprived of a chromosome

C. a repeat of a particular DNA sequence in the same chromosome or in nonhomologous ones

D. $(2n + 1)$; three chromosomes of the same kind are present in a set of chromosomes

E. a piece of the chromosome is inadvertently left out during the repair process

F. inhibits microtubule assembly; prevents chromosome movement

G. a chromosome segment that has been cut out and rejoined at the same place, but backward

Answers: 1. F   2. E   3. C   4. G   5. B   6. A
7. D

E   69. Matching II. Match the cause of the disorder with the disorder.

1 _____ Down syndrome

2 _____ galactosemia

3 _____ hemophilia

4 _____ Turner syndrome

A. autosomal recessive inheritance; lactose metabolism is blocked

B. nondisjunction of the twenty-first chromosomal pair

C. X-linked recessive inheritance

D. nondisjunction of the sex chromosomes

Answers: 1. B   2. A   3. C   4. D

M 70. Matching III. Match each of the following phenotypic defects with its most used method of treatment.

1 _____ diabetes   A. chemotherapy

2 _____ cleft lip   B. diet modification

3 _____ phenylketonuria (PKU)   C. environmental adjustments

4 _____ sickle-cell anemia   D. surgical correction

5 _____ Wilson's disorder

Answers: 1. B   2. D   3. B   4. C   5. A

Problems

D 71. In cats the allele *B* produces black, while *b* produces yellow. Neither gene is dominant, and in the heterozygous state the phenotype is a combination of yellow and black spots called tortoiseshell. The alleles *B* and *b* are X-linked. If a tortoiseshell cat has three tortoiseshell kittens and two black kittens, give the genotype and phenotype of the tomcat that produced them, and give the sex of the kittens.

D 72. An X-linked recessive gene (*c*) produces red–green colorblindness. A woman with normal vision whose father was colorblind marries a colorblind man.
 a. What are the possible genotypes for the mother of the colorblind man?
 b. What are the possible genotypes for the father of the colorblind man?
 c. What are the chances that the first son will be colorblind?
 d. What are the chances that the first daughter will be colorblind?

D 73. In cats an X-linked pair of alleles, *B* and *b*, controls color of fur. The alleles are incompletely dominant: *B* produces black, *b* produces yellow, and *Bb* produces tortoiseshell.
 a. A yellow cat had a litter of two tortoiseshell kittens and one yellow. What is the sex of the yellow kitten?
 b. A tortoiseshell cat brings home a litter of black, yellow, and tortoiseshell kittens. The color of which sex would tell you the color of the tomcat that produced them?
 c. A yellow male is crossed with a tortoiseshell female. If the female has all male kittens in her litter of four, what color(s) would they be?
 d. A tortoiseshell cat brings home her litter of black, yellow, and tortoiseshell kittens. By what method could you possibly decide whether the male parent was the black tomcat next door?

D 74. If a father and a son are both colorblind and the mother has normal vision, is it likely that the son inherited colorblindness from his father?

D 75. If a human recessive X-linked characteristic occurred with a 10-percent frequency, what would its frequency be in males and females?

D 76. In humans an X-linked disorder called coloboma iridia (a fissure in the iris) is a recessive trait. A normal couple has an afflicted daughter. The husband sues the wife for divorce on the grounds of infidelity. Would you find in his favor?

D 77. In *Drosophila* a narrow reduced eye is called a bar-eye. It is due to a dominant X-linked allele (*B*), while the full wild-type is due to the recessive gene (*B+*). Give the F_1 and F_2 genotypic and phenotypic expectations of a cross of a homozygous wild-type female with a bar-eyed male.

D 78. If the gene for yellow body color (*y*) is an X-linked recessive and its dominant counterpart (*y*+) produces wild body colors, give the phenotypes expected and their frequencies for the following four crosses:
 a. yellow female x wild male
 b. wild carrier female x wild male
 c. wild carrier female x yellow male
 d. homozygous wild female x yellow male

D 79. Two *Drosophila* are crossed several times, with a total number of offspring of 106 females and 48 males. There is too great a deviation from the expected 1:1 ratio for chance alone to account for the difference. What other factor could account for this difference?

D 80. White eyes in *Drosophila* is a mutation that turned out to be X-linked recessive. Would you expect that the first time the white eye was discovered it was in a male or a female?

D 81. Hemophilia is an X-linked recessive gene. A normal woman whose father had hemophilia marries a normal man. What are the chances of hemophilia in their children?

D 82. Colorblindness is an X-linked recessive gene. Two normal-visioned parents produce a color-blind child.
 a. Is this child male or female?
 b. What are the genotypes of the parents?
 c. What are the chances that their next child will be a colorblind daughter?

D 83. If an X-linked recessive gene is expressed in 4 percent of the men, what proportion of women would express the recessive trait?

D 84. Red–green color blindness is an X-linked recessive trait. Two normal-visioned parents have a colorblind son. Indicate the genotype and phenotype of each parent and the son.

D 85. There is an autosomal gene that controls baldness, and its expression is sex influenced, so that the gene for baldness (*B*) is dominant in males but recessive in females. In females the allele B^1 for nonbaldness is dominant over the gene for baldness. If a heterozygous nonbald woman marries a nonbald man, what will be the appearance of their children? Work out the possibilities for each sex.

D 86. Short index fingers (shorter than ring fingers) are dominant in males and recessive in females, while long index fingers (as long or longer than ring fingers) are dominant in females and recessive in males. Give the F_2 genotype and phenotype resulting from the cross of a male with long fingers with a female with short fingers.

Classification Questions

Answer questions 87–91 in reference to the five items listed below.
 a. 12
 b. 23
 c. 24
 d. 46
 e. 47

D 87. How many chromosomes does each somatic cell have in a human male who has two X chromosomes?

D 88. Following a gene duplication event involving only five loci, how many chromosomes will a human female have?

D 89. How many chromosomes are present in the somatic cells of a child born with Down syndrome (trisomy 21)?

D   90.   How many chromosomes are present in each cell of the germ cell line for a tetraploid species where its normal complement of chromosomes is 48?

D   91.   The normal sperm cell of a particular species carries 11 chromosomes. Following nondisjunction in the formation of secondary spermatocytes and their subsequent fertilization of normal ova, some of the zygotes will have 21 chromosomes, others will have 22, and the remainder will have how many chromosomes?

Answers: 87. e   88. d   89. e   90. c   91. b

Answer questions 92–96 in reference to the five processes listed below. Note that to answer questions 92–96 you need to know that the sequence of amino acids directly reflects the sequence of genes that coded for their placement.

       a.   an inversion
       b.   a deletion
       c.   a gene duplication
       d.   a translocation
       e.   an addition

D   92.   Homologous sets of genes ABCDEF and aBCdEF are located on nonhomologous chromosomes. Crossing over between them is suppressed because their locations are the result of ____.

D   93.   Homologous sets of genes ABCDEF and AEDCBF are located on homologous chromosomes. Crossing over between them is suppressed because of ____.

D   94.   A small region of a protein from three species is sequenced and found to be as follows:
       species X is alanine, glycine, glycine, threonine, alanine
       species Y is alanine, glycine, threonine, alanine
       species Z is alanine, valine, glycine, threonine, alanine

       The difference in the amino acid sequence of species Y is most likely due to ____.

D   95.   A small region of a protein from three species is sequenced and found to be as follows:
       species X is alanine, valine, threonine, alanine
       species Y is alanine, glycine, threonine, alanine
       species Z is alanine, valine, glycine, threonine, alanine

       The differences in the amino acid sequence of species Z is most likely due to ____.

D   96.   The nucleotide sequences of homologous regions of DNA of two species is AATGCCCCGTTA and AATGCCCCGCTTA. If this is not the result of a nucleotide base-pair addition, then it is most likely the result of ____.

Answers: 92. d   93. a   94. b   95. e   96. b

Answer questions 97–101 in reference to the five disorders listed below:

       a.   galactosemia
       b.   Turner syndrome
       c.   AIDS
       d.   hemophilia
       e.   Down syndrome

D   97.   For which disorder is both a phenotypic and a genotypic cure *potentially* possible?

D   98.   Which disorder is an autosomal recessive disorder?

M   99.   Which disorder is an X-linked recessive trait?

E   100.   Which disorder is also known as trisomy 21?

D   101.   Which disorder is due to a sex chromosome abnormality probably caused by nondisjunction of sex chromosomes at meiosis?

Answers: 97. a   98. a   99. d   100. e   101. b

Answer questions 102–106 in reference to the five items listed below:
- a. surgical correction
- b. chemotherapy
- c. genetic screening
- d. genetic counseling
- e. gene therapy

M   102.   Wilson's disorder can be treated by which of the above methods?

M   103.   Which method is most often used to provide a phenotypic cure for a genetic disorder?

M   104.   Once the risks have been determined, which method is an effective way of dealing with a genetic disorder prior to its occurrence in a child?

M   105.   Radiation treatment of a cancer victim is an example of

M   106.   The substitution of a normal allele for a defective allele via the methods of genetic engineering would be an example of

Answers: 102. b   103. a   104. d   105. b   106. e

Selecting the Exception

D   107.   Four of the five answers listed below provide evidence that genes are located on chromosomes. Select the exception.
- a. the chromosome number is cut in half by meiosis
- b. original chromosome number is restored by fertilization
- c. some genes tend to be inherited together
- * d. environmental factors may influence gene expression
- e. there are two sets of chromosomes, one maternal and one paternal, in diploid forms

M   108.   Four of the five answers listed below are related conditions in which abnormal numbers of chromosomes are present. Select the exception.
- a. monosomy
- b. Down syndrome
- c. nondisjunction
- * d. complete chromosome set
- e. trisomy

E   109.   Four of the five answers listed below are organisms widely used in genetic research. Select the exception.
- a. peas
- b. fruit flies
- c. *Neurospora*
- * d. dogfish shark
- e. *E. coli*

M 110. Four of the five answers listed below are conditions caused by chromosomal nondisjunction. Select the exception.
    a. Down syndrome
*   b. Huntington's disorder
    c. Turner syndrome
    d. Klinefelter syndrome
    e. trisomy 21

M 111. Four of the five answers listed below are therapeutic measures applied to affected individuals. Select the exception.
*   a. prenatal diagnosis
    b. chemotherapy
    c. surgical correction
    d. diet modification
    e. environmental adjustment

M 112. Four of the five answers listed below are methods of current or potential use in reducing the number of defective genes in a population. Select the exception.
    a. genetic counseling
    b. gene replacement
    c. mutagen reduction
*   d. diet modification
    e. genetic screening

D 113. Four of the five answers listed below are caused by recessive genes. Select the exception.
*   a. Huntington's disorder
    b. phenylketonuria
    c. colorblindness
    d. hemophilia
    e. albinism

Answers to problems in Chapter 10

71. *BY* black, tortoiseshell female, black males
72. a. *Cc* or *cc*   b. *CY* or *cY*   c. 1/2   d. 1/2
73. a. male   b. female   c. 1/2 yellow 1/2 black   d. black female kitten
74. No, males inherit all sex-linked traits from the mother.
75. Males 10 percent, females 1 percent
76. Yes, the daughter would have to inherit the recessive trait from both parents.
77. *B+B+* x *BY* → *F₁*: *B+B* wild female *B+Y* wild male *F₂*: 1/4 *BY* bar male
    1/4 *B+Y* wild male 1/4 *B+B+* wild female 1/4 *B+B* wild female
78. a. yellow male wild female
    b. 1/4 wild male 1/4 yellow male 1/4 wild female 1/4 wild carrier female
    c. 1/4 wild male 1/4 yellow male 1/4 yellow female 1/4 wild carrier female
    d. 1/2 wild carrier female 1/2 wild male
79. A sex-linked recessive lethal gene expressed in the males, who received it from their mothers
80. Male
81. All females would be normal but 1/2 of them would be carriers; 1/2 of the males would have hemophilia, the other 1/2 normal.
82. a. male   b. *Cc* × *CY*   c. no chance to produce a colorblind daughter
83. $4/100 \times 4/100 = 16/10{,}000$, or 4 out of 2,500

84. father CY, mother Cc, son cY
85. $BB^1 \times B^1B^1 \rightarrow BB^1 + B^1B^1$; all daughters nonbald, 1/2 sons bald, 1/2 sons nonbald
86. F_2: 3/4 males with short fingers, 1/4 males with long fingers F_2: 3/4 females with long fingers, 1/4 females with short fingers

CHAPTER 11
DNA STRUCTURE AND FUNCTION

Multiple-Choice Questions

DISCOVERY OF DNA FUNCTION

M   1.   The significance of Fred Griffith's experiment in which he used two strains of *Streptococcus pneumoniae* is that
  a. the semiconservative nature of DNA replication was finally demonstrated.
* b. it demonstrated that harmless cells had become permanently transformed through a change in the bacterial hereditary system.
  c. it established that pure DNA extracted from disease-causing bacteria transformed harmless strains into killer strains.
  d. it demonstrated that radioactively labeled bacteriophages transfer their DNA but not their protein coats to their host bacteria.
  e. all of the above

M   2.   Which statement is NOT true about Fred Griffith's experiments?
  a. Mice injected with S bacteria die.
* b. Mice injected with heat-killed S bacteria die.
  c. Mice injected with heat-killed S bacteria and live R bacteria die.
  d. Mice injected with R bacteria live.
  e. S bacteria are transformed into harmless R bacteria.

E   3.   Which scientist(s) identified the transforming substance involved in changing R bacteria to S?
* a. Avery
  b. Griffith
  c. Chargaff
  d. Hershey and Chase
  e. Pauling

E   4.   Bacteriophages are
  a. large bacteria.
  b. pathogens (disease-producing bacteria).
* c. viruses.
  d. cellular components.
  e. protistans.

M   5.   The significance of the experiments in which ^{32}P and ^{35}S were used is that
  a. the semiconservative nature of DNA replication was finally demonstrated.
  b. it demonstrated that harmless bacterial cells had become permanently transformed through a change in the bacterial hereditary system.
  c. it established that pure DNA extracted from disease-causing bacteria transformed harmless strains into killer strains.
* d. it demonstrated that radioactively labeled bacteriophages transfer their DNA but not their protein coats to their host bacteria.
  e. none of the above

D   6. If a mixture of viruses labeled with radioactive sulfur and phosphorus is placed in a
         bacterial culture,
         a. the bacteria will absorb radioactive sulfur.
      * b. the bacteria will absorb radioactive phosphorus.
         c. the bacteria will absorb both radioactive sulfur and phosphorus.
         d. the bacteria will not absorb either sulfur or phosphorus.
         e. the viruses will not attach to the bacteria.

E   7. Nucleic acid contains
         a. sulfur.
      * b. phosphorus.
         c. potassium.
         d. iron.
         e. manganese.

M   8. Which statement is false?
         a. Protein molecules contain no phosphorus.
      * b. Hershey and Chase discovered that ^{35}S and not ^{32}P had been incorporated into the
              hereditary system of the bacteria.
         c. Bacteriophages are viruses that inject their nucleic acid genetic code into bacteria and
              use the bacterial genetic apparatus to make viral proteins.
         d. Each nucleotide is composed of a five-carbon sugar, a phosphate group, and either a
              purine or a pyrimidine.
         e. Viruses are particles of nucleic acid encased in protein.

M   9. Sulfur is
      * a. found in proteins but not nucleic acids.
         b. found in bacteria.
         c. found in nucleic acid but not proteins.
         d. needed for bacteriophages to attach to bacteria.
         e. needed for the enzyme that splits the wall of bacteria.

DNA STRUCTURE

M   10. In the pairing of two nucleotides within the double helix
          a. hydrogen bonds are used.
          b. adenine and thymine bind together.
          c. purines bind with pyrimidines.
          d. double-ring nitrogenous bases connect to single-ring bases.
       * e. all of the above

E   11. A nucleotide may contain a
          a. purine.
          b. pentose.
          c. phosphate group.
          d. pyrimidine.
       * e. all of the above

M   12. From X-ray diffraction data, which of the following was determined about DNA?
          a. The molecule had uniform diameter.
          b. The molecule was long and narrow.
          c. Part of the molecule repeated itself often.
          d. The shape of the molecule could be spiral.
       * e. all of the above

M 13. Rosalind Franklin's research contribution was essential in
   a. establishing the double-stranded nature of DNA.
   b. establishing the principle of base pairing.
 * c. establishing most of the principal structural features of DNA.
   d. sequencing DNA molecules.
   e. determining the bonding energy of DNA molecules.

M 14. James Watson and Francis Crick
   a. established the double-stranded nature of DNA.
   b. established the principle of base pairing.
   c. explained how DNA's structure permitted it to be replicated.
   d. proposed the concept of the double-helix.
 * e. all of the above

E 15. In the bonding of nitrogenous bases
   a. adenine is paired with cytosine.
   b. adenine is paired with guanine.
   c. cytosine is paired with thymine.
 * d. guanine is paired with cytosine.
   e. two of the above

E 16. The DNA molecule could be compared to a
   a. hairpin.
 * b. ladder.
   c. key.
   d. globular mass.
   e. flat plate.

E 17. In DNA, complementary base pairing occurs between
   a. cytosine and uracil.
   b. adenine and guanine.
   c. adenine and uracil.
 * d. adenine and thymine.
   e. all of the above

M 18. Adenine and guanine are
 * a. double-ringed purines.
   b. single-ringed purines.
   c. double-ringed pyrimidines.
   d. single-ringed pyrimidines.
   e. amino acids.

M 19. Rosalind Franklin used which technique to determine many of the physical characteristics of DNA?
   a. transformation
   b. transmission electron microscopy
   c. density-gradient centrifugation
 * d. X-ray diffraction
   e. all of the above

E 20. In DNA molecules
 * a. the nucleotides are arranged in a linear, unbranched pattern.
   b. the nitrogenous bases are found on the outside of the molecule.
   c. the pentose–phosphate pattern runs the same way on each DNA strand.
   d. all of the above
   e. none of the above

M   21. Which statement is true?
*   a. The hydrogen bonding of cytosine to guanine is an example of complementary base pairing.
       b. Adenine always pairs up with guanine in DNA, and cytosine always teams up with thymine.
       c. Each of the four nucleotides in a DNA molecule has the same nitrogen-containing base.
       d. When adenine base pairs with thymine, they are linked by three hydrogen bonds.
       e. In the DNA of all species, the amount of purines never equals the amount of pyrimidines.

E   22. Each DNA strand has a backbone that consists of alternating
       a. purines and pyrimidines.
       b. nitrogen-containing bases.
       c. hydrogen bonds.
*   d. sugar and phosphate molecules.
       e. amines and purines.

DNA REPLICATION

M   23. The appropriate adjective to describe DNA replication is
       a. nondisruptive.
*   b. semiconservative.
       c. progressive.
       d. natural.
       e. lytic.

E   24. Replication of DNA
       a. produces RNA molecules.
       b. produces only new DNA.
*   c. produces two molecules, each of which is half-new and half-old DNA joined lengthwise to each other.
       d. generates excessive DNA, which eventually causes the nucleus to divide.
       e. is too complex to characterize.

DNA REPAIR

M   25. DNA polymerase
       a. is an enzyme.
       b. adds new nucleotides to a strand.
       c. proofreads DNA strands to see that they are correct.
       d. derives energy from ATP for synthesis of DNA strands.
*   e. all of the above

ORGANIZATION OF DNA IN CHROMOSOMES

E   26. Proteins associated with DNA in eukaryotes are
       a. repressors.
       b. tryptophans.
*   c. histones.
       d. nucleosomes.
       e. operons.

E   27. Histone–DNA units are called
       a. polysomes.
       b. ribosomes.
*   c. nucleosomes.
       d. chromocenters.
       e. vesicles.

M   28.   The DNA molecule is associated with histone in

    *   a.   looped series.

         b.   scattered introns.

         c.   hairpin lattices.

         d.   tightly coiled complexes.

         e.   lampbrushes.

Matching Questions

D   29.   Matching. Choose the one most appropriate answer for each.

1 _____ Avery and colleagues

2 _____ Rosalind Franklin

3 _____ Fred Griffith

4 _____ Hershey and Chase

5 _____ Friedrich Miescher

6 _____ Watson and Crick

A. discovered that the hereditary system of one strain of bacteria could be transformed by materials from another strain of bacteria

B. first to discover DNA and isolate it from fish sperm

C. in 1944, reported that DNA was the "transforming principle"

D. the first to build a scale model of DNA and to describe it explicitly in a publication

E. the first to demonstrate, through the use of radioactive isotopes, that DNA, not protein, was the substance transmitted through generations of cells

F. obtained excellent X-ray diffraction photographs that suggested that DNA was a long, thin molecule with regularly repeating structures; also said that DNA had to be helical like a circular stairway

Answers: 1. C   2. F   3. A   4. E   5. B   6. D

Classification Questions

Answer questions 30–34 in reference to the five nucleotides listed below:

         a.   guanine

         b.   cytosine

         c.   pyrimidine

         d.   thymine

         e.   uracil

E   30.   Early data indicated that within a species the amount of adenine was always equal to the amount of which of the above?

E   31.   Which nucleotide is not incorporated into the structure of the DNA helix?

D   32.   Which nucleotide is a double-ringed molecule?

M   33.   If one chain of a DNA molecule had a purine at a given position, what would its complement be on the other chain?

M   34.   Two hydrogen bonds connect adenine to _____ in the DNA molecule.

Answers: 30. d   31. e   32. a   33. c   34. d

Selecting the Exception

M   35. Four of the five answers listed below are bases used to construct nucleic acids. Select the exception.
          a. cytosine
          b. adenine
          c. thymine
          d. guanine
    *   e. phenylalanine

D   36. Four of the five answers listed below are correctly paired. Select the exception.
    *   a. A – C
          b. C – G
          c. A – T
          d. T – A
          e. purine – pyrimidine

CHAPTER 12
FROM DNA TO PROTEINS

Multiple-Choice Questions

TRANSCRIPTION AND TRANSLATION: AN OVERVIEW

E   1. The DNA molecule is usually made up of how many strands?
         a. 1
     *   b. 2
         c. 3
         d. 6
         e. 12

E   2. The RNA molecule is made up of how many strands?
     *   a. 1
         b. 2
         c. 3
         d. 6
         e. 12

E   3. In terms of their nitrogenous base component, how many different kinds of RNA molecules
         are there?
         a. 3
     *   b. 4
         c. 5
         d. 6
         e. 12

E   4. What is the form of RNA that carries the code from the DNA to the site where the protein
         is assembled?
     *   a. messenger RNA
         b. nuclear RNA
         c. ribosomal RNA
         d. transfer RNA
         e. structural RNA

M   5. Which of the following carries amino acids to ribosomes, where amino acids are linked into
         the primary structure of a polypeptide?
         a. mRNA
     *   b. tRNA
         c. hnRNA
         d. rRNA
         e. all of the above

M   6. Transfer RNA differs from other types of RNA because it
         a. transfers genetic instructions from cell nucleus to cytoplasm.
         b. specifies the amino acid sequence of a particular protein.
     *   c. carries an amino acid at one end.
         d. contains codons.
         e. none of the above

TRANSCRIPTION OF DNA INTO RNA

E   7.   The nitrogenous base found in DNA but not in RNA is
   - a. adenine.
   - b. cytosine.
   - c. guanine.
   - d. uracil.
   - *   e. thymine.

E   8.   Which substance is found in RNA but not in DNA?
   - a. thymine
   - b. deoxyribose
   - *   c. ribose
   - d. guanine
   - e. cytosine

E   9.   The nitrogenous base found in RNA but not in DNA is
   - a. adenine.
   - b. cytosine.
   - c. guanine.
   - *   d. uracil.
   - e. thymine.

E   10.   Uracil will pair with
   - a. ribose.
   - *   b. adenine.
   - c. cytosine.
   - d. thymine.
   - e. guanine.

M   11.   The synthesis of an RNA molecule from a DNA template strand is
   - a. replication.
   - b. translation.
   - *   c. transcription.
   - d. DNA synthesis.
   - e. metabolism.

E   12.   The relationship between strands of RNA and DNA is
   - a. antagonistic.
   - b. opposite.
   - *   c. complementary.
   - d. an exact duplicate.
   - e. unrelated.

M   13.   Transcription
   - a. occurs on the surface of the ribosome.
   - b. is the final process in the assembly of a protein.
   - *   c. occurs during the synthesis of any type of RNA from a DNA template.
   - d. is catalyzed by DNA polymerase.
   - e. all of the above

M   14.   Which of the following dominates in the process of transcription?
   - *   a. RNA polymerase
   - b. DNA polymerase
   - c. phenylketonuria
   - d. transfer RNA
   - e. all of the above

M   15. In transcription
          a. several RNA molecules are made from the same DNA molecule.
          b. promoters are needed so that RNA polymerase can bind to DNA.
          c. DNA produces messenger RNA.
          d. a specific enzyme called RNA polymerase is required.
     *   e. all of the above

M   16. The portion of the DNA molecule that is translated is composed of
          a. introns.
          b. anticodons.
     *   c. exons.
          d. transcriptons.
          e. both c and d, but not a or b

M   17. The portion of the DNA molecule that is not translated and is a noncoding portion of DNA is
          composed of
     *   a. introns.
          b. anticodons.
          c. exons.
          d. transcriptons.
          e. both c and d, but not a or b

M   18. In transcription
          a. several amino acids are assembled by the messenger RNA molecules at one time.
     *   b. a special sequence called a promoter is necessary for transcription to begin.
          c. certain polypeptide sequences are governed by one ribosome, while other sequences are
              produced by other ribosomes.
          d. the transfer RNA molecules arrange the messenger RNA codons into the appropriate
              sequence.
          e. none of the above

M   19. When a gene transcription occurs, which of the following is produced?
          a. more DNA
          b. protein or polypeptide sequences
     *   c. messenger RNA
          d. enzymes
          e. genetic defects

TRANSLATION OF mRNA

E   20. The genetic code is made up of units consisting of how many nucleotides?
          a. 2
     *   b. 3
          c. 5
          d. 6
          e. 12

E   21. There are how many different kinds of amino acids in proteins?
          a. 3
          b. 6
          c. 12
     *   d. 20
          e. 28

M   22. There are how many different kinds of RNA codons?
              a. 3
              b. 12
              c. 28
         *   d. 64
              e. 120

M   23. If the codon consisted of only two nucleotides, there would be how many different kinds
            of codons?
              a. 4
              b. 8
         *   c. 16
              d. 32
              e. 64

M   24. The concept that a set of three nucleotides specifies a particular amino acid provides the
            basis for
              a. the one gene, one enzyme hypothesis.
              b. the one gene, one polypeptide hypothesis.
         *   c. the genetic code.
              d. biochemical reactions among nucleic acids.
              e. all of the above

M   25. Of all the different codons that exist, three of them
              a. are involved in mutations.
              b. do not specify a particular amino acid.
              c. cannot be copied.
              d. provide punctuation or instructions such as "stop."
         *   e. both b and d

E   26. Each "word" in the mRNA language consists of how many letters?
         *   a. three
              b. four
              c. five
              d. more than five
              e. none of the above

D   27. If each nucleotide coded for a single amino acid, how many different types of amino acids
            could be combined to form proteins?
         *   a. 4
              b. 16
              c. 20
              d. 64
              e. none of the above

M   28. If the DNA triplets were ATG–CGT, the mRNA codons would be
              a. AUGCGU.
              b. ATGCGT.
         *   c. UACGCA.
              d. UAGCGU.
              e. none of the above

M   29. If the DNA triplets were ATG–CGT, the tRNA anticodons would be
         *   a. AUGCGU.
              b. ATGCGT.
              c. UACGCA.
              d. UAGCGU.
              e. none of the above

E   30. Ribosomes function as
        a. a single unit.
    *   b. two-part units.
        c. three-part units.
        d. four-part units.
        e. a multidivisional unit.

MUTATION AND PROTEIN SYNTHESIS

E   31. The difference between normal hemoglobin and sickle-cell hemoglobin is in the
        a. heme portion of the molecules.
        b. number of chains of amino acids.
    *   c. substitution of a specific amino acid for another specific amino acid.
        d. addition of one amino acid to the normal hemoglobin molecule.
        e. loss of only one amino acid from the normal hemoglobin molecule.

M   32. A gene mutation
        a. is a change in the nucleotide sequence of DNA.
        b. may be caused by environmental agents.
        c. may arise spontaneously.
        d. can occur in all organisms.
    *   e. all of the above

E   33. Mutations can be
        a. random.
        b. beneficial.
        c. harmful.
        d. heritable.
    *   e. all of the above

THE NATURE OF GENE CONTROL

D   34. During the early part of a young mammal's life, the *E. coli* in the young offspring's
        intestinal tract are exposed to high levels of which of the following that later generations of
        E. coli will never be exposed to?
        a. glucose
        b. ribose
        c. cellulose
    *   d. lactose
        e. fructose

M   35. A regulator gene produces which of the following?
    *   a. repressor protein
        b. regulatory enzyme
        c. promoter
        d. operator
        e. transcriber

M   36. A repressor protein binds with
        a. messenger RNA.
    *   b. the operator.
        c. the regulator.
        d. a product.
        e. a substrate.

M 37. The region that determines the rate at which a certain mRNA chain is to be synthesized.
   a. heterogeneous nuclear DNA
   b. repressor gene
  * c. promoter sequence
   d. operator sequence
   e. all of the above

M 38. Genes located in different regions of the body during embryonic development may be
   a. turned on and off.
   b. never turned on.
   c. turned on and left on.
   d. activated for only a short time in one cell and a long time in another cell.
  * e. all of the above

E 39. Cells of all multicellular organisms arise during mitosis from a single cell known as a(n)
   a. gamete.
  * b. zygote.
   c. embryo.
   d. clone.
   e. fetus.

E 40. Which term refers to the processes by which cells with identical genotypes become structurally and functionally distinct from one another?
   a. metamorphosis
   b. metastasis
   c. cleavage
  * d. differentiation
   e. induction

M 41. The mosaic effect in human females can be observed in
   a. skin color.
   b. hair color.
   c. distribution of fat cells.
  * d. distribution of sweat glands.
   e. all of the above

M 42. Cancer cells
   a. have altered plasma membranes.
   b. are unable to attach to other cells.
   c. divide to produce high densities of cells.
   d. have a different metabolism, using glycolysis even when oxygen is available.
  * e. all of the above

D 43. Which characteristic seems to be most uniquely correlated with metastasis?
   a. loss of nuclear–cytoplasmic controls governing cell growth and division
  * b. changes in recognition factors on membrane surfaces
   c. "puffing" in the polytene chromosomes
   d. the massive production of cyclic adenosine monophosphate and its secretion into the environment
   e. none of the above

M 44. The spread of a cancer from one site to others in the body is known as
   a. benign tumor.
  * b. metastasis.
   c. malignant tumor.
   d. remission.
   e. both a and c, but not b or d

E   45. The specific name given to a cancer-producing chemical is
        a. pathogen.
    *   b. carcinogen.
        c. teratogen.
        d. mutagen.
        e. oncogene.

Matching Questions

D   46. Matching. Choose the best matching element.

1 _____ anticodon	A.	RNA-directed synthesis of polypeptide chains
2 _____ codon	B.	sites at which RNA polymerases can bind and initiate transcription
3 _____ messenger RNA		
4 _____ promoters	C.	binds to small subunit platform of a ribosome
5 _____ transcription	D.	guided and catalyzed by RNA polymerases
6 _____ translation	E.	a tRNA triplet opposite an amino acid
	F.	a set of three nucleotides

Answers: 1. E   2. F   3. C   4. B   5. D   6. A

Classification Questions

Answer questions 47–51 in reference to the five RNA codons listed below:

        a. AUG
        b. UAA
        c. UUU
        d. UUA
        e. AAA

D   47. Which codon terminates a coding region?

D   48. The anticodon AAA would pair with which of the above?

M   49. A single mutation involving the second letter of codon AUA would convert it to what?

M   50. A DNA codon of ATT would be complementary to which RNA codons?

M   51. Which codon codes for an amino acid and indicates the beginning of a coding region?

Answers: 47. b   48. c   49. e   50. b   51. a

Answer questions 52–56 in reference to the five items of gene regulation listed below:

        a. operon
        b. operator
        c. promoter
        d. lactose
        e. regulator gene

M   52. Which item contains regulator, promoter, and operator regions?

D   53. A repressor protein can shut down transcription by binding to which item?

M   54.   Which item codes for the production of the repressor?

D   55.   When the repressor is inactivated, RNA polymerase can bind to which item and allow transcription to occur?

M   56.   The molecule that can activate the operon is represented by which item?

Answers: 52. a   53. b   54. e   55. c   56. d

Selecting the Exception

E   57.   Three of the four answers listed below are different forms of a class of nucleic acids. Select the exception.
*   a. template
     b. ribosomal
     c. messenger
     d. transfer

M   58.   Three of the four answers listed below are involved in gene action. Select the exception.
     a. replication
     b. transcription
     c. translation
*   d. polymerization

D   59.   Four of the five answers listed below are related pairings. Select the exception.
     a. double-stranded DNA–messenger RNA
     b. purine–pyrimidine
     c. codon–anticodon
     d. small subunit–large subunit
*   e. promoter–terminator

D   60.   Four of the five answers listed below describe changes at the chromosomal level. Select the exception.
*   a. base substitution
     b. duplication
     c. translocation
     d. deletion
     e. inversion

M   61.   Four of the five answers listed below are sources of genetic variation. Select the exception.
     a. crossing over
     b. mutation
*   c. asexual reproduction
     d. chromosome aberration
     e. sexual reproduction

D   62.   Four of the five answers listed below are components of a nucleotide. Select the exception.
     a. pentose sugar
*   b. amino acid
     c. pyrimidine
     d. phosphate group
     e. purine

D   63. Four of the five answers listed below are related by a common number. Select the exception.
         a. number of nucleotides in a codon
         b. number of building blocks (parts) in a nucleotide
         c. number of stop codons
      * d. number of types of DNA
         e. number of types of RNA

D   64. Three of the four answers listed below are steps in translation. Select the exception.
         a. initiation
      * b. replication
         c. chain elongation
         d. termination

D   65. Four of the five answers listed below are features of the lactose operon. Select the exception.
         a. regulator
      * b. terminator
         c. operator
         d. promoter
         e. structural gene

D   66. Four of the five answers listed below are descriptions of cancer cells. Select the exception.
      * a. abnormal shaped nucleus
         b. decline in ability to adhere to substrates
         c. changes in the plasma membrane
         d. abnormal growth and division
         e. cytoplasm shrinks and becomes disorganized

E   67. Four of the five answers listed below are carcinogens. Select the exception.
      * a. egg white
         b. asbestos
         c. radiation with X-ray
         d. components in cigarette smoke
         e. ultraviolet radiation

CHAPTER 13
RECOMBINANT DNA AND GENETIC ENGINEERING

Multiple-Choice Questions

RECOMBINANT DNA TECHNOLOGY

M   1. Recombinant DNA
     a. has occurred in sexually reproducing forms.
     b. can be produced with new biological techniques.
     c. occurs with viral infections of various forms of life.
     d. has produced changes that resulted in evolution.
   * e. all of the above

E   2. New genetic combinations result from
     a. crossing over.
     b. sexual reproduction.
     c. mutations.
     d. exchange of genes between different species.
   * e. all of the above

M   3. The process by which one bacterial cell transfers DNA to another is
     a. fission.
     b. gametic fusion.
   * c. conjugation.
     d. lysis.
     e. none of the above

E   4. Small circular molecules of DNA in bacteria are called
   * a. plasmids.
     b. desmids.
     c. pili.
     d. F particles.
     e. transferrins.

E   5. Enzymes used to cut DNA molecules in recombinant DNA research are
     a. ligases.
   * b. restriction enzymes.
     c. transcriptases.
     d. DNA polymerases.
     e. replicases.

M   6. The fragments of chromosomes split by restriction enzymes
     a. have fused ends.
     b. have specific sequences of nucleotides.
     c. have sticky ends.
     d. form a circle.
   * e. both b and c

E   7. A tangelo is a combination
     a. orange and lemon.
     b. orange and tangerine.
     c. navel orange and tangerine.
     d. tangerine and cantaloupe.
   * e. tangerine and grapefruit.

D 8. Plasmids
   a. are self-reproducing circular molecules of DNA.
   b. are sites for inserting genes for amplification.
   c. may be transferred between different species of bacteria.
   d. may confer the ability to donate genetic material when bacteria conjugate.
   * e. all of the above

M 9. The "natural" use of restriction enzymes by bacteria is to
   a. integrate viral DNA.
   * b. destroy viral DNA.
   c. repair "sticky ends."
   d. copy the bacterial genes.
   e. clone DNA.

M 10. Restriction enzymes
   a. often produce staggered cuts in DNA that are useful in splicing genes.
   b. are like most enzymes in being very specific in their action.
   c. are natural defense mechanisms evolved in bacteria to guard against or counteract bacteriophages.
   d. are used along with ligase and plasmids to produce a DNA library.
   * e. all of the above

M 11. Which of the following enzymes joins the paired sticky ends of DNA fragments?
   a. reverse transcriptase
   b. restriction enzymes
   * c. DNA ligase
   d. DNA polymerase
   e. transferase

M 12. RNA can manufacture DNA via the action of
   a. DNA polymerase.
   b. RNA polymerase.
   * c. reverse transcriptase.
   d. ligase.
   e. restriction endonuclease.

M 13. A collection of DNA fragments produced by restriction enzymes and incorporated into plasmids is called
   a. copied DNA.
   b. transcribed DNA.
   c. DNA amplification.
   * d. a DNA library.
   e. plasmid DNA.

D 14. For polymerase chain reaction to occur,
   a isolated DNA molecules must be primed.
   b. all DNA fragments must be identical.
   c the DNA must be separated into single strands.
   d. a sticky end must be available for the ligase enzyme to function.
   * e. a and c are correct, but b and d are not

D 15. Probes for cloned genes use
   * a. complementary nucleotide sequences labeled with radioactive isotopes.
   b. certain media with specific antibodies.
   c. specific enzymes.
   d. certain bacteria sensitive to the genes.
   e. all of the above

D   16. Because it has no introns, researchers prefer to use _____ when working with human genes.
*   a. cDNA
     b. cloned DNA
     c. hybridized DNA
     d. RFLPs
     e. viral DNA

D   17. Multiple copies of DNA can be produced by
     a. cloning a DNA library.
     b. genetic amplification.
     c. the use of reverse transcriptase.
     d. the action of DNA polymerase.
*   e. all of the above

APPLICATIONS OF THE NEW TECHNOLOGY

M   18. Which statement is true?
     a. There is no danger involved in recombinant DNA research in humans.
     b. There is no danger involved in recombinant DNA research in bacteria.
     c. There is no danger in releasing recombinant organisms into the environment.
*   d. Stringent safety rules make the use of recombinant DNA research possible.
     e. It is safe to conduct recombinant DNA research in plants.

M   19. Gene therapy
     a. has not yet been used successfully with mammals.
     b. is a surgical technique that separates chromosomes that have failed to segregate properly during meiosis II.
     c. has been used successfully to treat victims of Huntington's disorder by removing the dominant damaging autosomal allele and replacing it with a harmless one.
*   d. offers the possibility of replacing defective alleles with normal ones.
     e. all of the above

M   20. Ice-minus bacteria
     a. were released into the environment.
     b. have been genetically engineered to delete a harmful gene.
     c. will reduce the chance of ice forming on commercial plants such as strawberries.
     d. field trials generated protests by environmental activists.
*   e. all of the above

D   21. The use of RFLPs for "genetic fingerprinting" is based on
     a. the type of gel used in electrophoresis.
     b. identical alleles at loci.
*   c. differences of locations where enzymes make their cuts.
     d. differences between blood and semen DNA.
     e. bonding of DNA to RNA.

D   22. Which of the following statements about restriction fragment length polymorphism is false?
     a. RFLPs can be used as a genetic fingerprint.
     b. RFLPs are based on variations in alleles at the same locus.
     c. RFLPs reflect the fact that molecular differences in alleles alter the site where restriction enzymes function.
*   d. RFLPs can be used to distinguish between identical twins.
     e. RFLPs have greatly increased the number of sites involved in mapping the human genome.

Classification Questions

Answer questions 23–27 in reference to the five items listed below:

    a. restriction enzymes
    b. recombinants
    c. plasmids
    d. clones
    e. restriction sites

M   23. Bacterial populations containing thousands or millions of identical copies of one to several genes are _____.

D   24. When one uses the techniques of genetic engineering to move a novel or foreign piece of DNA into the DNA of an organism, these new DNA regions are known as _____.

M   25. The pieces of DNA that are moved by a genetic engineer from one organism to another are first incorporated into _____.

E   26. The sole function of these is to cut apart foreign DNA molecules.

D   27. Which of the above may contain all of the other entities?

Answers: 23. d   24. b   25. c   26. a   27. d

Answer questions 28–32 in reference to the four items listed below:

    a. cDNA
    b. a restriction enzyme
    c. reverse transcriptase
    d. a DNA library

M   28. Which of the above is from a viral source and catalyzes reactions to construct DNA strands from mRNA?

E   29. Any DNA copied from mRNA transcripts is known as _____.

E   30. A nuclease whose only function is to cut apart foreign DNA entering a cell is _____.

M   31. Collections of DNA fragments produced by restriction enzymes and incorporated into cloning vectors are _____.

D   32. Which of the above is a type of bacterial colony probe constructed of radioactively labeled DNA subunits?

Answers: 28. c   29. a   30. b   31. d   32. a

Selecting the Exception

M   33. Four of the five answers listed below are aspects of the process known as gene splicing. Select the exception.
    a. cloning vector
    b. restriction enzymes
    c. sticky ends
    d. exposed base pairs
  * e. crossing over

M 34. Four of the five enzymes below are used in genetic engineering. Select the exception.
   a. ligase
   b. reverse transcriptase
   c. restriction
 * d. replicase
   e. DNA polymerase

M 35. Four of the five statements below are true of cloned DNA. Select the exception.
   a. The plasmid used is the cloning vector.
   b. Identical copies are produced.
 * c. Cloned DNA is produced by reverse transcriptase.
   d. Multiple copies are produced.
   e. Cloned DNA is manufactured in bacteria cells.

CHAPTER 14
MICROEVOLUTION

Multiple-Choice Questions

EMERGENCE OF EVOLUTIONARY THOUGHT

M 1. The forelimbs of early mammals were similar in all features except
   a. embryonic origin.
   b. position on the body.
   c. number.
 * d. function.
   e. composition.

E 2. The pelvic girdle is
   a. part of the backbone of vertebrates.
   b. a place where the forelimbs are attached.
 * c. a place where the hindlimbs are attached.
   d. completely absent in snakes, which do not have legs.
   e. found only during embryonic development and is not present in many mature vertebrates.

E 3. Fossils found in the lowest geological strata are generally the most
   a. advanced.
   b. complex.
 * c. primitive.
   d. widespread.
   e. specialized.

E 4. In the early 1800s, creationist thinking would have included all of the following EXCEPT
   a. All species are links in a great chain.
   b. The key to understanding nature is to discover all the links in the great chain.
   c. All species originated in one place and at approximately the same time.
 * d. Species become modified over time.
   e. Nature was perfect in the original creation.

E 5. Darwin's mentor, who obtained Darwin's position on the H.M.S. *Beagle*, was
   a. Alfred Russel Wallace.
 * b. John Henslow.
   c. Jean-Baptiste Lamarck.
   d. Georges Cuvier.
   e. Charles Lyell.

M 6. The place Darwin visited on his trip around the world that had the greatest impact on his thinking was
   a. the Canary Islands.
   b. Africa.
   c. the Hawaiian Islands.
 * d. the Galápagos Islands.
   e. Brazil.

M   7. The development of Darwin's theory of evolution by natural selection was based largely on his study of which of the following organisms?
        a. butterflies
        b. butterflies and Galápagos finches
        c. domestic animals
    *   d. domestic animals and Galápagos finches
        e. all three organisms

E   8. Thomas Malthus proposed that
        a. the food supply multiplied faster than the population.
    *   b. the population multiplied faster than the food supply.
        c. the food supply and population multiplied at the same rate.
        d. artificial selection was the key to evolution.
        e. natural selection was the key to evolution.

E   9. The person credited with being the codiscoverer of the theory of natural selection was
    *   a. Alfred Wallace.
        b. Charles Lyell.
        c. Thomas Malthus.
        d. James Hutton.
        e. John Henslow.

E   10. *Archaeopteryx* was a transitional form between
        a. birds and mammals.
        b. reptiles and mammals.
    *   c. birds and reptiles.
        d. fish and amphibians.
        e. amphibians and reptiles.

MICROEVOLUTIONARY PROCESSES

D   11. If the frequency of expression of a recessive trait in a population is 16 percent, the frequency of the recessive allele would be what percent?
        a. 16
        b. 25
    *   c. 40
        d. 50
        e. 67

M   12. If the frequency of a recessive allele is 36 percent, the frequency of the dominant allele would be what percent?
        a. 5
        b. 8
        c. 25
        d. 48
    *   e. 64

D   13. In the Hardy–Weinberg equation, the term q^2 refers to the frequency of
        a. a recessive allele of a given locus.
    *   b. the homozygous recessive genotype at a given locus.
        c. recessive alleles in a population.
        d. heterozygotes in a population.

M 14. If the frequency of the recessive allele is 30 percent, the frequency of the heterozygous carrier would be what percent?
  * a. 42
    b. 9
    c. 27
    d. 60
    e. 80

D 15. In a population that is in Hardy–Weinberg equilibrium, the frequency of the recessive homozygous genotype is 0.49. The percentage of the population that is heterozygous is
    a. 51.
    b. 49.
  * c. 42.
    d. 7.
    e. 3.

M 16. The Hardy–Weinberg rule
  * a. is useful in determining the extent to which a sexually reproducing population is evolving.
    b. is used to predict when genetic drift will occur in a sexually reproducing population.
    c. is useful in determining the extent to which polyploidy is occurring in specific plant populations.
    d. is used to predict when specific groups of organisms will become extinct.
    e. all of the above

D 17. Suppose you have a population of guinea pigs in which two-thirds of the alleles for coat color specify black and one-third specify white. According to the Hardy–Weinberg rule, what will be the ratio of these alleles in the gene pool in future generations, provided all the guinea pigs reproduce?
    a. 1:1
  * b. 2:1
    c. 3:1
    d. 0.67: 0.11

D 18. Of 400 people who dwell on a Pacific island, 16 are homozygous recessive for a trait that has only two different types of alleles in the population. The number of heterozygous people is
    a. 256.
    b. 32.
    c. 64.
  * d. 128.
    e. 384.

M 19. For which group of individuals of the same species are there no restrictions to random mating among its members?
    a. individual
    b. species
  * c. population
    d. polyploid
    e. all of the above

M 20. The maintenance of Hardy–Weinberg equilibrium is encouraged
    a. when sexual selection occurs.
    b. when mutations occur.
    c. in small populations.
  * d. when there is no gene flow between different populations.
    e. all of the above

M   21. Which statement is NOT true?
        a. Migration leads to genetic variation.
    *   b. Dominant genes always occur more frequently in a population than recessive genes do.
        c. Nonrandom mating may result in changes in gene frequency.
        d. The Hardy–Weinberg law applies to large, stable populations.
        e. Crossing over increases variation.

E   22. New alleles arise by
    *   a. mutation.
        b. migration.
        c. genetic drift.
        d. random mating.
        e. independent assortment.

E   23. New variations of genes may be produced by
        a. immigration.
        b. mutation.
        c. crossing over.
        d. sexual reproduction.
    *   e. all of the above

M   24. What accounts for the fact that polydactylism is prevalent and Tay-Sachs disease virtually absent in one human population in the United States while Tay-Sachs disease is prevalent and polydactylism virtually absent in another?
        a. Natural selection has promoted these differences since humans live in many different environments.
        b. Mutation rates differ between different loci.
    *   c. There is little gene flow between the two populations.
        d. The populations are small, and therefore genetic drift is a major factor in the determination of allele frequencies.

M   25. New alleles that appear by mutation
        a. are inherently disadvantageous to their bearers.
        b. are seldom advantageous or disadvantageous in themselves.
        c. either have or lack survival value only in the context of their environment.
    *   d. both b and c
        e. both a and b

M   26. The introduction of a small population onto an island that results in a limited gene pool for a population best describes
        a. the Hardy–Weinberg law.
        b. genetic drift.
        c. the bottleneck effect.
    *   d. the founder principle.
        e. the effect of genetic isolation.

E   27. Which are sources of new alleles within a population?
        a. genetic recombination
        b. meiosis
    *   c. mutation
        d. genetic drift

E   28. Of the following, which does NOT characterize a population in Hardy–Weinberg equilibrium?
        a. large population size
        b. no mutation
    *   c. differential reproduction
        d. absence of gene flow

M   29. The sharp reduction of the gene pool and the numbers of a population through a severe epidemic is an example of
   - a. natural selection.
   - b. genetic isolation.
   - * c. the bottleneck effect.
   - d. the founder principle.
   - e. all of the above

E   30. The influence of genetic drift on allele frequencies increases as
   - a. gene flow increases.
   - * b. population size decreases.
   - c. mutation rate decreases.
   - d. the number of heterozygous loci increases.

M   31. When a population goes through a bottleneck,
   - * a. genetic drift is likely to occur.
   - b. mutation rates increase.
   - c. extinction rates decrease.
   - d. natural selection decreases in intensity.

D   32. Immigration of individuals to a population in Hardy–Weinberg equilibrium will NOT upset the equilibrium if
   - * a. they are beyond the age of reproduction.
   - b. females and males are in equal proportions.
   - c. they mate randomly in the new population.
   - d. they arrive in large numbers.

D   33. Although there are as many starlings in North America as there are in Europe, genetic variability in the North American population is reduced relative to that in Europe because
   - a. there are more environments in Europe.
   - * b. the North American population is derived from a small founder population.
   - c. there is more gene flow in Europe.
   - d. there is less mutation in North America.

E   34. All of the following are components of Darwin's principle of natural selection EXCEPT
   - * a. new alleles are constantly produced through mutation.
   - b. populations exhibit great variation.
   - c. organisms produce more offspring than can be sustained by the environment.
   - d. over time, adaptive phenotypes increase in frequency within a population.

E   35. Which of the following evolve?
   - * a. populations
   - b. genera
   - c. kingdoms
   - d. a and b

EVIDENCE OF NATURAL SELECTION

M   36. A color mutation in a moth from light to dark
   - a. is an advantage in industrial environments.
   - b. may be beneficial under changing environmental conditions.
   - c. produces a form of moth that will have a better chance for survival in some environments.
   - d. may be easily spotted by predators in some environments.
   - * e. all of the above

M   37. The HbS allele (sickle cell) occurs at a higher frequency in Africa than it does in the United States because
        a. it is a dominant allele in Africa and a recessive one in the United States.
        b. genetic recombination occurs at different rates in different human populations.
  * c. natural selection favors heterozygotes in Africa, but favors homozygous normal individuals in the United States.
        d. the U.S. population is descended from a small group of individuals who possessed the allele at a high frequency.

D   38. The phenotype of the horseshoe crab has remained virtually unchanged for more than 250 million years due to the
        a. lack of variability in most loci in horseshoe crab DNA.
        b. absence of natural selection.
        c. relative lack of horseshoe crab predators.
  * d. relatively stable environment in which the horseshoe crab lives.

M   39. Stabilizing selection occurs when
        a. the environment controls which organisms will survive.
        b. humans determine which organisms will survive.
  * c. the extremes of the population have a lesser chance to survive.
        d. the extremes of the population have a better chance to survive.
        e. the organisms on one extreme of the population have a better chance to survive than those on the other extreme.

M   40. Directional selection occurs when
        a. the environment controls which organisms will survive.
        b. humans determine which organisms will survive.
        c. the extremes of the population have a lesser chance to survive.
        d. the extremes of the population have a better chance to survive.
  * e. the organisms on one extreme of the population have a better chance to survive than do those on the other extreme.

M   41. In an unchanging environment, selection in a well-adapted population is
        a. directional.
        b. disruptive.
  * c. stabilizing.
        d. absent.

E   42. Artificial selection occurs when
        a. the environment controls which organisms will survive.
  * b. humans determine which organisms will survive.
        c. the extremes of the population have a lesser chance to survive.
        d. the extremes of the population have a better chance to survive.
        e. the organisms on one extreme of the population have a better chance to survive than those on the other extreme.

E   43. An insect that exhibits resistance to a pesticide
        a. developed the resistance in response to the pesticide.
        b. mutated when exposed to the pesticide.
  * c. inherited genes that made it resistant to the pesticide.
        d. none of the above

E   44. In a certain bird species, clutch size (the number of eggs laid by a female in one breeding season) ranges from four to eight and the most frequent clutch size is six. This phenomenon is an example of
  a. sexual selection.
  * b. stabilizing selection.
  c. disruptive selection.
  d. directional selection.

E   45. Male northern sea lions are nearly twice the size of females because
  a. males live longer than females.
  b. predators of the sea lions favor males.
  * c. males compete to mate with females.
  d. each male must protect the one female with which he mates.

SPECIATION

E   46. A species is composed of
  a. related organisms.
  b. a group of reproductive females.
  * c. populations that have the potential to interbreed and produce fertile offspring.
  d. organisms located in the same habitat.
  e. all males and females in the same geographical range with the same ecological requirements.

E   47. The term *reproductive isolation mechanism* refers to
  a. specific areas where males compete or display for females.
  b. the process by which sexual selection evolves within a population.
  * c. a blockage of gene flow between populations.
  d. the inability of a species to continue reproduction.

M   48. Members of two different bird species mate and produce viable fertile offspring. The courtship song of the hybrid is not recognized by members of either parent species. This is an example of
  a. speciation.
  b. balanced polymorphism.
  * c. behavioral isolation.
  d. sexual selection.

D   49. Incompatibilities between the developing embryo and the maternal organism that cause the embryo to abort spontaneously may prevent individuals of different populations from producing fertile offspring. Such differences may be which of the following?
  * a. isolating mechanisms
  b. allele frequencies
  c. mutations
  d. founder effects
  e. gene flow

M   50. Two individuals are members of the same species if they
  a. possess the same number of chromosomes.
  b. breed at the same time.
  c. are phenotypically indistinguishable.
  * d. can mate and produce fertile offspring.

M   51.   Which is NOT an example of an isolating mechanism?
             a. species-specific courtship rituals
     *   b. Hardy–Weinberg equilibrium
             c. the founder effect
             d. earthquakes and floods
             e. all of the above

E   52.   Complete reproductive isolation is evidence that what has occurred?
             a. extinction
     *   b. speciation
             c. polyploidy
             d. hybridization
             e. gene flow

Classification Questions

Answer questions 53–56 in reference to the four evolutionary processes listed below:

          a. mutation
          b. gene flow
          c. genetic drift
          d. natural selection

M   53.   Which is most likely to lead to the loss of genetic variation in a small population?

E   54.   Which process produces new genetic variation within a species?

M   55.   Which process can rapidly offset the effects of genetic isolation when two populations come into secondary contact?

D   56.   The reduced contribution of one phenotype in comparison to another in the next generation is an example of what?

Answers: 53. c   54. a   55. b   56. d

Selecting the Exception

M   57.   Four of the five answers listed below are sources of variation in a population. Select the exception.
             a. mutation
             b. sexual reproduction
             c. crossing over
             d. independent assortment
     *   e. law of dominance

D   58.   Four of the five answers listed below are characteristics of an unchanging, nonevolving population. Select the exception.
             a. random mating
             b. no mutation
     *   c. differential survival
             d. no migration or gene flow
             e. infinitely large population

E   59. Four of the five answers listed below are characteristics of mutations. Select the exception.
    *   a. predictable
            b. lethal or beneficial
            c. random
            d. effects depend on environment
            e. heritable

M   60. Four of the five answers listed below are portions of the theory of natural selection. Select the exception.
            a. Variation is heritable.
            b. Heritable traits vary in adaptability.
            c. More organisms are produced than can survive.
    *   d. The largest and strongest always contribute more genes to the next generation.
            e. Natural selection is the result of differential reproduction.

E   61. Four of the five answers listed below are types of selection exhibited by nature. Select the exception.
    *   a. artificial
            b. disruptive
            c. stabilizing
            d. directional
            e. sexual

M   62. Four of the five answers listed below are examples of disruptive selection. Select the exception.
    *   a. pesticide resistance
            b. sexual dimorphism
            c. sickle-cell anemia
            d. balanced polymorphism
            e. differential mortality

E   63. Four of the five answers listed below are isolating mechanisms. Select the exception.
            a. geographic
            b. behavioral
            c. temporal (time)
            d. gametic
    *   e. external fertilization

D   64. Four of the five answers listed below can upset genetic equilibrium. Select the exception.
    *   a. interbreeding
            b. genetic drift
            c. mutation
            d. natural selection
            e. gene flow

CHAPTER 15
LIFE'S ORIGINS AND MACROEVOLUTION

Multiple-Choice Questions

EVIDENCE OF MACROEVOLUTION

E   1. The punctuational model of evolutionary change proposes that most morphological change occurs
      a. gradually within a species.
      b. rapidly within a species.
      c. gradually during speciation.
   * d. rapidly during speciation.

M   2. According to the punctuated equilibrium model of speciation, a tree of descent would be characterized by
   * a. vertical lines with horizontal branchings.
      b. vertical lines with branchings at narrow angles.
      c. broad-angled lines with horizontal branches.
      d. broad-angled lines with branching at narrow angles.

E   3. The fossil record is incomplete because
      a. very few organisms were preserved as fossils.
      b. organisms tend to decay before becoming a fossil.
      c. animals with hard parts are preserved more easily.
      d. geological processes may destroy fossils.
   * e. all of the above

M   4. The study of comparative morphology has revealed the conservative nature of the genes responsible for
      a. food procurement.
      b. reproductive behavior.
   * c. embryonic development.
      d. size.

M   5. The convergence in external morphology of sharks, penguins, and porpoises is attributed to
      a. reduced genetic variability in these groups.
   * b. selection pressures that are common to these groups.
      c. reproductive isolation of these groups.
      d. identical genes in all three groups.

M   6. Which serve as examples of convergence?
   * a. penguins and porpoises
      b. panthers and tigers
      c. apes and monkeys
      d. sharks, skates, and rays
      e. mice, rats, and gerbils

E   7. Which mutations are NOT subject to natural selection?
      a. lethal
      b. physiological
   * c. neutral
      d. morphological
      e. beneficial

M   8.   The concept of a molecular clock is based on the idea that
*   a.   neutral mutations occur at regular rates.
       b.   genetic relatedness can be determined by timing antibody–antigen reactions.
       c.   radioactive isotopes decay at a constant rate.
       d.   speciation is a rapid event.

M   9.   All of the following are useful indicators of phylogenetic relatedness EXCEPT
       a.   base sequences in DNA.
       b.   amino acid sequences in a protein.
*   c.   similar ecological requirements.
       d.   similar embryonic development.

M   10. Phylogenetic relationships, when determined solely by the study of comparative
          morphology, may be incorrect due to
       a.   morphological divergence.
*   b.   convergence.
       c.   adaptive radiation.
       d.   extinction.

D   11. Which of the following contributes to adaptive radiation within a lineage?
       a.   extinction of competitors
       b.   new phenotypic characteristics
       c.   genetic uniformity
*   d.   a and b
       e.   a, b, and c

M   12. All radioactive dating methods used to assign time boundaries to geologic intervals are
          based on
       a.   comparing the relative amounts of stable elements in various rock samples.
       b.   comparing the half-lives of all of the isotopes present in a rock sample.
*   c.   comparing the known, invariant decay rates of certain radioactive isotopes to the
            measured amounts of these isotopes and their decay products in different kinds of rocks.
       d.   determining how deep the rock samples were buried; the deeper rocks are invariably
            older than those rocks situated closer to the surface.
       e.   all of the above

E   13. Fossil evidence of the earliest living organisms now dates back
       a.   570 million years.
       b.   1.4 billion years.
*   c.   more than 3.5 billion years.
       d.   more than 5 billion years.
       e.   4004 B.C.

M   14. Life on earth began how many years ago?
       a.   6,000
       b.   350,000
       c.   35,000,000
       d.   350,000,000
*   e.   3,500,000,000

E   15. The half-life of a radioactive isotope
       a.   is variable depending on environmental conditions.
       b.   is the length of time it takes to leave a living organism.
       c.   is a way to determine the age of a fossil.
       d.   is the length of time for half of a given sample of a radioactive substance to change.
*   e.   both c and d

M   16. The rate of radioactive decay is
     a. constant for any one isotope.
     b. completely independent of environmental influences.
     c. based on an unstable ratio of neutrons to protons in the nucleus of the atom.
     d. different for each different isotope considered.
   * e. all of the above

E   17. The acquisition of a key evolutionary innovation by a species gives evidence for the concept of
     a. uniformitarianism.
     b. gradualism.
     c. convergence.
   * d. adaptive radiation.
     e. special creation.

M   18. When compared to many higher plant lineages, the duration of the average mammalian lineage is
     a. longer.
   * b. shorter.
     c. of equal length.
     d. too varied to draw any generalizations.

E   19. Background extinction is a measure of
     a. the rate of species turnover at the end of geological eras.
     b. the number of species that suffer extinction at the beginning of geological eras.
   * c. the steady rate of species turnover within a lineage throughout most of their evolutionary history.
     d. the lowest rate of species turnover within a lineage observed within a geological era.

M   20. Explanations for mass extinction include all of the following EXCEPT
     a. collisions between the earth and other bodies in the solar system.
     b. continental movements.
   * c. adaptive radiation of new predator species in many lineages.
     d. alterations in sea level.

M   21. Which of the following has been used to measure more precisely the relatedness of primates?
   * a. cytochrome c
     b. blood type
     c. family trees
     d. convergence
     e. fossils

MACROEVOLUTION AND EARTH HISTORY

E   22. The most recent geological era is the
   * a. Cenozoic.
     b. Mesozoic.
     c. Carboniferous.
     d. Paleozoic.
     e. Proterozoic.

E   23. Which Paleozoic geological period is the most recent?
     a. Carboniferous
   * b. Permian
     c. Cambrian
     d. Devonian
     e. Ordovician

E   24. Which Paleozoic geological period is the most ancient?
- a. Carboniferous
- b. Permian
- * c. Cambrian
- d. Devonian
- e. Ordovician

E   25. Which epoch is the most recent?
- a. Eocene
- * b. Pleistocene
- c. Paleocene
- d. Miocene
- e. Pliocene

E   26. Which geological era is the most recent?
- * a. Cenozoic
- b. Mesozoic
- c. Proterozoic
- d. Archean
- e. Paleozoic

E   27. Which geological era is the most ancient?
- a. Cenozoic
- b. Mesozoic
- c. Proterozoic
- * d. Archean
- e. Paleozoic

E   28. Geological time is divided into major divisions known as
- * a. eras.
- b. epochs.
- c. periods.
- d. all of the above

E   29. The geologic time scale is subdivided on the basis of
- a. the appearance of different radioactive isotopes in different strata.
- b. levels of background extinction.
- * c. periods of mass extinction.
- d. a and b

E   30. Most of today's mammals appeared during the
- a. Triassic.
- b. last few million years of the Cretaceous.
- * c. first 10–15 million years of the Paleocene.
- d. Pleistocene ice ages.
- e. most recent geological time period.

E   31. The solar system is approximately how many years old?
- a. 10–12 billion
- * b. 4.6–5 billion
- c. 750 million
- d. 400 million
- e. 200 million

E   32. The primitive earth's atmosphere did NOT contain
             a. water vapor.
             b. free nitrogen.
             c. free hydrogen.
        *   d. free oxygen.
             e. inert gases.

E   33. Many of the organic compounds essential for life, such as amino acids and nucleotides,
             could NOT assemble spontaneously in the presence of
             a. hydrogen.
        *   b. free oxygen.
             c. carbon dioxide.
             d. nitrogen.
             e. argon.

M   34. The earth is able to maintain water in a liquid state on the surface by virtue of
             a. insufficient life to use up the available water.
             b. the distance of the earth from the sun.
             c. the availability of oxygen in the atmosphere.
             d. the size of the earth.
        *   e. both b and d

M   35. The early atmosphere of the earth
        *   a. originated when gases from beneath the slowly solidifying crust were vented by
                 vulcanism.
             b. did not exist before 1 billion years ago.
             c. probably consisted of hydrogen, methane, nitrogen, ammonia, and hydrogen sulfide, but
                 no water vapor.
             d. all of the above

E   36. Organic compounds break down spontaneously in the presence of _____; hence, life
             probably never would have emerged if the ancient atmosphere had been the same as the
             present one.
             a. carbon dioxide
             b. hydrogen
        *   c. oxygen
             d. nitrogen
             e. silica

E   37. Experiments like those first performed by Stanley Miller in 1953 demonstrated that
             a. DNA forms readily and reproduces itself.
        *   b. many of the lipids, carbohydrates, proteins, and nucleotides required for life can form
                 under abiotic conditions.
             c. complete, functioning prokaryotic cells are formed after approximately three months.
             d. a lipid–protein film will eventually be formed by thermal convection.
             e. all of the above

E   38. Which of the following was NOT included in Miller's reaction chamber, which contained
             substances intended to duplicate the atmosphere of ancient earth?
        *   a. carbon dioxide
             b. methane
             c. ammonia
             d. water vapor
             e. both b and c

E 39. Who demonstrated the possibility of producing organic compounds from gases and water if the mixture is bombarded with a continuous spark discharge?
* a. Miller
b. Starr
c. Thompsen
d. Pauling
e. Platt

E 40. The Miller experiment designed to study the early synthesis of organic compounds included all of the following molecules EXCEPT
a. methane.
b. ammonia.
c. water.
* d. oxygen.

M 41. Protein synthesis on the primordial earth may have been catalyzed by _____ before the evolution of enzymes.
a. DNA
b. carbohydrates
c. amino acids
* d. RNA
e. lightning

M 42. The formation of polypeptide chains under abiotic conditions was important because they served as
a. a supply of structural units.
b. enzymes to catalyze reactions.
c. subunits in the formation of DNA.
d. subunits in the formation of RNA.
* e. both a and b

M 43. What step occurred first in the evolution of life?
a. formation of lipid spheres
b. formation of protein-RNA systems
c. formation of membrane-bound protocells
* d. spontaneous formation of lipids, proteins, carbohydrates, and nucleotides under abiotic conditions
e. formation of ATP

M 44. Which step in the evolution of life is the most complex and occurred last?
a. formation of lipid spheres
b. formation of protein-RNA systems
* c. formation of membrane-bound protocells
d. spontaneous formation of lipids, proteins, carbohydrates, and nucleotides under abiotic conditions
e. formation of ATP

D 45. Contemporary hypotheses concerned with the origin of life focus on what two characteristics of living systems?
a. energy conversion and development of a nucleus
b. self-replication and utilization of oxygen
* c. plasma membranes and self-replication
d. growth and transcription

M   46. The earliest organisms were probably unicellular
         a. autotrophs.
         b. aerobes.
    *   c. heterotrophs.
         d. eukaryotes.

M   47. The presence of free oxygen in the atmosphere
         a. was a result of the accumulation of the by-products of photosynthesis.
         b. prevented the further spontaneous generation of life.
         c. provided the opportunity to extract more energy through aerobic respiration.
         d. did not occur immediately after the earth was formed.
    *   e. all of the above

M   48. When free oxygen (O_2) became available in the atmosphere,
         a. some organisms changed their metabolism.
         b. oxygen was used as a dumping place for hydrogen ions and electrons.
         c. some cells and forms of life became extinct.
         d. aerobic respiration emerged.
    *   e. all of the above

E   49. The large land mass that contained all the continents was called
         a. Laurasia.
    *   b. Pangea.
         c. Gondwanaland.
         d. Atlantis.
         e. all of the above

M   50. What mud-crawling, mud-burrowing crustaceans eventually had 600 genera living during the Cambrian Period?
         a. jawless fishes
         b. cephalopods
         c. brachiopods
    *   d. trilobites
         e. isopods

E   51. During which geologic era did Pangea break up?
         a. Archean
         b. Paleozoic
         c. Cenozoic
         d. Proterozoic
    *   e. Mesozoic

D   52. Plate tectonic theory is based on
         a. a thermal convection model, in which cool material in the earth's mantle rises and spreads laterally beneath the crustal plates.
         b. the idea that the earth's crust is fragmented into rigid crusts that are sinking slowly beneath crustal plates.
         c. the idea that coacervate formation causes continents to drift apart slowly on their crustal plates.
    *   d. observations that the sea floor is slowly spreading away from oceanic ridges due to thermal convection in the mantle.
         e. all of the above

D   53. Which characterizes the earth during the Cambrian period?
*   a. trilobites abundant, extensive shallow seas at tropical latitudes
     b. active predators, land masses at the poles
     c. adaptive radiation of fish, land masses at the poles
     d. first eukaryotes, Pangea land mass

M   54. What was the most abundant and conspicuous animal during the Cambrian period?
     a. primates
*   b. trilobites
     c. fish
     d. cephalopods
     e. sea scorpions

M   55. Insects became abundant during which period?
*   a. Carboniferous
     b. Devonian
     c. Silurian
     d. Ordovician
     e. Cambrian

E   56. Fossil fuels were formed in which period?
*   a. Carboniferous
     b. Devonian
     c. Silurian
     d. Ordovician
     e. Cambrian

D   57. The great burst of diversification in metazoan families, especially those with marine representatives, occurred during which geological period?
     a. Silurian
     b. Devonian
*   c. Ordovician
     d. Carboniferous

M   58. Much of the fossil fuel used by humans today represents the organic remains of organisms that lived during which geological era?
*   a. Carboniferous
     b. Devonian
     c. Silurian
     d. Permian

M   59. All earth's land mass was located in a single continent, Pangea, during which period?
     a. Cretaceous
     b. Permian
     c. Triassic
     d. Jurassic
*   e. both b and c

M   60. The largest extinction the world has ever known occurred at the end of which period?
     a. Cretaceous
*   b. Permian
     c. Triassic
     d. Jurassic
     e. Tertiary

M   61.   Mammals originated during which period?
- a. Cretaceous
- b. Permian
- * c. Triassic
- d. Jurassic
- e. Tertiary

M   62.   The flowering plants appeared during which period?
- * a. Cretaceous
- b. Permian
- c. Triassic
- d. Jurassic
- e. Tertiary

M   63.   The greatest mass extinction in the history of life on earth occurred between which two geological periods?
- a. Devonian and Carboniferous
- b. Silurian and Devonian
- * c. Triassic and Permian
- d. Cretaceous and Tertiary

M   64.   Present evidence suggests that birds evolved from ancestral
- a. turtles.
- b. mammals.
- * c. dinosaurs.
- d. therapsids.

E   65.   The dinosaurs disappeared at the end of which period?
- * a. Cretaceous
- b. Permian
- c. Triassic
- d. Jurassic
- e. Tertiary

D   66.   Spore-bearing plants became dominant during which period?
- * a. Carboniferous
- b. Devonian
- c. Silurian
- d. Ordovician
- e. Cambrian

E   67.   The extensive adaptive radiation of the mammals occurred during which geological era?
- a. Paleozoic
- b. Cretaceous
- * c. Cenozoic
- d. Mesozoic

M   68.   Sidney Fox found that if heated protein chains were allowed to cool in water they would
- a. form nitrogen, which would escape as a gas.
- b. form proteinoids.
- * c. form small, stable spheres or microspheres.
- d. clot and form a complex latticework frame for chemical reactions.
- e. break down into the original amino acids that the protein chain was made from.

ORGANIZING THE EVIDENCE—CLASSIFICATION SCHEMES

E 69. Which of the following includes all the others?
  a. family
* b. phylum
  c. species
  d. class
  e. order

E 70. Which includes all related genera?
* a. family
  b. phylum
  c. species
  d. class
  e. order

M 71. Phylogeny refers to what aspects of individuals?
  a. morphological traits
* b. evolutionary relationships
  c. physiological characteristics
  d. behavioral features
  e. all of the above

E 72. The most widely accepted classification system in use today was proposed by
  a. Charles Darwin.
  b. James Hutton.
  c. Jean-Baptiste Lamarck.
* d. Robert Whittaker.
  e. Alfred Russel Wallace.

D 73. The assigning of scientific names is called
  a. gradualism.
  b. convergence.
  c. classification.
* d. taxonomy.
  e. phylogeny.

Matching Questions

D   74.   Matching. Write the most appropriate letter by the best matching element.

1 _____ adaptive radiation

2 _____ Archean

3 _____ Cenozoic

4 _____ convergence

5 _____ gradualism

6 _____ Mesozoic

7 _____ Paleozoic

8 _____ Proterozoic

9 _____ punctuation

A. mammals, birds, and flowering plants evolve mostly during this era

B. the traditional model of speciation that states that most morphological change occurs within species as a result of genetic drift, directional selection, and other processes by which allele frequencies change

C. an era that harbored the oldest definite fossils known

D. two or more species from dissimilar, only distantly related lineages adopt a similar way of life and come to resemble one another rather closely

E. an era that ended with the great Permian extinction about 240 million years ago

F. an era during which free oxygen became abundant in Earth's atmosphere, and the first forms of life evolved into more complex, multicellular types 2.5 billion years ago until 570 million years ago

G. an era that ended with the massive Cretaceous extinction that wiped out the dinosaurs

H. an alternative model of speciation that says most morphological change occurs rapidly during speciation

I. Darwin's finches on the Galápagos Islands are an example of this kind of spectacular evolutionary success

Answers: 1. I   2. C   3. A   4. D   5. B   6. G

                 7. E   8. F   9. H

Classification Questions

Answer questions 75–78 in reference to the five taxonomic categories listed below:

     a. genus
     b. species
     c. order
     d. family
     e. phyla

E   75.   Which category is not included in any of the other listed categories?

E   76.   Which category is included in each of the other categories?

M   77.   The term *Hominidae* is an example of _____.

E   78.   Humans belong to the taxon *Homo*. Which category denotes the taxonomic category of *Homo*?

Answer questions 79–83 in reference to the four terms listed below:

    a. gradualism
    b. convergence
    c. punctuation
    d. divergence

M   79. The porpoise and the penguin are examples of _____.

M   80. The accumulation of allelic differences between two species over a period of 2 million years is an example of _____.

M   81. The rapid divergence of two reproductively isolated groups following speciation is an example of _____.

D   82. Wings of pterosaurs, birds, and bats are examples of _____.

D   83. Most morphological change occurs within species by changes in allele frequencies. This is an example of _____.

Answers: 79. b   80. a   81. c   82. b   83. a

Selecting the Exception

D   84. Four of the five answers listed below are habitats favoring fossil preservation. Select the exception.
    * a. deserts
    b. swamp
    c. tar pits
    d. seafloor
    e. caves

D   85. Four of the five answers listed below are related by a common era. Select the exception.
    a. Permian
    b. Ordovician
    c. Carboniferous
    * d. Cretaceous
    e. Cambrian

D   86. Four of the five answers listed below are related by a similar relationship. Select the exception.
    a. Mesozoic
    * b. Tertiary
    c. Cenozoic
    d. Proterozoic
    e. Archean

D   87. Four of the five answers listed below are related by a common era. Select the exception.
    * a. Polycene
    b. Miocene
    c. Oligocene
    d. Pliocene
    e. Paleocene

D   88. Four of the five answers listed below are periods of mass extinctions. Select the exception.
          a. Ordovician
*   b. Silurian
          c. Cretaceous
          d. Permian
          e. Triassic

M   89. Four of the five answers listed below are components of the mixture used in Miller's experiment. Select the exception.
          a. hydrogen
*   b. oxygen
          c. methane
          d. ammonia
          e. water

D   90. Four of the five answers listed below are related by a common association. Select the exception.
          a. archaebacteria
          b. methanogens
          c. halophiles
*   d. cyanobacteria
          e. thermoacidophiles

D   91. Four of the five answers listed below have a common relationship. Select the exception.
          a. protistans
          b. plants
          c. animals
*   d. fungi
          e. methanogens

CHAPTER 16
HUMAN EVOLUTION

Multiple-Choice Questions

THE MAMMALIAN HERITAGE

E   1.   Which feature do mammals share in common with all vertebrates?
- a. hair
- * b. a column of individual backbones
- c. milk
- d. internal development

E   2.   Mammals are the only vertebrates that possess
- a. teeth.
- b. a backbone.
- c. a brain.
- * d. mammary glands.
- e. sensory organs.

M   3.   A mammal with well-developed premolars and molars would likely be eating mostly
- a. meat.
- * b. plant matter.
- c. insects.
- d. decayed materials.
- e. none of these

PRIMATE ORIGINS

M   4.   The most primitive living primate is the
- a. Old World monkey.
- b. lemur.
- c. New World monkey.
- * d. tree shrew.
- e. tarsier.

M   5.   Which of the following is a brachiator, that is, uses long arms to hang from overhead branches as it moves from tree to tree?
- a. tree shrew
- * b. ape
- c. lemur
- d. human

E   6.   Which is NOT an anthropoid?
- a. orangutan
- * b. lemur
- c. spider monkey
- d. gibbon

E   7.   Bipedalism is most highly developed in
- a. hominoids.
- b. apes.
- * c. humans.
- d. monkeys.
- e. prosimians.

M 8. In the course of the evolution of existing primate groups, there has been a general decrease in
* a. number of offspring produced by a female.
   b. body size.
   c. life span.
   d. duration of infant dependency.

E 9. All but which factor were important evolutionary adaptations in primates?
   a. enhanced stereoscopic vision
   b. upright position
   c. an opposable thumb
* d. the development of a restricted or specialized diet
   e. brain expansion and elaboration

M 10. Which feature is NOT characteristic of the evolutionary trends in primates?
   a. longer life span
   b. longer gestation period
   c. longer infant dependency
   d. longer periods between pregnancies
* e. larger litters

M 11. Which characteristic is NOT considered to have been a key character in early primate evolution?
   a. eyes adapted for discerning color and shape in a three-dimensional field
   b. body and limbs adapted for tree climbing
* c. greater jaw and dental specialization
   d. eyes adapted for discerning movement in a three-dimensional field
   e. opposable thumb and forefinger

M 12. Humans are least closely related to the
   a. chimpanzee.
   b. orangutan.
   c. gorilla.
* d. tarsier.
   e. gibbon.

M 13. The primates first arose about how many million years ago?
   a. 75
* b. 60
   c. 50
   d. 40
   e. 30

E 14. All of the placental mammals apparently arose from ancestral forms of
* a. Insectivora, which includes omnivorous shrews and moles.
   b. Carnivora, which includes dogs, cats, and seals.
   c. Rodentia, which includes mice and beavers.
   d. Metatheria, which includes the opossum and kangaroo.
   e. Primate, which means first.

M 15. Primitive primates generally live
* a. in tropical and subtropical forest canopies.
   b. in temperate savanna and grassland habitats.
   c. near rivers, lakes, and streams in the East African Rift Valley.
   d. in caves with abundant supplies of insects.
   e. all of the above

M   16. The diet of the direct ancestors of primates did NOT include
    *   a. grass.
          b. insects.
          c. fruits.
          d. seeds.

THE HOMINIDS

M   17. Hominids evolved when the climate was becoming
          a. wetter and hotter.
          b. wetter and cooler.
          c. drier and hotter.
    *   d. drier and cooler.

D   18. How long ago did the hominid evolutionary line diverge from that leading to the great apes?
          a. about 3 million years ago
    *   b. somewhere between 6 million and 4 million years ago
          c. during the Eocene epoch
          d. less than 2 million years ago
          e. about 1.5 million years ago

E   19. Hominids are characterized as being
          a. insectivores.
          b. herbivores.
          c. carnivores.
    *   d. omnivores.
          e. none of the above

E   20. The early hominid fossils are found in
    *   a. Africa.
          b. Asia.
          c. Australia.
          d. the South Pacific.
          e. Europe.

M   21. Which is a hominid?
          a. chimpanzee
    *   b. *Australopithecus*
          c. baboon
          d. a and b
          e. a, b, and c

M   22. Fossils of the earliest known hominids are how many million years old?
          a. more than 20
          b. about 10
    *   c. approximately 4
          d. less than 0.5

M   23. The conclusion that early hominids were bipedal is based on examination of
          a. the angles made by the bones that articulate with the pelvis.
          b. fossil footprints.
          c. imprints of motor cortex in fossilized craniums.
    *   d. a and b
          e. a, b, and c

M 24. It is thought that the earliest tools were employed by hominids to
       a. assist in locomotion.
       b. provide protection.
   *   c. facilitate the processing of food.
       d. ward off predators.

E 25. The oldest "manufactured" tools have been found in
       a. North America.
       b. Eurasia.
   *   c. Africa.
       d. Australia.

M 26. The geographical distribution of hominids changed dramatically during the Pleistocene
       period due to the migrations of
       a. *Australopithecus robustus.*
       b. *Australopithecus boisei.*
   *   c. *Homo erectus.*
       d. *Homo sapiens.*

D 27. Bipedal behavior and a skeleton adapted for bipedalism were not weeded out by natural
       selection because they
       a. improved stability during standing.
   *   b. enabled the forelimbs to efficiently manipulate the environment.
       c. accelerated the development of binocular vision.
       d. a and b
       e. a, b, and c

M 28. Plasticity specifically refers to the ability to
       a. interbreed with many forms.
   *   b. respond to a wide range of demands.
       c. spread into a large number of habitats.
       d. reproduce rapidly.
       e. function as pioneers in the process of succession.

M 29. The primate fossil named Lucy was a(n)
       a. dryopith.
   *   b. australopith.
       c. cercopith.
       d. prosimian.
       e. hominid.

M 30. Fossil evidence suggests the earliest members of the genus *Homo* were
       a. social.
       b. omnivorous.
       c. tool makers.
       d. a and b
   *   e. a, b, and c

M 31. Which statement about Neanderthals is false?
       a. The oldest Neanderthal fossils are 500,000 years old.
       b. Neanderthal settlements show little evidence of tools.
       c. Neanderthal brains were larger than those of modern humans.
   *   d. a and b are false
       e. a, b, and c are all false

M 32. The species *Homo sapiens* is thought to be how many years old?
    a. 10,000–25,000
    b. 30,000–60,000
    c. 60,000–95,000
    d. 85,000–120,000
  * e. 200,000–300,000

M 33. About 40,000 years ago, what kind of evolution replaced biological evolution in the shaping of modern humans?
  * a. cultural
    b. behavioral
    c. chemical
    d. psychological
    e. morphological

M 34. In an evolutionary context, plasticity refers to
    a. the influence of culture on evolution.
    b. the ability of an individual to alter its phenotype.
  * c. the ability of a population to adapt to changing selection pressures.
    d. the importance of hand movements in the efficient utilization of tools.

M 35. A hominid of Europe and Asia that became extinct about 35,000 years ago was
    a. a dryopith.
    b. *Australopithecus*.
    c. *Homo erectus*.
  * d. Neanderthals.

Matching Questions

D 36. Matching I. Choose the one most appropriate answer for each.

1 _____ anthropoids

2 _____ australopith

3 _____ ceboids

4 _____ cercopithecoids

5 _____ hominoids

6 _____ Neanderthals

7 _____ Primates

8 _____ prosimians

A. a group that includes apes and humans

B. a population of *Homo sapiens* that lived from at least 100,000 to as recently as 35,000 years ago; tool users and artisans

C. the order that includes animals with freely swiveling limbs, mobile grasping digits, upright body posture, good depth perception, and exquisite neural control

D. organisms in a suborder that includes New World and Old World monkeys, apes, and humans

E. a group that includes New World monkeys only

F. organisms in a suborder that includes tree shrews, tarsiers, lemurs, and others

G. a group that includes Old World monkeys only

H. bipedal organisms from about 3.8 to 1 million years ago, with essentially human bodies and ape-shaped heads; brains no larger than those of chimpanzees

Answers: 1. D   2. H   3. E   4. G   5. A   6. B
7. C   8. F

D   37.   Matching II. Choose the one most appropriate answer for each.

1 _____ *Australopithecus*

2 _____ *Homo erectus*

3 _____ *Homo sapiens*

4 _____ Neanderthals

A.   lived from approximately 100,000 to 35,000 years ago; skilled tool makers and artisans

B.   lived about 1.5 million years ago until 300,000 years ago; cranial capacity approximately 1,000 cubic centimeters; bipedal

C.   humans since 300,000 years ago

D.   Lucy; between 3.8 to 1 million years ago

Answers: 1. D   2. B   3. C   4. A

Classification Questions

Answer questions 38–41 in reference to the four hominids listed below:

    a. *Homo habilis*
    b. *Homo erectus*
    c. *Homo sapiens*
    d. *Australopithecus afarensis*

M   38.   To which species did the Neanderthals belong?

D   39.   Which species is designated as the first hominid?

M   40.   Which species was the first known to use fire?

D   41.   Which species was the first definitely known to use tools?

Answers: 38. c   39. d   40. b   41. a

Selecting the Exception

M   42.   Four of the five answers listed below are prosimians. Select the exception.
    a. tree shrews
*   b. monkeys
    c. lemurs
    d. tarsiers
    e. lorises

E   43.   Three of the four answers listed below are anthropoids. Select the exception.
*   a. tarsier
    b. Old World monkey
    c. human
    d. ape

M   44.   Three of the four answers listed below are trends in hominid evolution. Select the exception.
    a. strong social bonding
    b. enhanced vision
*   c. upright vertebral column
    d. omnivorous feeding behavior

D   45. Four of the five answers listed below are related by a similar evolutionary characteristic in *Homo*. Select the exception.
  a. small thin face
  b. high skull
  c. large cranial capacity
  d. larger body size
* e. specialized teeth

CHAPTER 17
VIRUSES, BACTERIA, AND PROTISTANS

Multiple-Choice Questions

VIRUSES

E   1.   Which statement is NOT true?
       a.   Viruses are not able to move by themselves.
       b.   Viruses are not able to reproduce by themselves.
   *   c.   Viruses are not structurally organized.
       d.   Some biologists consider that viruses are forms of life and other biologists consider them to be nonlife.
       e.   Viruses contain instructions to manufacture themselves.

E   2.   When a virus takes over the machinery of a cell, it forces the cell to manufacture
       a.   more mitochondria for energy for the virus.
       b.   more liposomes to isolate themselves from water.
       c.   more food particles.
   *   d.   more viral particles.
       e.   more Golgi bodies so that the cell will secrete the excess viruses.

M   3.   The lysogenic pathway is characterized by
   *   a.   passive replication of viral DNA.
       b.   extensive transcription of viral DNA.
       c.   destruction of the bacterial host.
       d.   a and b
       e.   a, b, and c

M   4.   Which disease is NOT caused by a virus?
       a.   smallpox
       b.   polio
       c.   influenza
   *   d.   syphilis
       e.   herpes

D   5.   Which virus is an RNA virus?
       a.   adenovirus
   *   b.   retrovirus
       c.   parvovirus
       d.   Herpes virus
       e.   papovavirus

M   6.   A virus is characterized by all of the following EXCEPT
   *   a.   enzymes of respiration.
       b.   nucleic acid core.
       c.   noncellular organization.
       d.   protein coat.

E   7.   Plant viruses are transmitted primarily by
       a.   wind.
       b.   water.
       c.   bacteria.
   *   d.   animals.

M   8. Which statement about viruses is true?
    a. They were the first forms of life to evolve.
    b. They do not attack plants.
    c. They are able to reproduce without using other organisms.
    d. They are made of protein only.
*   e. They include some forms that are able to attack bacteria.

BACTERIA

E   9. Viroids differ from viruses in that the former lack
    a. a nucleic acid core.
*   b. a protein coat.
    c. the ability to reproduce.
    d. a and b

M   10. Flu pandemics are caused by the spread of
    a. pathogenic bacteria.
*   b. RNA viruses.
    c. DNA viruses.
    d. parasitic protozoans.

E   11. Which of the following does NOT belong to the protistans?
*   a. bacteria
    b. protozoans
    c. chrysophytes
    d. dinoflagellates
    e. euglenids

E   12. Spherical bacteria are called
    a. bacilli.
    b. spirilla.
*   c. cocci.
    d. bacteriophages.
    e. all of the above

M   13. A helical or spiral bacterium is called a
*   a. spirillum.
    b. bacillus.
    c. coccus.
    d. both b and c

M   14. Peptidoglycan is
    a. found in the chromosomes of most bacteria.
*   b. composed of polysaccharides crosslinked with proteins.
    c. composed of long polypeptides held together by disulfide bridges.
    d. a unique combination of protein lipid and fat.
    e. both a and c

M   15. Which statement is NOT characteristic of bacteria?
*   a. Some may be completely naked.
    b. Some may have hairlike structures called pili.
    c. Some may have rigid cell walls.
    d. Some may have flagella and move about.
    e. Some may have a thin polysaccharide covering.

E   16. All of the following are characteristics of at least some of the Monera EXCEPT
      a. photosynthesis.
      b. heterotrophy.
      c. chemosynthesis.
   *   d. multicellularity.

M   17. Which statement about bacteria is true?
      a. They are diploid organisms.
      b. They produce gametes.
   *   c. They possess circular DNA molecules.
      d. They are eukaryotic.

E   18. In bacteria, DNA is found
      a. in the nucleus alone.
      b. in organelles alone.
      c. in both the nucleus and organelles.
   *   d. as a single circular thread, and possibly as additional pieces.
      e. as particles scattered throughout the entire bacterial cell.

D   19. Some bacteria resemble viruses in that they
      a. perform photosynthesis.
   *   b. are obligate intracellular parasites.
      c. are aerobic.
      d. employ RNA as the genetic material.

D   20. The following human disorders can be caused by bacteria EXCEPT
      a. diarrhea.
      b. Lyme disease.
   *   c. malaria.
      d. botulism.

D   21. Endospores are produced by
      a. Chrysophytes.
   *   b. bacteria.
      c. protozoans.
      d. viruses.

M   22. Which statement is true of all autotrophic bacteria?
      a. They produce molecular oxygen.
      b. They synthesize sugar.
      c. They are anaerobic.
   *   d. They synthesize ATP.

D   23. Gram-positive bacteria react to which of the following, whereas Gram-negative bacteria do NOT?
      a. presence of oxygen
   *   b. presence of a chemical stain
      c. presence of light
      d. absence of carbohydrates
      e. presence of magnetic fields

M   24. When nutrients are scarce, some bacteria
      a. engage in conjugation.
      b. switch to photosynthesis.
   *   c. form endospores.
      d. become pathogenic.
      e. divide.

M 25. Endospores
  a. are resistant bodies.
  b. enable some bacteria to survive for long periods of time.
  c. may contain concentrated poisons.
  * d. all of the above

E 26. The strongest poison known to humans is produced by
  * a. *Clostridium botulinum.*
  b. *Clostridium tetani.*
  c. fer-de-lance snakes.
  d. certain nettles in Java.
  e. curare.

PROTISTANS

M 27. The bacterium *E. coli*
  a. is a normal inhabitant of the human intestinal tract.
  b. produces conditions that prevent invasion by other bacteria.
  c. enhances digestion, particularly the digestion of fats.
  d. produces vitamin K.
  * e. all of the above

D 28. Each statement concerning the bacterium *E. coli* is true EXCEPT:
  a. it synthesizes vitamins that are essential to its mammalian host.
  b. it can act as a pathogen.
  c. it can prevent colonization of the gut by pathogens.
  * d. it is capable of photosynthesis.

M 29. *E. coli*
  a. is rarely found in the intestinal tract of people who live in industrially developed countries.
  * b. may cause high infant mortality by producing severe diarrhea.
  c. is photosynthetic and autotrophic.
  d. causes fecal material to move through the colon at a slow rate and frequently causes constipation.
  e. all of the above

M 30. Heterocysts are regions in filamentous cyanobacteria
  a. that can break and allow for reproduction by fragmentation.
  b. where endospores are formed.
  c. where the filament is attached to its substrates.
  * d. where nitrogen fixation occurs.
  e. where photosynthesis occurs.

E 31. Which is a swamp gas?
  a. carbon monoxide
  b. carbon dioxide
  c. ammonia sulfide
  * d. methane
  e. hydrogen sulfide

M 32. The type of bacterium most likely to be found in a swamp is
  a. thermoacidophilic.
  b. halophilic.
  c. cyanobacteria.
  * d. methanogens.
  e. *E. coli.*

M 33. Which type of bacterium would likely be found in hot springs?
* a. thermophiles
   b. halophiles
   c. cyanobacteria
   d. methanogens
   e. *E. coli*

M 34. Which terms accurately describe the Archebacteria?
   a. extinct, aerobic
   b. extinct, anaerobic
   c. present, aerobic
* d. present, anaerobic

M 35. The methane-producing bacteria (methanogens) belong to the
* a. archaebacteria.
   b. prokaryotes.
   c. eukaryotes.
   d. urkaryotes.
   e. eubacteria.

M 36. According to Lynn Margulis, the organelles of the eukaryotes
   a. evolved separately from the nucleus.
   b. are structures that broke off from the nucleus.
   c. represent inpouchings from the plasma membrane.
* d. are descendants of symbiotic organisms engulfed by a larger organism.
   e. are obligate parasites.

E 37. Multicellular organisms first appeared how many years ago?
   a. 7,500,000,000
   b. 3,000,000,000
* c. 900,000,000
   d. 70,000,000
   e. 7,000,000

D 38. Which of the following is the strongest evidence for the hypothesis that present-day eukaryotic aerobes are the descendants of the successful symbiotic association of anaerobes and mitochondria?
   a. mitochondria can produce ATP
   b. a mitochondrion can survive indefinitely when removed from a eukaryotic cell
* c. a mitochondrion has its own set of DNA molecules
   d. fossilized mitochondria are older than the oldest fossilized eukaryotes

E 39. Between 1.3 billion and 700 million years ago, what arose first?
   a. prokaryotes
* b. eukaryotes
   c. amphibians
   d. stromatolites
   e. flowering plants

E 40. All of the following are advantages of multicellularity EXCEPT
   a. division of labor.
   b. greater metabolic efficiency.
* c. lower extinction rates.
   d. larger-sized organisms possible.

M   41.   Which of the following is NOT true of *Euglena*?
      *   a.   It moves by pseudopodia.
         b.   It contains chloroplasts.
         c.   It can detect light sources by using an eyespot.
         d.   Its cell body is not surrounded by a cell wall.
         e.   none of the above; all statements are true

E   42.   The most primitive forms of life were the
         a.   archaebacteria.
      *   b.   ancestral prokaryotes.
         c.   eukaryotes.
         d.   urkaryotes.
         e.   eubacteria.

E   43.   The simplest of the eukaryotes are the
      *   a.   protistans.
         b.   plants.
         c.   fungi.
         d.   animals.
         e.   both a and c

M   44.   "Red tides" and extensive fish kills are caused by population "blooms" of
         a.   *Euglena.*
      *   b.   specific dinoflagellates.
         c.   diatoms.
         d.   *Plasmodium.*
         e.   fish.

M   45.   Dinoflagellates are characterized by all of the following EXCEPT:
         a.   they secrete neurotoxins that can kill fish.
         b.   they possess flagella that fit in grooves.
         c.   they kill shellfish such as clams, oysters, scallops, and mussels.
      *   d.   they have two shells that fit together like petri plates.
         e.   they are photosynthetic.

M   46.   "Red tide" neurotoxins are produced by members of which phylum?
         a.   Chrysophyta
      *   b.   Pyrrophyta
         c.   Sarcomastigophora
         d.   Ciliophora

E   47.   Protozoans are classified on the basis of their
         a.   photosynthetic nature.
         b.   life cycle.
         c.   unique structures.
      *   d.   type of motility.
         e.   feeding habitats.

E   48.   Protozoans are placed into four groups on the basis of
         a.   cell membrane and cell wall components.
         b.   heterotrophic or autotrophic mode of nutrition.
      *   c.   means of locomotion.
         d.   characteristics of the nucleus.

E   49.   As defined in your textbook, all protists are
   a. autotrophic.
   b. heterotrophic.
 * c. unicellular.
   d. multicellular.

D   50.   Protozoans cause all of the following diseases EXCEPT
   a. dysentery.
   b. African sleeping sickness.
   c. malaria.
 * d. elephantiasis.
   e. trichomonal infections of the reproductive tract.

M   51.   Certain euglenids are unique among the Protista in that they
   a. possess flagella.
   b. reproduce by longitudinal fission.
 * c. are heterotrophic and autotrophic.
   d. are multicellular.

E   52.   Pseudopodia are characteristic of which of the following groups of protozoans?
   a. ciliated
   b. flagellated
 * c. amoeboid
   d. sporozoan

D   53.   Which of the following specialized structures is NOT correctly paired with a function?
   a. gullet–ingestion
   b. cilia–food gathering
 * c. contractile vacuole–digestion
   d. anal pore–waste elimination
   e. ribosome–protein synthesis

M   54.   The sporozoan parasite *Plasmodium* infects cells of which of the following?
   a. blood
   b. liver
   c. brain
 * d. a and b
   e. a, b, and c

D   55.   All of the following are members of the same kingdom EXCEPT
   a. *Amoeba.*
 * b. *Clostridium.*
   c. *Euglena.*
   d. *Paramecium.*

E   56.   Structurally, the most complex unicellular organisms are
   a. viruses.
   b. bacteria.
   c. dinoflagellates.
 * d. ciliates.

M   57.   For an organism to be considered truly multicellular,
   a. its cells must be heterotrophic.
 * b. there must be division of labor and cellular specialization.
   c. the organisms cannot be parasitic.
   d. the organisms must at least be motile.
   e. the individual cells must be able to survive alone.

D 58. Which of the following are NOT able to carry on photosynthesis?
    a. cyanobacteria
    b. euglenids
    c. chrysophyta
  * d. protozoans
    e. dinoflagellates

Matching Questions

D 59. Matching. Match all applicable letters with the appropriate terms. A letter may be used more than once, and a blank may contain more than one letter.

1 _____ *Amoeba proteus*	A. Eubacteria
2 _____ *Anabaena*	B. Archaebacteria
3 _____ *Clostridium botulinum*	C. Virus
4 _____ diatoms	D. Protista
5 _____ *Escherichia coli*	E. Gram-positive
6 _____ foraminifera	F. Gram-negative
7 _____ golden algae	G. photosynthetic autotroph
8 _____ Herpes virus	H. dinoflagellates
9 _____ methanogens	I. obtain food by using pseudopodia
10 _____ *Paramecium*	J. causes malaria
11 _____ *Plasmodium*	K. a sporozoan
12 _____ thermoacidophiles	L. a ciliate
13 _____ *Volvox*	M. cause cold sores and a type of venereal disease
	N. live in "glass" houses
	O. live in hardened shells that have thousands of tiny holes

Answers:
  1. D, I   2. A, F, G   3. A, E   4. D, G, N   5. A, F
  6. D, O   7. D, G   8. C, M   9. B   10. D, L
  11. D, K, J   12. B   13. D, G

Classification Questions

Answer questions 60–64 in reference to the five groups of organisms listed below:
    a. eubacteria
    b. archaebacteria
    c. euglenids
    d. dinoflagellates
    e. protozoans

D 60. To which group do modern, blue-green algae belong?

M 61. Which is the only group represented by modern bacteria?

D 62. Methanogenic bacteria, common in the shallow seas of the Carboniferous Period, belonged to which group?

M 63. Organisms responsible for the red tides along ocean coasts belong to which group?

M 64. Chagas Disease, or American Trypanosomiasis, which eventually killed Charles Darwin, is caused by a species in which group?

Answers: 60. a   61. a   62. a   63. d   64. e

Answer questions 65–69 in reference to the four groups of protozoans listed below:
   a. Mastigophora
   b. Sarcodina
   c. Sporozoa
   d. Ciliophora

E 65. The common amoeba, *Amoeba proteus*, is a member of which group?

M 66. The radiolarians, which produce glass shells, are members of which group?

M 67. The malarial parasite *Plasmodium* is a member of which group?

M 68. Which group derives its motility from the presence of a flagellum?

M 69. An organism commonly used in competition experiments is the *Paramecium*, which belongs to which group?

Answers: 65. b   66. b   67. c   68. a   69. d

Selecting the Exception

E 70. Three of the four answers listed below are descriptions of bacterial shape. Select the exception.
   a. coccus
   b. bacillus
 * c. pili
   d. spirillum

M 71. Four of the five answers listed below are members of the same kingdom. Select the exception.
 * a. archaebacteria
   b. protozoa
   c. chrysophyte
   d. dinoflagellate
   e. euglenoid

M 72. Four of the five answers listed below are bacterial structures. Select the exception.
   a. endospore
   b. pilus
   c. capsule
 * d. eyespot
   e. heterocyst

D 73. Four of the five answers listed below are related by a common category. Select the exception.
   a. rhinoviruses
 * b. poxviruses
   c. togaviruses
   d. retrovirus
   e. enteroviruses

D 74. Four of the five answers listed below are related by a similar category. Select the exception.
   a. Herpes viruses
   b. papovaviruses
   c. parvoviruses
 * d. paramyxoviruses
   e. adenoviruses

D 75. Four of the five answers listed below are protozoans. Select the exception.
   a. amoeboids
 * b. dinoflagellates
   c. ciliates
   d. sporozoans
   e. flagellates

D 76. Four of the five answers listed below are cellular. Select the exception.
 * a. viroid
   b. diatom
   c. trypanosome
   d. trichosome
   e. dinoflagellate

CHAPTER 18
FUNGI AND PLANTS

Multiple-Choice Questions

PART I. KINGDOM OF FUNGI

E   1. Saprobes are
       a. cytoplasmic organelles.
       b. metabolic by-products.
  *   c. organisms that feed on dead material.
       d. parasites of plants.
       e. an evolutionary dead end.

E   2. Fungi
       a. are producers.
  *   b. are generally saprobes.
       c. usually have life cycles in which the diploid phase dominates.
       d. include *Fucus* and liverworts.
       e. are typically marine forms.

M   3. Which fungus relies on extracellular digestion and absorption of energy-rich substances found in living organisms?
       a. slime molds
       b. saprobic
  *   c. parasitic
       d. plasmodial
       e. autotrophic

E   4. All fungi are
       a. unicellular.
       b. multicellular.
       c. autotrophic.
  *   d. heterotrophic.

M   5. All fungi
       a. are saprobes.
  *   b. perform extracellular digestion.
       c. are parasites.
       d. a and b
       e. a, b, and c

E   6. In most true fungi the individual cellular filaments of the body are called
       a. mycelia.
  *   b. hyphae.
       c. mycorrhizae.
       d. asci.
       e. gills.

M   7. In what way do fungi reproduce?
       a. asexually, through spores
       b. budding of the parent body
       c. sexually, through gametes
       d. a and b
  *   e. a, b, and c

D   8.   The major difference between a mature zygospore and a spore produced in the zygomycete sporangium is that the mature zygospore
         a. produces gametes.
         b. is metabolically active.
      * c. is diploid.
         d. is produced asexually.

E   9.   Fungi are classified on the basis of differences in
         a. cell wall composition.
         b. modes of nutrition.
      * c. reproductive structures.
         d. mode of locomotion.

M   10.   Zygospores are produced by
         a. plants only.
      * b. fungi only.
         c. algae only.
         d. plants and fungi.
         e. none of the above

E   11.   Yeasts are members of which of the following?
      * a. sac fungi
         b. club fungi
         c. imperfect fungi
         d. water molds
         e. zygospore-forming fungi

M   12.   Which organism is a member of zygospore-forming fungi?
         a. water mold
         b. smut or rust
      * c. bread mold
         d. mushroom

E   13.   Mushrooms are members of which of the following?
         a. sac fungi
      * b. club fungi
         c. imperfect fungi
         d. water molds
         e. zygospore-forming fungi

D   14.   Imperfect fungi are those that lack (or do not show)
         a. spores.
      * b. sexual reproduction.
         c. cross walls within hyphae.
         d. rhizoids.

SYMBIOSIS BETWEEN FUNGI AND PLANTS

M   15.   Which factor is the most important algal contribution to the fungal component of a lichen?
         a. improved water conservation
         b. mechanical protection from being blown away
      * c. photosynthetically derived food
         d. less overlap between individual algal cells
         e. pigment for camouflage

M   16. A lichen is a composite organism made up of
  a. two different fungi.
  * b. a fungus and an alga.
  c. a fungus and a gymnosperm.
  d. a fungus and a bryophyte.

M   17. Mycorrhizae and plants exhibit
  * a. mutualism.
  b. parasitism.
  c. commensalism.
  d. competition.
  e. all of the above

PART II. KINGDOM OF PLANTS

M   18. In the life cycle of primitive plants, which of the following predominates?
  * a. haploid stage
  b. diploid stage
  c. large sporophyte body
  d. both b and c
  e. both a and c

E   19. The first group with flowers were
  a. algae.
  b. fern allies.
  c. ferns.
  * d. angiosperms.
  e. gymnosperms.

M   20. All of the following are characteristic of the major trends in terrestrial autotroph evolution EXCEPT
  a. development of vascular tissue.
  b. adaptation to environmental stress.
  c. nonmotile gametes.
  d. fertilization by biotic vectors.
  * e. reduction of the sporophyte phase.

M   21. Ferns are more advanced than mosses because mosses lack which structure found in ferns?
  a. spores
  b. cuticle
  * c. xylem
  d. sporophytes
  e. pollen

E   22. Most freshwater algae belong to which division?
  a. red algae
  * b. green algae
  c. brown algae
  d. blue-green algae
  e. golden brown algae

M   23. The mosses and liverworts are members of which division?
  a. red algae
  b. green algae
  c. ferns and horsetails
  * d. bryophytes
  e. flowering plants

M 24. The large plantlike kelps are members of the
    a. red algae.
    b. green algae.
*   c. brown algae.
    d. bryophytes.
    e. lycophytes.

M 25. Gametophytes are
    a. haploid plants that produce spores.
    b. diploid plants that produce spores.
*   c. haploid plants that produce gametes.
    d. diploid plants that produce gametes.
    e. diploid or haploid plants that produce gametes.

M 26. In complex land plants the diploid stage is resistant to adverse environmental conditions, such as dwindling water supplies and cold weather. The diploid stage progresses through which sequence?
    a. gametophyte → male and female gametes
    b. spores → sporophyte
*   c. zygote → sporophyte
    d. zygote → gametophyte

M 27. The increased complexity among the different divisions of land plants is paralleled by increased complexity of which of the following?
    a. male gamete
    b. female gamete
    c. gametophyte
*   d. sporophyte
    e. all of the above

M 28. A gametophyte is
    a. a gamete-producing plant.
    b. haploid.
    c. the plant produced by the fusion of gametes.
    d. the dominant generation in the higher plants.
*   e. both a and b

M 29. Angiosperms are more advanced than gymnosperms because gymnosperms lack which structure found in angiosperms?
    a. independent gametophytes
    b. pollen grains
*   c. fruits
    d. roots

M 30. Algae are found in the kingdom
    a. Plantae.
    b. Monera.
    c. Protista.
*   d. both a and c
    e. both a and b

E 31. Red algae
    a. are primarily marine organisms.
    b. can participate in reef building.
    c. contain phycobilin pigments.
*   d. all of the above

M   32. Stemlike structures, gas-filled floats, and a thick leathery surface are found in species of
            a. red algae.
   *   b. brown algae.
            c. bryophytes.
            d. green algae.
            e. blue-green algae.

M   33. Which pigment is NOT characteristic of green algae (chlorophytes)?
            a. chlorophyll *a*
            b. xanthophyll
            c. carotenoids
   *   d. phycobilins
            e. chlorophyll *b*

M   34. Which statement about Bryophyta is NOT true?
   *   a. The archegonium produces sperm.
            b. The sporangium produces spores.
            c. The sporophyte is parasitic and attached to the gametophyte.
            d. Meiosis precedes spore formation.
            e. Bryophytes require water for sexual reproduction.

M   35. The unicellular alga *Chlamydomonas*
            a. lacks a gametophyte generation.
            b. lacks a sporophyte generation.
            c. lacks a haploid and a diploid phase.
   *   d. possesses both a haploid and a diploid phase.

M   36. Bryophytes
            a. rely on isogamy for sexual reproduction.
            b. have vascular systems that enable them to survive on land.
            c. include lycopods, horsetails, and ferns.
   *   d. none of the above
            e. all of the above

E   37. Mosses are
            a. algae.
   *   b. bryophytes.
            c. vascular plants.
            d. gymnosperms.
            e. extinct.

M   38. Which statement is false?
            a. Mosses do not have xylem and phloem.
            b. Mosses do not have true leaves.
            c. Mosses do not have true stems.
            d. Mosses use rhizoids, not roots, for attachment and absorption.
   *   e. Mosses are different from all other plants in that they have an independent sporophyte generation and a dependent gametophyte generation.

M   39. All are Bryophytes EXCEPT
            a. hornworts.
            b. liverworts.
   *   c. lycopods.
            d. mosses.

M 40. Which is NOT characteristic of the Bryophytes?
    a. sporangium
    b. antheridium
    c. diploid zygote
*   d. megaspores

M 41. In horsetails, lycophytes, and ferns,
*   a. spores give rise to gametophytes.
    b. the main plant body is a gametophyte.
    c. the sporophyte bears sperm- and egg-producing organs.
    d. all of the above

D 42. Which statement concerning fertilization in ferns is true?
    a. It occurs within an archegonium.
    b. It requires water.
    c. The fertilization product is a seed.
*   d. a and b
    e. a, b, and c

E 43. Which are seed plants?
    a. cycads and ginkgos
    b. conifers
    c. angiosperms
*   d. all of the above

E 44. Which of the following is NOT a conifer?
    a. pine
    b. fir
    c. cedar
*   d. ginkgo
    e. cypress

D 45. Which plant is NOT a gymnosperm?
    a. cycad
    b. spruce
*   c. palm
    d. ginkgo

E 46. What are major sources of pulp, lumber, and numerous industrial products?
    a. cycads
    b. ginkgos
*   c. conifers
    d. hardwoods
    e. all of the above

M 47. What is the most appropriate term for a mature pollen grain?
    a. megaspore
    b. microsporangium
*   c. microgametophyte
    d. microgamete
    e. all of the above

E 48. The group of plants that has the most species is
    a. mosses.
    b. ferns.
    c. gymnosperms.
*   d. dicots.
    e. monocots.

E   49.   A pine tree is
- a. an angiosperm.
- b. a haploid plant body.
- *   c. a sporophyte.
- d. a living fossil.
- e. all of the above

M   50.   All are monocots EXCEPT
- a. iris.
- b. wheat.
- *   c. maple.
- d. grass.

M   51.   Dependence on animal vectors for fertilization and dispersal is characteristic of many species of
- a. ferns.
- *   b. angiosperms.
- c. mosses.
- d. conifers.

M   52.   Which is a vascular plant?
- a. bryophyte
- *   b. fern
- c. red algae
- d. green algae
- e. brown algae

M   53.   Microspores mature into
- a. ovules.
- b. seeds.
- *   c. pollen grains.
- d. anthers.

M   54.   The vast majority of plant species are
- a. algae.
- b. bryophytes.
- c. gymnosperms.
- *   d. angiosperms.

E   55.   The conifers, such as pines and junipers, are examples of the
- *   a. gymnosperms.
- b. angiosperms.
- c. bryophytes.
- d. filicinae.
- e. none of the above

Classification Questions

Answer questions 56–60 in reference to the five groups of Fungi listed below:
- a. water molds
- b. zygospore-forming fungi
- c. sac fungi
- d. club fungi
- e. imperfect fungi

E   56.   The common mushroom bought in the supermarket is most likely a member of which group?

D 57. The potato blight of Ireland was probably caused by a flourishing population of *Phytophthora infestans*, which is a member of which group?

M 58. The yeast used in the fermentation of grape juice to produce the wines of the world is a member of which group?

M 59. The common black bread mold is a member of which group?

M 60. The delicious, edible morel is a member of which group?

Answers: 56. d   57. a   58. c   59. b   60. c

Answer questions 61–65 in reference to the four divisions of nonvascular plants listed below:

   a. red algae
   b. brown algae
   c. green algae
   d. bryophytes

M 61. Agar, used in science, medicine, and commercial foods, is extracted from members of what group?

M 62. Kelp, found in extensive beds off the coast of California, are members of which division?

D 63. Which division can be characterized as having sessile cells, phycobilins as an accessory photosynthetic pigment, and immobile sperm?

M 64. During the summer months, most eutrophic freshwater lakes have large populations of species of which division?

E 65. Liverworts are members of which division?

Answers: 61. a   62. b   63. a   64. c   65. d

Selecting the Exception

M 66. Four of the five answers listed below are terms used in describing fungi. Select the exception.
   a. hyphae
 * b. peptidoglycan
   c. saprobic
   d. spore
   e. mycelium

D 67. Four of the five answers listed below are related to a common fungal group. Select the exception.
 * a. club structure
   b. imperfect fungi
   c. *Penicillium*
   d. no sexual reproduction known
   e. cause most of the human fungal diseases

M 68. Four of the five answers listed below are related by the quantity of chromosomes present. Select the exception.
   a. spores
 * b. sporophyte
   c. egg
   d. sperm
   e. gametophyte

D   69. Four of the five answers listed below are related by absence of vascular tissue. Select the exception.

   * a. lycophytes
      b. bryophytes
      c. red algae
      d. brown algae
      e. green algae

D   70. Four of the five answers listed below are parts of the gametophyte generation. Select the exception.

      a. rhizoid
   * b. sporangium
      c. antheridium
      d. archegonium
      e. spores

E   71. Four of the five answers listed below are conifers. Select the exception.

      a. hemlock
      b. spruce
      c. fir
   * d. palm
      e. pine

D   72. Four of the five answers listed below are portions of the gametophyte generation. Select the exception.

      a. pollen grains
      b. megaspore
   * c. ovule
      d. pollen tube
      e. male gametophyte

CHAPTER 19
ANIMALS

Multiple-Choice Questions

OVERVIEW OF THE ANIMAL KINGDOM

M   1. Which insulates various internal organs from the stresses of body-wall movement and bathes them in a liquid through which nutrients and waste products can diffuse?
*   a. a coelom
     b. mesoderm
     c. a mantle
     d. a water-vascular system
     e. all of the above

M   2. All animals are
*   a. multicellular, heterotrophic, and diploid.
     b. multicellular, heterotrophic, and haploid.
     c. multicellular, autotrophic, and diploid.
     d. multicellular, autotrophic, and haploid.

M   3. A digestive tract is said to be complete if it at least
     a. possesses specialized regions for different digestive tasks.
     b. produces acids and contains enzymes.
*   c. is a one-way tube with a mouth and an anus.
     d. is surrounded by muscle.

M   4. Creeping behavior and a mouth located toward the head end of the body may have led, in some evolutionary lines, to
     a. development of a circulatory system with blood.
     b. sexual reproduction.
     c. feeding on nutrients suspended in the water (filter feeding).
*   d. concentration of sense organs in the head region.
     e. radial symmetry.

PART I. THE INVERTEBRATES

E   5. Sponges are
     a. herbivores.
*   b. filter feeders.
     c. scavengers.
     d. predators.
     e. carnivores.

M   6. Mesoglea is found in which group?
     a. sponges
*   b. cnidarians
     c. nematodes
     d. annelids
     e. mollusks

E   7. Nematocysts are used in
           a. reproduction.
           b. excretion.
           c. locomotion.
           d. circulation.
       *   e. feeding.

M   8. Which is a stage in the life cycle of *Obelia*, a cnidarian?
           a. medusa
           b. planula
           c. polyp
       *   d. all of the above

M   9. A planula is
           a. a sedentary, attached, tree-shaped form found in corals.
       *   b. a swimming larval form with an outer ciliated epidermis.
           c. a kind of parasitic worm.
           d. a fleshy lobe that extends laterally from the body wall of a marine worm.
           e. a rasplike tongue.

M   10. Nematocysts are found only in
       *   a. cnidarians.
           b. nematodes.
           c. crustaceans.
           d. echinoderms.

M   11. Which body plan is characterized by simple gas exchange mechanisms, two-way traffic through a highly branched, saclike gut, and a thin, flat body with all cells fairly close to the gut?
           a. cnidarian
           b. nematode
           c. echinoderm
       *   d. flatworm

M   12. Bilateral symmetry is characteristic of
           a. cnidarians.
           b. sponges.
           c. jellyfish.
       *   d. flatworms.

M   13. Mesodermal tissue is absent in
           a. sponges.
           b. cnidarians.
           c. flatworms.
       *   d. a and b
           e. a, b, and c

D   14. An organism that possesses a scolex and proglottids lacks
           a. bilateral symmetry.
       *   b. a coelom.
           c. mesodermal tissue.
           d. a and b
           e. a, b, and c

M   15. A scolex is
     *   a. the anterior attachment organ of a tapeworm.
          b. the feeding organ of a fluke.
          c. an appendage of a sandworm.
          d. the egg of a sea star.
          e. the larva of an aquatic insect.

M   16. Which have a tough cuticle, a false coelom, and a complete digestive system and are facultative anaerobes?
     *   a. nematodes
          b. cnidarians
          c. flatworms
          d. echinoderms
          e. porifera

M   17. A segmented body plan is common to each group EXCEPT
          a. arthropods.
          b. chordates.
          c. annelids.
     *   d. nematodes.

D   18. Which are deuterostomes?
          a. annelids
     *   b. chordates
          c. arthropods
          d. mollusks
          e. all of the above

D   19. Which is a deuterostome?
     *   a. bird
          b. squid
          c. fly
          d. earthworm

M   20. Which annelid structure may resemble the ancestral structure from which the vertebrate kidney evolved?
          a. trachea
     *   b. nephridium
          c. mantle
          d. parapodia
          e. none of the above

D   21. Which of the following is most closely related to an organism that possesses setae and nephridia and exhibits coordinated movements of circular and longitudinal muscle?
          a. millipede
          b. tapeworm
     *   c. polychaete
          d. hookworm

E   22. Nephridia are
          a. circulatory organs.
          b. respiratory organs.
     *   c. urinary organs.
          d. endocrine organs.
          e. part of the nervous system.

E 23. The animal group that contains the greatest number of named species is
    a. mollusks.
* b. arthropods.
    c. nematodes.
    d. chordates.

M 24. Which adaptation has contributed to the success of the insects?
    a. specialized sensory organs
    b. wings
    c. high reproductive capacity
    d. a and b
* e. a, b, and c

M 25. Exoskeletons are most characteristic of which of the following?
    a. mollusks
* b. arthropods
    c. echinoderms
    d. chordates
    e. annelids

E 26. The unique tissue adaptation for respiration used by many arthropods, including insects, is
    a. gills.
    b. lunglike chambers.
* c. tracheae.
    d. mantle.

M 27. The exoskeleton of a butterfly provides all EXCEPT
    a. physical protection.
    b. physical support.
    c. an anti-desiccant surface.
* d. a respiratory surface.

D 28. Which is NOT a chelicerate?
    a. tick
* b. mosquito
    c. spider
    d. scorpion

M 29. Based on the criterion of segmentation, which organism most closely resembles the earliest ancestral arthropod?
    a. dragonfly
* b. millipede
    c. tick
    d. crab

M 30. In the course of evolution, the thorax of an insect has become specialized for
    a. digestion.
    b. reproduction.
* c. locomotion.
    d. excretion.

D 31. Which animal belongs to a subphylum different from that of the other four?
    a. tick
* b. shrimp
    c. mite
    d. spider
    e. scorpion

M   32. A radula is which of the following?
   a. foot
 * b. tonguelike
   c. ear
   d. sensitive hair
   e. balance organ

D   33. Which is most closely related to an organism that possesses a mantle and a radula?
   a. lobster
   b. rotifer
 * c. octopus
   d. sand dollar

M   34. A mantle is found only among the
   a. arthropods.
   b. annelids.
   c. echinoderms.
 * d. mollusks.
   e. chordates.

D   35. The mollusks with the most complex nervous systems are
   a. chitons.
 * b. cephalopods.
   c. gastropods.
   d. bivalves.

D   36. Which is NOT a protostome?
   a. earthworm
   b. crayfish or lobster
 * c. sea star
   d. squid
   e. all of the above

E   37. A water-vascular system is characteristic of the
   a. arthropods.
   b. annelids.
   c. chordates.
   d. mollusks.
 * e. echinoderms.

PART II. VERTEBRATES AND THEIR KIN

D   38. Parasites of humans are found in each group EXCEPT
   a. flatworms.
   b. nematodes.
   c. annelids.
 * d. echinoderms.

M   39. The water-vascular system is unique to
   a. cnidarians.
   b. bivalves.
 * c. echinoderms.
   d. annelids.

M   40.   Which statement is NOT true?
         a.   All chordates have notochords.
         b.   All chordates have pharyngeal pouches or slits.
         c.   All chordates have dorsal tubular nerve cords.
    *   d.   All chordates are vertebrates.
         e.   Chordates are found in all major types of environments.

D   41.   Which group contains organisms that produce free-living larvae?
         a.   cnidarians
         b.   echinoderms
         c.   chordates
         d.   a and b
    *   e.   a, b, and c

M   42.   In filter-feeding chordates, which structure has cilia that create water currents and mucous sheets that capture nutrients suspended in the water?
         a.   notochord
         b.   differentially permeable membrane
         c.   filiform tongue
    *   d.   gill slit
         e.   jaw

M   43.   The feeding behavior of true fishes is dependent on highly developed
         a.   parapodia.
         b.   notochords.
    *   c.   sense organs.
         d.   gill slits.
         e.   motile organs.

E   44.   In true fishes the gills primarily serve which function?
    *   a.   gas exchange
         b.   feeding
         c.   water elimination
         d.   both feeding and gas exchange
         e.   all of the above

M   45.   The invertebrate chordates are
    *   a.   filter feeders.
         b.   scavengers.
         c.   herbivores.
         d.   predators.
         e.   parasites.

M   46.   The heart in amphibians
         a.   pumps blood more rapidly than the heart of fish.
         b.   is efficient enough for amphibians but would not be for birds and mammals.
         c.   has three chambers (one ventricle and two atria).
    *   d.   all of the above

M   47.   Which group has a heart of no more than three chambers?
         a.   birds
    *   b.   amphibians
         c.   cartilaginous fish
         d.   bony fish
         e.   mammals

E 48. Sharks, rays, and skates belong to what group?
   a. birds
   b. amphibians
 * c. cartilaginous fish
   d. bony fish
   e. reptiles

M 49. The most primitive vertebrates are members of the group of
 * a. jawless fishes.
   b. amphibians.
   c. cartilaginous fish.
   d. birds.
   e. bony fish.

M 50. Which sequence most accurately describes the complete path of blood through the circulatory system of a fish?
   a. atrium → ventricle → gill capillaries → atrium → ventricle → all other capillaries
   b. atrium → ventricle → gill capillaries
   c. gill capillaries → atrium → ventricle → all other capillaries
 * d. gill capillaries → all other capillaries → atrium → ventricle

M 51. The vertebrate jaw first appeared in which organism?
 * a. fishes
   b. amphibians
   c. reptiles
   d. birds
   e. mammals

E 52. The vertebrate lung first appeared in which organism?
 * a. fishes
   b. amphibians
   c. reptiles
   d. birds
   e. mammals

M 53. Which of the following is most responsible for freeing vertebrates from dependence on watery habitats?
   a. lungs
   b. paired appendages
 * c. the shelled eggs
   d. the four-chambered heart

M 54. Which adaptation is (are) common to insects and mammals?
 * a. jointed appendages
   b. closed circulatory system
   c. lungs
   d. a and b
   e. a, b, and c

E 55. Sharks differ from most other fish in that they lack
   a. lungs.
   b. scales.
 * c. bone.
   d. paired appendages.

E   56. Exchange of respiratory gases through the skin is a characteristic of many
         a. fish.
     *   b. amphibians.
         c. reptiles.
         d. mammals.

D   57. An organism that possesses feathers must also possess
         a. malphighian tubules.
         b. a three-chambered heart.
     *   c. a dorsal nerve cord.
         d. a pseudocoelom.

Matching Questions

D   58. Matching. Choose the most appropriate answer(s) for each. A letter may be used once or
         more or not at all.

    1 _____ amphibians   A. vertebrates
    2 _____ annelids   B. invertebrate chordates
    3 _____ arthropods   C. planarians, flukes, and tapeworms
    4 _____ birds   D. nematode, *Trichinella spiralis*
    5 _____ cnidarians   E. snails, squids, and limpets
    6 _____ echinoderms   F. insects
    7 _____ flatworms   G. collar cells present
    8 _____ jawless fishes   H. jellyfish, corals, and sea anemones
    9 _____ lancelets   I. crustaceans and ticks
    10 _____ mammals   J. polychaetes and leeches
    11 _____ reptiles   K. nematocysts
    12 _____ roundworms   L. sea urchins, crinoids, and brittle stars
    13 _____ sponges   M. thickened cuticle and hardened exoskeleton
    14 _____ bony fishes   N. earthworms
    15 _____ sea squirts   O. polyp and/or medusa
                                     P. water-vascular system
                                     Q. four-chambered heart
                                     R. whales
                                     S. salamanders and toads
                                     T. salmon and seahorses
                                     U. lizards and dinosaurs

Answers: 1. A, S   2. J, N   3. F, I, M   4. A, Q   5. H, K, O
           6. L, P   7. C   8. A   9. B   10. A, Q, R
          11. A, U, Q   12. D   13. G   14. A, T   15. B

Classification Questions

Answer questions 59–63 in reference to the five animal phyla listed below:

    a. sponges
    b. cnidarians
    c. flatworms
    d. nematodes
    e. annelids

M   59. Members of which group have a false body cavity?

D   60. Members of which group have a brain with nerve cords and a branched gut and lack a circulatory system?

M   61. Members of which group have a brain with a double ventral nerve cord, a complete gut, and a circulatory system that is usually closed?

E   62. Which phylum contains the most primitive species of the Animal Kingdom?

M   63. Tapeworms are members of which phylum?

Answers: 59. d   60. c   61. e   62. a   63. c

Answer questions 64–68 in reference to the five animal groups listed below:

    a. annelids
    b. arthropods
    c. mollusks
    d. echinoderms
    e. chordates

D   64. Trilobites were members of which group?

D   65. The larval stage in this group has bilateral symmetry while the adult stage exhibits radial symmetry.

E   66. Although most are enclosed by hardened shells, the group name literally means "soft body."

E   67. Which group has the greatest number of species?

D   68. The lancelet is a member of which group?

Answers: 64. b   65. d   66. c   67. b   68. e

Selecting the Exception

M   69. Four of the five answers listed below are characteristics of the majority of animals. Select the exception.
    a. multicellular
*   b. exhibits alternation of generations
    c. usually motile at least during part of their life cycle
    d. usually diploid sexually reproducing forms of life
    e. usually heterotrophic

D   70. Four of the five answers listed below are members of a common group. Select the exception.
    a. jellyfish
    b. hydra
*   c. sea squirts
    d. corals
    e. sea anemones

D   71. Four of the five answers listed below are members of a common group. Select the exception.
        a. sea star
*   b. sea anemone
        c. sea urchin
        d. sea lily
        e. sea cucumber

D   72. Four of the five answers listed below are members of a common group. Select the exception.
        a. lancelet
        b. jawed fish
        c. jawless fish
        d. sea squirt
*   e. squid

D   73. Four of the five answers listed below possess some type of coelom. Select the exception.
        a. nematodes
        b. annelids
        c. arthropods
        d. mollusks
*   e. flatworms

M   74. Four of the five answers listed below are characteristics of cnidarians. Select the exception.
        a. planula larvae
        b. polyp form
        c. mesoglea
        d. nematocyst
*   e. pharynx

M   75. Four of the five answers listed below are found in flatworms. Select the exception.
        a. proglottid
*   b. setae
        c. scolex
        d. flame cell
        e. first form to develop a mesoderm

M   76. Four of the five answers listed below are parasites. Select the exception.
*   a. planaria
        b. fluke
        c. nematodes
        d. leech
        e. tapeworm

M   77. Four of the five answers listed below are descriptive of annelids. Select the exception.
        a. first segmented form
        b. possess nephridia
*   c. jointed appendages
        d. setae
        e. complete gut with closed circulatory system and coelom

E   78. Four of the five answers listed below are crustaceans. Select the exception.
        a. crabs
        b. shrimps
        c. lobsters
*   d. centipedes
        e. barnacles

M 79. Four of the five answers listed below are grasshopper mouthparts. Select the exception.
*   a. proboscis
    b. maxilla
    c. palps
    d. mandible
    e. labrum

M 80. Four of the five answers listed below are molluscan body features. Select the exception.
    a. gills
    b. head and foot
    c. mantle
*   d. carapace
    e. radula

M 81. Four of the five answers listed below are characteristics of adult sea stars. Select the exception.
    a. spiny skin
    b. tube foot
    c. water-vascular system
*   d. bilateral symmetry
    e. ampulla

CHAPTER 20
PLANT TISSUES

Multiple-Choice Questions

THE PLANT BODY: AN OVERVIEW

E   1.   Approximately how many species of plants are known?
   - a. 100,000
   - b. 180,000
   - * c. 265,000
   - d. 360,000
   - e. 480,000

E   2.   A cotyledon is which of the following?
   - a. embryonic root
   - b. seed cover
   - c. flower part
   - * d. seed leaf
   - e. fruit

M   3.   Plant tissue noted for photosynthesis, storage, and secretion is
   - a. vascular cambium.
   - * b. parenchyma.
   - c. collenchyma.
   - d. sclerenchyma.
   - e. none of the above

M   4.   Parenchyma cells are specialized for and involved in all of the following activities EXCEPT
   - a. photosynthesis.
   - b. structure of fruits.
   - * c. conduction of food.
   - d. secretion.
   - e. food storage.

M   5.   The chewy, stringy cells in celery are which cells?
   - a. xylem
   - * b. collenchyma
   - c. phloem
   - d. sclerenchyma
   - e. parenchyma

M   6.   The gritty stone cells of pears, the hard cells of seed coats, and plant fibers are examples of
   - a. xylem.
   - b. collenchyma.
   - c. phloem.
   - * d. sclerenchyma.
   - e. parenchyma.

E   7.   Cells that are the main water-conducting cells of a plant are
   - a. sclereids.
   - * b. xylem tubes.
   - c. sieve tubes.
   - d. parenchyma.
   - e. all of the above

M   8. The cells that function with the sieve tubes are the
         a. vessels.
   *   b. companion cells.
         c. adjunct cells.
         d. sclereids.
         e. periderm.

E   9. The cell walls of epidermal cells are filled with which of the following to reduce water loss?
   *   a. cutin
         b. pectin
         c. lignin
         d. suberin
         e. chitin

M   10. Perpetually young tissues where cells retain the ability to divide are
         a. vascular.
   *   b. meristematic.
         c. protective.
         d. photosynthetic.
         e. all of the above

PRIMARY STRUCTURE OF SHOOTS

M   11. Which statement is NOT generally true of monocot stems?
         a. They do not undergo secondary growth.
         b. They are not tapered along their length.
         c. Their vascular bundles are scattered throughout the ground tissue.
   *   d. Monocot stems have a single central vascular cylinder.
         e. all of the above

M   12. Leaf primordia arise
         a. as part of the periderm.
         b. as part of secondary growth.
   *   c. at the nodes.
         d. as a result of differentiation of cambium cells.
         e. from the lateral, not the apical, meristem.

E   13. Buds are produced
         a. in the angles where leaves attach to stems.
         b. at the very ends of stems.
         c. at the nodes.
         d. by the apical meristem.
   *   e. all of the above

M   14. The stalk that supports the individual dicot leaf is the
         a. vascular bundle.
   *   b. petiole.
         c. node.
         d. bundle sheath.
         e. stomata.

E   15. Deciduous plants
         a. are nonvascular.
         b. are evergreen.
         c. shed their leaves as winter approaches.
         d. may retain their dead brown leaves over the winter and shed them only when new leaves emerge.
   *   e. both c and d

E   16. The main photosynthetic area of a leaf is composed of
   *   a. mesophyll.
            b. cortex.
            c. xylem.
            d. epidermis.
            e. none of the above

M   17. Photosynthesis takes place in the
            a. stomata.
            b. vascular bundles.
            c. cuticle.
            d. lower and upper epidermis.
   *   e. mesophyll tissue.

PRIMARY STRUCTURE OF ROOTS

E   18. Roots are involved in all the following activities EXCEPT
            a. support.
            b. food storage.
   *   c. food production.
            d. anchorage.
            e. absorption and conduction.

M   19. The carrot
            a. has a taproot system.
            b. uses food stored in the root to produce flowers, fruits, and seeds.
            c. takes two years to complete its life cycle.
            d. does not develop adventitious roots and has very limited lateral roots.
   *   e. all of the above

E   20. Mitosis takes place in which region of the root?
            a. zone of maturation
            b. root cap
            c. zone of elongation
   *   d. apical meristem region
            e. region of differentiation

M   21. Which gives rise to lateral roots?
            a. endodermis
            b. cortex
            c. epidermis
   *   d. pericycle
            e. pith

WOODY PLANTS

M   22. If all of the phloem were stripped from around a tree in a process known as girdling,
            a. the plant would stop growing.
            b. the vascular cambium would be destroyed so that the plant could no longer grow.
            c. the shoot system would get no moisture or minerals.
   *   d. the roots would starve and eventually the plant would die.
            e. there would be no problems unless the tree became infected by insects and fungi.

M   23.   Which is part of the lateral meristem?
*   a. cork cambium
     b. procambium
     c. protoderm
     d. ground meristem
     e. all of the above

M   24.   Annual growth rings are formed in woody stems principally through the activities of the
     a. pericycle.
     b. pith.
*   c. vascular cambium.
     d. mesophyll.
     e. endodermis.

M   25.   Secondary xylem is formed in association with the
     a. pith.
*   b. inner face of vascular cambium.
     c. outer face of vascular cambium.
     d. inner face of cork cambium.
     e. outer face of cork cambium.

M   26.   Which provides horizontal transport of material in stems and roots?
*   a. ray cells
     b. vessels
     c. the pericycle
     d. the cortex
     e. the secondary phloem

M   27.   Which environment would be most likely to produce trees without annual rings?
*   a. tropical rain forest
     b. northern evergreen forest
     c. areas with alternating wet and dry seasons
     d. temperate-deciduous forests
     e. none of the above, because annual rings are characteristic of all trees

M   28.   Which tissue will not be crushed or sloughed off by the growing of the stem?
*   a. vascular cambium
     b. epidermis
     c. cortex
     d. pith
     e. endodermis

M   29.   Lateral meristems
     a. are groups of dividing cells.
     b. are responsible for increases in the width of a stem or root.
     c. are called cambium.
     d. produce secondary growth only.
*   e. all of the above

Matching Questions

D   30.   Choose the one most appropriate answer for each.

1 _____ companion cells

2 _____ cork cambium

3 _____ fusiform initials

4 _____ meristems

5 _____ mesophyll

6 _____ pericycle

7 _____ primordium

8 _____ sclereids

9 _____ sieve tube members

10 _____ vascular bundles

11 _____ xylem vessels

12 _____ collenchyma

13 _____ bark

14 _____ endodermis

15 _____ epidermis

16 _____ parenchyma

17 _____ periderm

18 _____ phloem

19 _____ pith

20 _____ sclerenchyma

21 _____ stoma

22 _____ vascular cambium

23 _____ xylem

A. collection of strands of all types of conducting tissue

B. cells that help sieve tube members

C. a part of the vascular column just inside endodermis; gives rise to lateral roots

D. ground tissue that is "stringy" in consistency

E. living cells that conduct food from photosynthetic source to storage sink

F. tissue providing support; example is hemp fibers

G. gives rise to periderm

H. tissue transporting water and minerals upward

I. unspecialized plant tissue that will form specific organs later

J. outer layer of cells over primary plant body

K. replaces the epidermis in plants that undergo secondary growth

L. openings for air and water vapor movement into/out of leaf

M. produce vascular tissue arranged parallel to stem axis

N. individual dead cells that conduct water

O. tissue transporting food from source to sink

P. the thickest and principal photosynthetic region of the leaf

Q. single layer of cells that controls water movement into xylem

R. regions of high mitotic activity

S. tissue specializing in photosynthesis, storage, secretion

T. cells with thick walls; abundant in shells of nuts and "stones" of fruit

U. ground tissue located centrally within a ring of vascular bundles

V. all living and nonliving tissues between vascular cambium and stem surface

W. develops into secondary xylem and phloem

Answers:

1. B	2. G	3. M	4. R	5. P	6. C
7. I	8. T	9. E	10. A	11. N	12. D
13. V	14. Q	15. J	16. S	17. K	18. O
19. U	20. F	21. L	22. W	23. H	

Classification Questions

Answer questions 31–35 in reference to the five plant tissues listed below:

    a. parenchyma
    b. collenchyma
    c. sclerenchyma
    d. xylem
    e. phloem

M   31. Ground tissue of plants, contains hardened cells, forming nut shells

E   32. Vascular tissue that conducts and distributes food to plant cells

E   33. Vascular tissue that conducts water and dissolved salts throughout a plant

D   34. Vascular tissue of a plant composed of dead cells with recesses, pits, open ends

M   35. Plant tissue involved in photosynthesis and storage

Answers: 31. c   32. e   33. d   34. d   35. a

Answer questions 36–41 in reference to the plant tissues listed below:

    a. vascular cambium
    b. cork cambium
    c. pericycle
    d. ground tissue
    e. dermal tissue

D   36. Which tissue gives rise to periderm?

D   37. Which tissue gives rise to the protective covering that forms the bark of a tree?

M   38. Which tissue makes up the bulk of the plant body?

M   39. Which tissue gives rise to secondary phloem and xylem?

M   40. Which tissue gives rise to lateral roots?

D   41. Which tissue gives rise to the xylem and phloem of an older tree?

Answers: 36. b   37. b   38. d   39. a   40. c   41. a

Selecting the Exception

M   42. Four of the five answers listed below are related by a common region of the plant body. Select the exception.
    a. leaf
  * b. root cap
    c. node
    d. axillary bud
    e. stem

M   43. Four of the five answers listed below are characteristic of monocots. Select the exception.
    a. flower parts in threes or multiples of three
    b. pollen grains have one pore
    c. one cotyledon in seed
  * d. vascular tissue arranged in a ring
    e. veins in leaf are parallel

D 44. Four of the five answers listed below are characteristic of dicots. Select the exception.
   a. secondary growth
   b. net venation
   c. flower parts in fours or fives
   d. two seed leaves
  * e. pollen grains with one pore or furrow

M 45. Four of the five answers listed below are types of ground tissue. Select the exception.
   a. ground tissue
  * b. xylem
   c. sclerenchyma
   d. parenchyma
   e. collenchyma

D 46. Four of the five answers listed below are functions of parenchyma tissue. Select the exception.
  * a. support
   b. wound healing
   c. food storage
   d. conduct photosynthesis
   e. regeneration of lost parts

D 47. Four of the five answers listed below are characteristic of sclerenchyma cells. Select the exception.
   a. sclereid
   b. found in seed coats
  * c. retain the ability to divide after differentiation
   d. gritty texture of pear cells
   e. used in manufacture of paper, textiles, and rope

D 48. Four of the five answers listed below are characteristics of xylem. Select the exception.
   a. dead at maturity
   b. cell walls impregnated with waterproofing substances
  * c. conducts dissolved food
   d. helps support plant body
   e. have pits in the walls of the cells

D 49. Four of the five answers listed below are characteristics of phloem. Select the exception.
  * a. consists only of cell walls
   b. characterized by channels across plant cell walls
   c. sieve plates found between some cells
   d. include accessory companion cells
   e. transports sugar

D 50. Four of the five answers listed below are tissues capable of cell division. Select the exception.
   a. cork cambium
   b. apical meristem
   c. procambium
  * d. periderm
   e. vascular cambium

M 51. Four of the five answers listed below are limited to the node region. Select the exception.
   a. leaf axil
   b. node
  * c. vascular bundle
   d. lateral bud
   e. leaf primordia

M 52. Four of the five answers listed below are parts of tissue found in a cross section of root. Select the exception.
   a. cortex
 * b. pith
   c. pericycle
   d. endodermis
   e. epidermis

M 53. Four of the five answers listed below are related to vascular tissue. Select the exception.
   a. conducts water and minerals
   b. vascular bundle
   c. translocation
   d. vein
 * e. pith

M 54. Four of the five answers listed below possess chloroplasts. Select the exception.
   a. mesophyll cell
 * b. epidermal cell
   c. sclereid cell
   d. palisade cell
   e. spongy cell

M 55. Four of the five answers listed below are functions of roots. Select the exception.
   a. support
 * b. synthesis of food
   c. absorption of water and minerals
   d. conduction of water and solutes
   e. anchorage

M 56. Four of the five answers listed below are related by a similar nature. Select the exception.
   a. adventitious
   b. tap
   c. fibrous
   d. lateral
 * e. insectivorous

D 57. Four of the five answers listed below are features of the pericycle. Select the exception.
   a. outermost tissue in the vascular column
   b. origins of branch roots
   c. found in the root, but not in the stem
 * d. site for food storage
   e. located inside the endodermis

D 58. Four of the five answers listed below are parts of a leaf. Select the exception.
   a. stoma
   b. cuticle
   c. mesophyll
 * d. node
   e. petiole

CHAPTER 21
PLANT NUTRITION AND TRANSPORT

Multiple-Choice Questions

FLIES FOR DINNER

E 1. The concentration of carbon dioxide in the atmosphere approximates how many parts per million?
   a. 3.5
   b. 35
 * c. 350
   d. 3,500
   e. 35,000

NUTRITIONAL REQUIREMENTS

E 2. Plants in general require a total of how many essential elements for their growth and survival?
   a. 6
   b. 12
 * c. 16
   d. 22
   e. 28

E 3. Which of the following elements required by plants do NOT come directly from the soil?
 * a. carbon
   b. nitrogen
   c. magnesium
   d. potassium
   e. iron

M 4. Which element is found as a component of amino acids, proteins, nucleic acids, and coenzymes?
 * a. nitrogen
   b. potassium
   c. sulfur
   d. phosphorus
   e. magnesium

M 5. Which element activates enzymes used in protein, starch, or sugar synthesis and helps maintain water–solute balance?
   a. nitrogen
 * b. potassium
   c. sulfur
   d. phosphorus
   e. magnesium

D 6. Which element is a component of two vitamins and most proteins?
   a. nitrogen
   b. potassium
 * c. sulfur
   d. phosphorus
   e. magnesium

D   7. Which element is a component of chlorophyll and activates enzymes used in photosynthesis, respiration, and protein synthesis?
     a. nitrogen
     b. potassium
     c. sulfur
     d. phosphorus
*   e. magnesium

M   8. Chlorosis and leaf droop are caused by a deficiency of
     a. nitrogen.
     b. potassium.
     c. sulfur.
     d. phosphorus.
*   e. magnesium.

E   9. Which is a micronutrient?
     a. sulfur
     b. calcium
     c. phosphorus
*   d. manganese
     e. magnesium

E   10. Chlorotic leaves turn
*   a. yellow.
     b. black.
     c. orange.
     d. red.
     e. transparent.

D   11. A plant will become chlorotic due to a lack of any of the following EXCEPT
     a. nitrogen.
*   b. phosphorus.
     c. magnesium.
     d. manganese.
     e. iron.

E   12. Most of the macronutrients and micronutrients function as
     a. food for plants.
     b. structural components for cells.
     c. elements needed for the development of mycorrhizae.
*   d. enzyme activators.
     e. all of the above

UPTAKE OF WATER AND NUTRIENTS

E   13. Nodules found on the roots of leguminous plants are involved in supplying which element for the plant?
     a. aluminum
     b. boron
     c. magnesium
*   d. nitrogen
     e. chlorine

E   14. Mycorrhizae are
         a. roots.
         b. bacteria.
      * c. fungus-roots.
         d. isolated plants.
         e. small animals found in agricultural soils.

M   15. Mycorrhizae
         a. increase plant growth.
         b. are symbionts.
         c. allow a plant to absorb more water.
         d. increase the surface area for absorption of water and minerals.
      * e. all of the above

M   16. Which statement is false?
         a. Annual grasses have fibrous root systems.
         b. Most dicots have a large taproot system.
         c. Mycorrhizae are mutually beneficial to the plants they infect.
      * d. Roots explore the soil and actively search for water.
         e. In mycorrhizal infection the fungus absorbs sugar and nitrogen compounds from the host plant.

M   17. The Casparian strip is associated with the
         a. epidermis.
         b. vascular tissue.
         c. cortex.
         d. root hairs.
      * e. endodermis.

M   18. The water and minerals absorbed by the roots usually first enter the
         a. pericycle.
         b. vascular tissue.
         c. cortex.
      * d. root hairs.
         e. endodermis.

E   19. The relationships of organisms in root nodules and mycorrhizae can be described as
         a. unfortunate.
         b. cohesion.
      * c. symbiotic.
         d. parasitic.
         e. exploitive.

M   20. Mineral uptake in plants occurs by way of
         a. leaves.
      * b. roots.
         c. stems.
         d. phloem.
         e. flowers.

E   21. Water inside all of the xylem cells is being pulled upward by
         a. turgor pressure.
      * b. negative pressures (tensions).
         c. osmotic gradients.
         d. pressure flow forces.
         e. all of the above

WATER TRANSPORT AND CONSERVATION

M 22. Most of the water moving into a leaf is lost through
　　　　　a. osmotic gradients.
*　　　　b. transpiration.
　　　　　c. pressure flow forces.
　　　　　d. translocation.
　　　　　e. all of the above

M 23. Most of the water that enters the plant
　　　　　a. leaves the plant through the root system.
*　　　　b. is lost through transpiration.
　　　　　c. remains in the plant to form the high concentration of water in plant tissue.
　　　　　d. remains in the plant to function in translocation.
　　　　　e. is used up in cellular metabolism.

E 24. Of all the water moving into a leaf, about what percent is used in photosynthesis, membrane functions, and other activities?
　　　　　a. 1
*　　　　b. 2
　　　　　c. 10
　　　　　d. 70
　　　　　e. 90

M 25. Which of the following causes transpiration?
　　　　　a. hydrogen bonding
*　　　　b. the drying power of air
　　　　　c. cohesion
　　　　　d. turgor pressure
　　　　　e. all of the above

M 26. Which theory of water transport states that hydrogen bonding allows water molecules to maintain a continuous fluid column as water is pulled from roots to leaves?
　　　　　a. pressure flow
　　　　　b. evaporation
*　　　　c. cohesion
　　　　　d. abscission
　　　　　e. fusion

M 27. Water moves through a plant because of
　　　　　a. transpirational pull.
　　　　　b. the cohesion of water molecules.
　　　　　c. the strength of hydrogen bonds holding water molecules together.
　　　　　d. the replacement of lost water molecules.
*　　　　e. all of the above

M 28. Water tension in a transpiring plant
　　　　　a. is exerted on a continuous column of water throughout the plant.
　　　　　b. is the result of the polar nature of water molecules.
　　　　　c. results in the loss of over 90 percent of the water the plant absorbs.
　　　　　d. will exert a pull on water molecules lower down in the plant's vascular system.
*　　　　e. all of the above

E   29. The waxy covering of the leaf is the
     *   a. cuticle.
          b. epidermis.
          c. Casparian strip.
          d. stomata.
          e. none of the above

E   30. The openings in leaves that function to exchange gases are called
          a. cuticles.
     *   b. stomata.
          c. guard cells.
          d. pits.
          e. pores.

E   31. The cells that surround stomata are
          a. endodermal cells.
     *   b. guard cells.
          c. mesophyll cells.
          d. vascular bundle cells.
          e. vessel cells.

E   32. Carbon dioxide enters the plant
          a. at night.
          b. when transpiration occurs.
          c. when the guard cells are turgid.
          d. when potassium ions leave the guard cells.
     *   e. both b and c

E   33. The cuticle
          a. conserves water.
          b. reduces absorption of carbon dioxide by the plant.
          c. reduces transpiration.
          d. helps prevent wilting.
     *   e. all of the above

M   34. Guard cells
          a. surround the stoma.
          b. control the opening to the interior of the leaf.
          c. become turgid when it becomes light if environmental conditions are not too hot or dry.
          d. absorb water from surrounding epidermal cells.
     *   e. all of the above

M   35. Usually, during the daytime
          a. carbon dioxide accumulates in leaf cells.
          b. turgor pressure in the guard cell decreases.
     *   c. water and potassium move into the guard cell.
          d. the guard cells close.
          e. water is conserved.

M   36. Water uptake depends on
          a. abscisic acid.
          b. cohesion.
     *   c. the concentration gradient.
          d. active transport.
          e. potassium pump.

TRANSPORT OF ORGANIC SUBSTANCES

M　37. The most common form of sugar transported to the roots is
  a. glucose.
  b. fructose.
 * c. sucrose.
  d. ribose.
  e. starch.

E　38. Carbohydrates are stored in plants in the form of
  a. cellulose.
  b. sucrose.
 * c. starch.
  d. fats.
  e. glucose.

E　39. Movement of soluble organic material through plants is known as
 * a. translocation.
  b. active transport.
  c. passive transport.
  d. transpiration.
  e. none of the above

E　40. Sugars are carried throughout the plant in which tissue?
  a. cortex
  b. parenchyma
  c. xylem
 * d. phloem
  e. cambium

E　41. Insects used to study the process of translocation in plants are
 * a. aphids.
  b. fruit flies.
  c. cockroaches.
  d. termites.
  e. grasshoppers.

D　42. The fluid in the phloem
  a. is under negative pressure.
  b. moves by active transport.
 * c. is under pressure equivalent to the air in a tire or greater.
  d. is responsible for the transpiration pull of material from roots.
  e. is chiefly water with dissolved minerals.

M　43. A car parked under a tree that gets spattered by sticky droplets has been covered by
  a. water and minerals that have been exuded from the tips of leaves.
 * b. droplets of honeydew that have been forced out of aphids.
  c. feces from herbivorous insects.
  d. material released from mistletoe in the upper limbs.
  e. drops of water produced by transpiration.

E　44. The movement of materials already in the phloem is described as
  a. source-to-sink.
  b. pressure flow.
  c. cohesion.
  d. active transport.
 * e. both a and b

M   45.   The source region in the pressure flow explanation of phloem transport is most often the
              a. root.
              b. flower.
              c. stem.
         *   d. leaf.
              e. soil.

M   46.   The sink region in the pressure flow explanation of phloem transport could be
              a. growing leaves.
              b. seeds.
              c. fruits.
              d. roots.
         *   e. all of the above

M   47.   Large pressure gradients arise in sieve tube systems by means of
              a. vernalization.
              b. abscission.
         *   c. osmosis.
              d. transpiration.
              e. all of the above

Matching Questions

D   48.   Choose the one most appropriate letter for each.

1 _____ companion cells   A. mouthpart of an aphid

2 _____ legumes   B. pipelines of the xylem

3 _____ mycorrhiza   C. a mutually beneficial association between a
                                         fungus and a young root
4 _____ nodules
                                     D. structures on roots that house nitrogen-fixing
5 _____ sieve tube members   bacteria

6 _____ stylet   E. pipelines of the phloem

7 _____ tracheids and vessels   F. evaporation from stems and leaves

8 _____ translocation   G. actively transport sucrose into sieve tube
                                         members
9 _____ transpiration
                                     H. dicot plants that tend to establish symbiotic
                                         relationships with nitrogen-fixing bacteria

                                     I. transport of organic molecules from source
                                         region to sink

Answers: 1. G   2. H   3. C   4. D   5. E   6. A
                7. B   8. I   9. F

Classification Questions

Answer questions 49–53 in reference to the five plant macronutrients listed below:

              a. nitrogen
              b. potassium
              c. calcium
              d. magnesium
              e. phosphorus

M   49.   Which nutrient helps to maintain turgor pressure?

E   50.   Nutrient that is an extremely important part of ATP.

M   51.   Nutrient that is an important part of the backbone structure of DNA.

D   52.   Which nutrient helps to cement cell walls together?

M   53.   Nutrient that is essential to formation of chlorophyll and acts as a cofactor for many enzymes.

Answers: 49. b   50. e   51. e   52. c   53. d

Answer questions 54–58 in reference to the five plant micronutrients listed below:

     a.   iron
     b.   boron
     c.   manganese
     d.   zinc
     e.   copper

D   54.   Which nutrient is used in synthesis of auxins?

M   55.   Which nutrient plays an important role in flowering and germination?

M   56.   Which nutrient is a cofactor in enzymes involved in carbohydrate metabolism?

E   57.   Which nutrient is an essential component of proteins involved in electron transport?

D   58.   Which nutrient plays an important role in the movement of plant hormones?

Answers: 54. d   55. b   56. e   57. a   58. b

Selecting the Exception

M   59.   Four of the five answers listed below are macronutrients. Select the exception.
     *   a.   manganese
        b.   potassium
        c.   calcium
        d.   magnesium
        e.   phosphorus

M   60.   Four of the five answers listed below are micronutrients. Select the exception.
        a.   molybdenum
        b.   copper
     *   c.   nitrogen
        d.   iron
        e.   chlorine

M   61.   Four of the five answers listed below are related by a common chemical nature. Select the exception.
        a.   protein
     *   b.   calcium carbonate
        c.   carbohydrate
        d.   lipid
        e.   nucleic acid

D   62. Four of the five answers listed below are elements whose deficiency symptoms include chlorosis. Select the exception.
    *   a. phosphorus
             b. iron
             c. chlorine
             d. copper
             e. magnesium

M   63. Four of the five answers listed below are related by their participation in water movement through plants. Select the exception.
             a. hydrogen bonds
             b. transpiration
             c. cohesion
             d. tension in xylem
    *   e. photosynthesis

D   64. Four of the five answers listed below are associated with transpiration. Select the exception.
             a. potassium ions pumped into guard cells
             b. water pressure builds up in guard cells
             c. photosynthesis occurs in guard cells
             d. carbon dioxide enters leaf
    *   e. presence of cuticle

M   65. Four of the five answers listed below are actions that cause stomata to open. Select the exception.
    *   a. sunlight decreases
             b. potassium ions build up guard cells
             c. water moves from epidermal cells to guard cells
             d. turgor pressure increases in guard cells
             e. guard cells carry on photosynthesis

M   66. Four of the five answers listed below are sinks for solute deposition. Select the exception.
             a. fruits
             b. roots
    *   c. flower blossoms
             d. seeds
             e. rapidly growing tissue

CHAPTER 22
PLANT REPRODUCTION AND DEVELOPMENT

Multiple-Choice Questions

REPRODUCTIVE MODES

E   1.   Which statement is false?
       a. Flowers are reproductive shoots.
*   b. Trees are gametophytes.
       c. Sporophyte plants reproduce asexually.
       d. Cells produced by mitosis are clones.
       e. Gametophytes are haploid.

M   2.   The least specialized part of the flower is a
       a. carpel.
       b. stamen.
       c. petal.
*   d. sepal.
       e. pistil.

M   3.   Which is NOT primarily related to asexual reproduction?
       a. rhizomes
*   b. pollination
       c. runner formation
       d. cloning and tissue culture
       e. all of the above

E   4.   Grasses reproduce by
       a. runners.
       b. corms.
       c. bulbs.
       d. tubers.
*   e. rhizomes.

GAMETE FORMATION IN FLOWERS

E   5.   Which of the following develops into seed?
       a. flower
       b. ovary
       c. carpel
*   d. ovule
       e. pistil

E   6.   The male part of a flower is the
       a. carpel.
*   b. stamen.
       c. petal.
       d. sepal.
       e. pistil.

E 7. The male part of a flower includes the
   a. carpel.
   b. stigma.
   c. filament.
   d. anther.
 * e. both c and d, but not a or b

E 8. The various flower parts are attached to the
   a. style.
 * b. receptacle.
   c. stigma.
   d. filament.
   e. sepal.

E 9. Stamens contain
   a. petals.
   b. sepals.
   c. stigmas.
   d. ovules.
 * e. anthers.

E 10. A stamen is
   a. composed of a stigma, a style, and an ovary.
   b. the mature male gametophyte.
 * c. the site where microspores are produced.
   d. part of the vegetative phase of an angiosperm.
   e. none of the above

E 11. The process during which the diploid set of chromosomes become haploid is
   a. metastasis.
   b. fertilization.
   c. cleavage.
 * d. meiosis.
   e. none of the above

E 12. The corolla is made up of
   a. sepals.
 * b. petals.
   c. pistils.
   d. pollen grains.
   e. anthers.

M 13. Which forms the outermost whorl of flower parts?
 * a. sepals
   b. petals
   c. anthers
   d. pistils
   e. stamens

E 14. Which of the following are produced within the anthers?
   a. ovules
   b. stamens
 * c. microspores
   d. female gametophytes
   e. none of the above

M   15.   The protective layers covering the ovule are the
               a. nucellus.
               b. endosperm.
        *   c. integuments.
               d. micropyle.
               e. embryo sac.

FROM POLLINATION TO FERTILIZATION

M   16.   Megaspores
               a. are haploid.
               b. are found in the embryo sac.
               c. will develop into the gametophyte.
               d. are female rather than male.
        *   e. all of the above

D   17.   The megaspore eventually divides into how many cells to form the embryo sac prior to
               fertilization?
               a. 3
               b. 4
        *   c. 7
               d. 8
               e. 16

E   18.   The female gametophyte is the
               a. nucellus.
               b. ovule.
        *   c. embryo sac.
               d. endosperm.
               e. ovary.

E   19.   The egg is
               a. diploid.
               b. tetraploid.
               c. polyploid.
               d. triploid.
        *   e. haploid.

E   20.   The primary function of the endosperm is
               a. protection.
               b. reproduction.
               c. growth.
        *   d. nutrition.
               e. water absorption.

E   21.   Pollination occurs on the
               a. micropyle.
        *   b. stigma.
               c. style.
               d. anther.
               e. embryo sac.

D 22. In flowering plants one sperm nucleus fuses with that of an egg and a zygote forms that develops into an embryo. Another sperm nucleus
   a. fuses with a primary endosperm cell to produce three cells, each with one nucleus.
   b. fuses with a primary endosperm cell to produce one cell with one triploid nucleus.
 * c. fuses with the diploid endosperm mother cell, forming a primary endosperm cell with a single triploid nucleus.
   d. fuses with one of the smaller megaspores to produce what will eventually become the seed coat.
   e. none of the above

E 23. The pollen tube grows to or through which of the following?
   a. stigma
   b. style
   c. ovary
   d. micropyle
 * e. all of the above

E 24. The endosperm is
   a. diploid.
   b. tetraploid.
   c. polyploid.
 * d. triploid.
   e. haploid.

E 25. The zygote is
 * a. diploid.
   b. tetraploid.
   c. polyploid.
   d. triploid.
   e. haploid.

M 26. The first seed-bearing plants were produced in the Devonian, about how many million years ago?
   a. 50
   b. 150
   c. 250
 * d. 390
   e. 450

M 27. Ovules and pollen sacs first arose on the surface of scales that were
   a. stems.
   b. leaves.
   c. flowers.
   d. found in cones.
 * e. both b and d, but not a or c

M 28. The evolution of flowers and insects is an example of
   a. parallel evolution.
   b. regressive evolution.
 * c. coevolution.
   d. convergent evolution.
   e. divergent evolution.

E 29. Insects are attracted to flowers by
   a. nectaries.
   b. specific colors.
   c. specific color patterns.
   d. floral odors.
   * e. all of the above

E 30. Bees use what wavelength to see patterns in flowers that humans cannot see?
   a. infrared light
   b. visible light
   * c. ultraviolet light
   d. gamma radiation
   e. X-rays

E 31. Which color are most insects unable to see?
   a. yellow
   b. blue
   * c. red
   d. green
   e. orange

M 32. Foul-smelling flowers may be pollinated by
   a. birds.
   * b. beetles and flies.
   c. bees and bumblebees.
   d. wasps.
   e. bugs and butterflies.

M 33. Bees will NOT visit flowers of what color?
   * a. red
   b. blue
   c. yellow
   d. purple
   e. white

M 34. Wind-pollinated plants
   a. include grasses.
   b. include deciduous trees.
   c. are usually found in dry, windy areas.
   d. do not have large, showy flowers and may not even have petals.
   * e. all of the above

EARLY DEVELOPMENT

E 35. The seed is produced by the development of the
   a. embryo.
   * b. ovule.
   c. ovary.
   d. zygote.
   e. pollen.

M 36. The seed coat forms from the
   a. zygote.
   b. cotyledon.
   c. nucellus.
   * d. integuments.
   e. micropyle.

M   37. What kind of fruit is formed from carpels of several associated flowers?
- a. aggregate
- b. simple
- * c. multiple
- d. fleshy
- e. dry

E   38. Fruit is produced from the development of the
- a. zygote.
- b. ovule.
- c. flowers.
- d. cotyledon.
- * e. ovary.

E   39. A seed leaf is which of the following?
- a. embryo
- b. coleoptile
- c. endosperm
- * d. cotyledon
- e. suspensor

M   40. Each of the following is a simple fruit EXCEPT
- a. pea.
- b. maple.
- * c. strawberry.
- d. wheat.
- e. sunflower.

M   41. The seeds of fleshy fruits are most likely to be spread by
- * a. animals.
- b. water.
- c. wind.
- d. explosion.
- e. insects.

E   42. Strawberries reproduce by
- * a. runners.
- b. corms.
- c. bulbs.
- d. tubers.
- e. rhizomes.

PATTERNS OF GROWTH AND DEVELOPMENT

M   43. The most critical factor affecting seed germination is
- a. increasing day length.
- b. oxygen availability.
- * c. water absorption.
- d. warmth.
- e. none is most critical; all are equal.

E   44. The signaling chemicals produced by one group of cells that affect distant target cells are called
- a. secretions.
- * b. hormones.
- c. steroids.
- d. polymers.
- e. enzymes.

M   45. Synthetic auxins are used as
        a. pesticides.
      * b. herbicides.
        c. fungicides.
        d. insecticides.
        e. all of the above

M   46. 2,4-D, a potent dicot weed killer, is a synthetic
      * a. auxin.
        b. gibberellin.
        c. cytokinin.
        d. phytochrome.
        e. none of the above

M   47. The most common synthetic "hormone" is
        a. 3,7-C.
      * b. 2,4-D.
        c. 1,5-K.
        d. 3,6-T.
        e. 1,4-X.

M   48. The "flowering" hormone is
        a. auxin.
        b. gibberellin.
        c. cytokinin.
      * d. florigen.
        e. ethylene.

M   49. The plant hormone that is gaseous is
        a. auxin.
        b. gibberellin.
        c. cytokinin.
        d. florigen.
      * e. ethylene.

M   50. The plant hormone that promotes cell division is
        a. auxin.
        b. gibberellin.
      * c. cytokinin.
        d. florigen.
        e. ethylene.

M   51. The plant hormone that promotes fruit ripening is
        a. auxin.
        b. gibberellin.
        c. cytokinin.
        d. florigen.
      * e. ethylene.

D   52. A plant hormone whose existence is conjectured but that has NOT been isolated or
        identified is
        a. auxin.
        b. gibberellin.
        c. cytokinin.
      * d. florigen.
        e. ethylene.

M   53. The plant hormone that promotes dormancy in plants and seeds is
     *   a. abscisic acid.
          b. auxin.
          c. gibberellic acid.
          d. ethylene.
          e. none of the above

M   54. The plant hormone thought to be involved with tropism is
          a. abscisic acid.
     *   b. auxin.
          c. gibberellic acid.
          d. ethylene.
          e. none of the above

M   55. The function of a coleoptile is
          a. food production.
          b. food storage.
     *   c. protection.
          d. translocation.
          e. absorption of water and minerals.

M   56. Studies on the growth of coleoptiles involve
          a. florigen.
          b. ethylene.
     *   c. auxin.
          d. abscisic acid.
          e. gibberellin.

M   57. What is the principal substance that causes phototropism in stems or leaves?
     *   a. auxin
          b. gibberellic acid
          c. abscisic acid
          d. ethylene
          e. all of the above

M   58. The primary root of a seedling grows down
          a. to avoid light.
          b. in response to gravity.
          c. because the cells on the top of the root grow faster than those on the bottom of the root.
          d. in response to different concentrations of auxin.
     *   e. all except a

M   59. Which substance is involved in thigmotropism?
     *   a. auxin
          b. gibberellic acid
          c. abscisic acid
          d. florigen
          e. none of the above

M   60. Which of the following is NOT promoted by the active form of phytochrome?
          a. seed germination
     *   b. root growth
          c. leaf expansion
          d. stem branching
          e. flower formation

D 61. Compared with young trees growing out in the open, young trees growing in a darker forest understory tend to have longer, thinner trunks with less branching; this developmental pattern is principally caused by
   a. phototropism.
   b. thigmotropism.
 * c. activated phytochrome being converted to inactive phytochrome.
   d. inactive phytochrome being converted to active phytochrome.
   e. none of the above

M 62. The pigment responsible for photoperiodism is
   a. chlorophyll.
   b. xanthophyll.
   c. anthocyanin.
 * d. phytochrome.
   e. photoerythrin.

E 63. Rhythms that are repeated every 24 hours are collectively and specifically known as
   a. sleep movements.
   b. tropisms.
   c. biorhythms.
 * d. circadian rhythms.
   e. the biological clock.

M 64. The active form of phytochrome is known as
   a. Pp.
   b. Pr.
 * c. Pfr.
   d. Pl.
   e. Pst.

M 65. Active phytochrome controls
   a. flowering and seed set.
   b. seed germination.
   c. stem branching and elongation.
   d. expansion of leaves.
 * e. all of the above

M 66. The value of a plant's sleep movements is possibly that they
   a. block moonlight from the lower leaves.
   b. reduce the amount of heat lost from the plant at night.
   c. allow heat transfer between leaves.
   d. speed the process of translocation between plant parts.
 * e. a and b, but not c and d

M 67. Phytochrome is converted from the inactive to the active form by being exposed to light of what color?
   a. far red
 * b. red
   c. yellow
   d. white
   e. blue

E 68. In the dark, plants cannot
   a. grow.
   b. respire.
   c. move.
 * d. form chlorophyll.
   e. form carotenoid pigment.

M 69. Day-neutral plants are
   a. short-day plants.
 * b. able to bloom when they are old enough.
   c. night-blooming plants.
   d. triggered to bloom by cold weather.
   e. none of the above

M 70. Which statement is true?
 * a. Long-day plants will never bloom in the tropics.
   b. Short-day plants bloom around noon.
   c. Short-day plants bloom in midsummer.
   d. Cocklebur is an example of a long-day plant.
   e. The flowering of day-neutral plants is controlled by the duration of darkness, not the duration of light.

M 71. Short-day plants
   a. flower in late summer.
   b. will not bloom until they have been exposed to a dark period longer than a critical length.
   c. flower in the fall.
   d. will not bloom if their dark period is interrupted by two to five minutes of light.
 * e. all of the above

M 72. It is thought that florigen is produced in the
   a. roots.
 * b. leaves.
   c. stem.
   d. flowers.
   e. petioles.

E 73. All the processes that lead to the death of a plant or any of its organs are called
   a. dormancy.
   b. vernalization.
   c. abscission.
 * d. senescence.
   e. none of the above

E 74. The aging of a plant is known as
 * a. senescence.
   b. vernalization.
   c. abscission.
   d. dormancy.
   e. chlorosis.

M 75. Senescence may be counteracted by
   a. auxins.
   b. abscisic acid.
 * c. cytokinin.
   d. gibberellic acid.
   e. florigen.

Matching Questions

D   76.   Matching I. Choose the one most appropriate answer for each.

1 _____ aggregate fruit

2 _____ anther

3 _____ carpel

4 _____ embryo sac

5 _____ endosperm mother cell

6 _____ megaspores

7 _____ micropyle

8 _____ microspores

9 _____ multiple fruit

10 _____ ovary

11 _____ ovule

12 _____ petal

13 _____ pollen grain

14 _____ sepal

15 _____ stigma

A. meiospores of anthers

B. site where pollen tube usually penetrates the ovule

C. after fertilization ripens into fruit tissue

D. a 2*n* cell that will help form nutrients for the developing plant embryo

E. cluster of matured ovaries attached to a common receptacle

F. modified leaves with pigments and fragrance-producing cells

G. immature male gametophyte

H. female reproductive organ

I. landing platform for pollen

J. pollen-bearing structure

K. meiospores of ovule

L. outermost whorl of leaf parts on a receptacle; generally green, but sometimes pigmented

M. female gametophyte

N. matured ovaries of several flowers fused together into a single mass (for example, pineapple, fig)

O. after fertilization will form a seed

Answers: 1. E   2. J   3. H   4. M   5. D   6. K
               7. B   8. A   9. N   10. C   11. O   12. F
               13. G   14. L   15. I

D   77.   Matching II. Choose the one most appropriate answer for each.

1 _____ abscisic acid

2 _____ annual

3 _____ biennial

4 _____ coleoptile

5 _____ ethylene

6 _____ florigen

7 _____ gibberellic acid

8 _____ phytochrome

9 _____ short-day plant

10 _____ target cell

11 _____ long-day plant

A. has receptor sites for a particular hormonal message

B. a hollow, cylindrical organ that protects young leaves growing within it

C. blue-green pigment that absorbs light energy

D. stimulates stomata closure and might trigger seed and bud dormancy

E. stimulates fruit ripening

F. reproduce in spring

G. produces only roots, stems, and leaves the first growing season and produces flowers the second year

H. flowers in autumn

I. the elusive hormone that controls flowering

J. lives for only one growing season

K. promotes stem elongation in dwarf plants

Classification Questions

Answer questions 78–82 in reference to the five flower parts listed below:

        a. anther
        b. stigma
        c. ovule
        d. ovary
        e. stamen

E   78. During fertilization of a flowering plant, the male gamete first adheres to which of the above structures?

M   79. A pollen tube ultimately grows into which structure?

M   80. Fertilization of a flowering plant occurs inside of which structure?

E   81. Which structure produces pollen?

M   82. Male gametogenesis occurs in which structure?

Answers: 78. b   79. c   80. c   81. a   82. a

Answer questions 83–87 in reference to the five flower parts listed below:

        a. megaspore
        b. microspore mother cell
        c. ovule
        d. ovary
        e. seed

M   83. Which structure gives rise to the female gametophyte?

E   84. Which structure is female and haploid?

M   85. Which of the above gives rise to haploid pollen grains?

D   86. The egg is ultimately derived from which structure?

M   87. During early development the plant embryo is most intimately associated with which structure?

Answers: 83. a   84. a   85. b   86. a   87. c

Answer questions 88–92 in reference to the five plant hormones listed below:

        a. auxins
        b. gibberellins
        c. cytokinins
        d. abscisic acid
        e. ethylene

M   88. Which hormones are most closely associated with cell division?

M   89. Which hormones are involved in stem elongation and closely related chemically to certain weed killers like 2,4-D?

D   90. Which hormone controls rate of transpiration?

E 91. Which hormone is a gas that promotes ripening?

M 92. Which hormone promotes bud and seed dormancy?

Answers: 88. c   89. a   90. d   91. e   92. d

Selecting the Exception

E 93. Four of the five answers listed below are related by gender. Select the exception.
    a. carpel
    b. ovary
  * c. stamen
    d. style
    e. stigma

M 94. Four of the five answers listed below are types of flower whorls. Select the exception.
  * a. receptacle
    b. stamen
    c. carpel
    d. petal
    e. sepal

E 95. Four of the five answers listed below are haploid. Select the exception.
    a. gametophyte
  * b. zygote
    c. sperm
    d. microspore
    e. gamete

E 96. Four of the five answers listed below are nonreproductive parts of a flower. Select the exception.
    a. receptacle
  * b. anther
    c. corolla
    d. petal
    e. sepal

M 97. Four of the five answers listed below are related by a common gender. Select the exception.
    a. micropyle
    b. integument
    c. embryo sac
  * d. microspore
    e. egg

E 98. Four of the five answers listed below are the results of fertilization. Select the exception.
    a. fruit
    b. seed
    c. embryo
  * d. pollen
    e. endosperm

E 99. Four of the five answers listed below are useful to flowers as means to attract vectors. Select the exception.
    a. nectar
    b. flower color
    c. color patterns
    d. pollen
  * e. wind

M   100.   Four of the five answers listed below are parts of a seed. Select the exception.
        *   a. ovary
             b. cotyledon
             c. meristem
             d. coleoptile
             e. endosperm

M   101.   Four of the five answers listed below are defined as simple fruits. Select the exception.
        *   a. pineapple
             b. maple
             c. pea
             d. lemon
             e. banana

E   102.   Four of the five answers listed below are adaptations to aid in dispersal of fruit. Select the exception.
             a. hooks
             b. spines
        *   c. smooth surface
             d. hairs
             e. sticky substances

D   103.   Three of the four answers listed below are effects caused by auxin. Select the exception.
             a. used as herbicide
        *   b. promotes cell division
             c. promotes cell elongation
             d. functions in tropism

D   104.   Three of the four answers listed below are effects caused by gibberellin. Select the exception.
             a. breaks dormancy in seeds in buds
             b. causes stem elongation
        *   c. triggers flower production
             d. overcomes genetic dwarfing

M   105.   Four of the five answers listed below are characteristics of ethylene. Select the exception.
             a. triggers dropping of leaves and fruits
             b. promotes fruit ripening
        *   c. triggers cell division
             d. a gas
             e. effects observed by ancient Chinese

M   106.   Four of the five answers listed below are stimulators that evoke plant tropisms. Select the exception.
             a. gravity
             b. touch
             c. mechanical stress
             d. light
        *   e. electrical current

M   107.   Four of the five answers listed below are flower responses that follow 24-hour cycles. Select the exception.
             a. sleep movements
             b. flowers open in the morning
             c. circadian rhythm
        *   d. photoperiodism
             e. flowers close at night

M   108. Four of the five answers listed below are plant activities affected by phytochrome. Select the exception.
* a. tropism
  b. stem elongation
  c. seed germination
  d. leaf expansion
  e. formation of flowers, fruits, and seeds

CHAPTER 23
TISSUES, ORGAN SYSTEMS, AND HOMEOSTASIS

Multiple-Choice Questions

ANIMAL STRUCTURE AND FUNCTION: AN OVERVIEW

E   1. Chemical and structural bridges link groups or layers of like cells, uniting them in structure and function as a cohesive
      a. organ.
      b. organ system.
    * c. tissue.
      d. cuticle.

E   2. The tissue that lines internal surfaces of the body is
    * a. epithelial.
      b. loose connective.
      c. supportive connective.
      d. fibrous.
      e. adipose.

M   3. Epithelial cells are specialized for all the following functions EXCEPT
      a. secretion.
      b. protection.
      c. filtration.
    * d. contraction.
      e. absorption.

E   4. The secretion of tears, milk, sweat, and oil are functions of what tissue?
    * a. epithelial
      b. loose connective
      c. lymphoid
      d. nervous
      e. adipose

M   5. Which of the following is NOT included in connective tissues?
      a. bone
    * b. skeletal muscle
      c. cartilage
      d. collagen
      e. blood

E   6. What type of tissue is blood?
      a. epithelial
      b. muscular
    * c. connective
      d. adipose
      e. noncellular fluid

M   7. Which epithelial cell is modified for diffusion?
      a. cuboidal
    * b. simple squamous
      c. simple columnar
      d. stratified squamous
      e. stratified columnar

M 8. The type of epithelial cell found in the lining of the stomach, intestinal tract, and part of the respiratory tract is
    a. simple cuboidal.
    b. simple squamous.
*   c. simple columnar.
    d. stratified.
    e. stratified columnar.

E 9. Exocrine glands secrete
    a. enzymes.
    b. sweat.
    c. milk.
    d. saliva.
*   e. all of the above

M 10. An extracellular ground substance is characteristic of
    a. muscle tissue.
    b. epithelial tissue.
*   c. connective tissue.
    d. nervous tissue.
    e. embryonic tissue.

M 11. Connective tissues include all the following EXCEPT
    a. cartilage.
    b. blood.
    c. bone.
    d. fat.
*   e. outer skin.

E 12. Dense fibrous tissues that connect muscle to bone are called
    a. muscles.
    b. cartilage.
    c. ligaments.
*   d. tendons.
    e. all of the above

M 13. Collagen fibers are characteristic of which tissue?
    a. muscle
    b. epithelial
*   c. connective
    d. nervous
    e. embryonic

M 14. Tendons connect
    a. bones to bones.
    b. bones to ligaments.
*   c. muscles to bones.
    d. bones to cartilage.
    e. all of the above

E 15. Cartilage is found
    a. in the nose.
    b. at the ends of bones.
    c. in the external ear.
    d. between vertebrae.
*   e. all of the above

E   16.   Adipose tissue cells are filled with
           a.   minerals.
   *   b.   fat.
           c.   cartilage.
           d.   fibers.
           e.   muscles.

M   17.   If its cells are striated and fused at the ends so that the cells contract as a unit, the tissue is
           a.   smooth muscle.
           b.   dense fibrous connective.
           c.   supportive connective.
   *   d.   cardiac muscle.
           e.   none of the above

E   18.   Muscle that is NOT striped and is involuntary is
           a.   cardiac.
           b.   skeletal.
           c.   striated.
   *   d.   smooth.
           e.   both a and d, but not b or c

E   19.   Cardiac muscle cells are
           a.   involuntary.
           b.   voluntary.
           c.   striated.
           d.   slow contracting.
   *   e.   both a and c

E   20.   Smooth muscles are
           a.   striated and voluntary.
           b.   isolated, spindle-shaped cells.
           c.   found in the walls of hollow structures such as blood vessels and the stomach.
           d.   involuntary and nonstriated.
   *   e.   all except a

MAJOR ORGAN SYSTEMS

E   21.   The endocrine system functions in
           a.   conduction.
           b.   contraction.
   *   c.   hormonal control of body functioning.
           d.   protection against disease.
           e.   cell production.

E   22.   Maintaining the volume and composition of body fluids is the direct responsibility of
         which system?
           a.   integumentary
           b.   immune
           c.   digestive
   *   d.   urinary
           e.   circulatory

M   23.   Which system is involved with heat production?
           a.   endocrine system
           b.   nervous system
   *   c.   muscular system
           d.   respiratory system
           e.   skeletal system

E   24. Integration of body functions is controlled by the
           a. respiratory system.
           b. nervous system.
           c. endocrine system.
           d. defense system.
       *   e. both b and c, but not a and d

M   25. Which system produces blood cells?
           a. endocrine
       *   b. skeletal
           c. muscular
           d. defense
           e. integumentary

HOMEOSTASIS AND SYSTEMS CONTROL

M   26. Which are examples of integrators?
       *   a. brain, spinal cord
           b. muscles, glands
           c. sensory cells in eye, tongue, and ear
           d. bones
           e. none of the above

E   27. The control of the temperature of the body is an example of which of the following?
           a. homeostatic mechanism
           b. positive feedback system
           c. endocrine function
           d. negative feedback system
       *   e. both a and d, but not b or c

M   28. Which is the correct sequence involved in the regulation of organ systems?
           a. stimulus, receptor, integrator, response, effector
           b. stimulus, response, integrator, receptor, effector
       *   c. stimulus, receptor, integrator, effector, response
           d. stimulus, integrator, receptor, effector, response
           e. stimulus, effector, integrator, receptor, response

M   29. An effector is a
           a. muscle.
           b. nerve.
           c. gland.
           d. receptor.
       *   e. both a and c

M   30. Which involves a positive feedback stimulation?
           a. temperature control
       *   b. sexual stimulation
           c. glucose concentration
           d. absorption of toxins
           e. muscle concentration

Matching Questions

D   31.   Choose the one most appropriate answer for each.

1 _____ adipose tissue	A. tendons are made of this
2 _____ blood	B. contains collagen and elastin; acts as a packing material that supports internal organs
3 _____ dense connective tissue	
4 _____ glandular epithelium	C. receives, conducts, and initiates signals in response to environmental changes
5 _____ loose connective tissue	
6 _____ interstitial fluid	D. stores fatty reserves
7 _____ neuron	E. offers resistance to mechanical injury and loss of internal fluids; also a barrier against microorganisms
8 _____ epidermis	
	F. secretes extracellular products such as sweat, mucus, tears, and shells
	G. fluid ground substance plus free cells; involved in transport, pH, and temperature stability
	H. extracellular fluid that bathes cells and tissues

Answers: 1. D   2. G   3. A   4. F   5. B   6. H
                7. C   8. E

Classification Questions

Answer questions 32–36 in reference to the five types of connective tissue listed below:

       a. loose tissue
       b. dense regular tissue
       c. adipose
       d. cartilage
       e. blood

E   32.   Tendons are composed of which of the above?

E   33.   The elasticity of skin is due to the presence of which kind of tissue?

M   34.   Which tissue plays an important role in stabilizing body temperature?

E   35.   Which tissue provides nourishment to each of the other connective tissues?

M   36.   Which tissue plays a particularly important role in the thermoregulation of marine mammals?

Answers: 32. b   33. a   34. e   35. e   36. c

Answer questions 37–41 in reference to the five organ systems listed below:

       a. circulatory
       b. lymphatic
       c. digestive
       d. endocrine
       e. respiratory

E   37.   The absorption of nutrients into the blood is the responsibility of which system?

E   38.   Which system includes the immune response?

M   39.   Airborne allergens are first encountered by which system?

E   40.   Which system rapidly transports many vital materials throughout the body?

E   41.   The production of hormones occurs in which system?

Answers: 37. c   38. b   39. e   40. a   41. d

Selecting the Exception

M   42.   Four of the five answers listed below are secreted by an exocrine gland. Select the exception.
       a.   wax
       b.   saliva
    *   c.   hormone
       d.   milk
       e.   mucus

D   43.   Four of the five answers listed below are related by a common tissue type. Select the exception.
       a.   adipose
       b.   bone
       c.   cartilage
       d.   blood
    *   e.   epithelium

M   44.   Four of the five answers listed below are functions of the skeleton. Select the exception.
    *   a.   controls body temperature
       b.   produces blood cells
       c.   protection
       d.   storage sites for calcium and phosphorus
       e.   muscle attachment

CHAPTER 24
PROTECTION, SUPPORT, AND MOVEMENT

Multiple-Choice Questions

INTEGUMENTARY SYSTEM

E   1. The word *integument* is derived from the word for
- a. protection.
- b. support.
- * c. covering.
- d. contraction.
- e. resistance.

E   2. Melanin protects the skin from
- a. desiccation.
- b. abrasion.
- * c. ultraviolet radiation.
- d. infrared damage.
- e. invasion by bacteria.

E   3. The integumentary system is responsible for all but which of the following?
- a. protection against bacterial attack
- b. protection against abrasion
- c. synthesis of certain vitamins
- * d. blood cell formation
- e. control of temperature and prevention of desiccation

E   4. The largest organ of the vertebrate body is which of the following?
- a. lungs
- b. liver
- c. stomach
- * d. skin
- e. small intestines

E   5. Vitamin D is required for _____ metabolism.
- a. sulfur
- b. phosphorus
- * c. calcium
- d. potassium
- e. zinc

M   6. Which of the following is NOT found in the epidermis?
- a. stratified epithelium
- * b. blood vessels
- c. tight cell junctions
- d. keratin
- e. melanin

E   7. Which of the following statements is false concerning the outermost layer of the epidermis?
- a. It is the first to feel any abrasion.
- b. Keratin provides waterproofing.
- c. Millions of cells are worn off daily.
- * d. Its cells are undergoing rapid cell division.
- e. It is called the stratum corneum.

SKELETAL SYSTEM

E 8. In spongy bone tissue the spaces are filled with
   - a. air.
   - b. blood.
   - c. cartilage.
   - * d. marrow.
   - e. lymph.

M 9. Haversian canals are characteristic of which tissue?
   - a. adipose
   - * b. bone
   - c. cartilage
   - d. epithelial
   - e. muscular

D 10. All but which of the following are associated with bone formation?
   - a. osteoblasts
   - b. cartilage
   - * c. osteoporosis
   - d. marrow cavity formation
   - e. calcium

M 11. The human axial skeleton includes all of the following EXCEPT
   - a. skull.
   - b. ribs.
   - * c. pectoral girdle.
   - d. sternum.
   - e. vertebral column.

E 12. Which of the following is NOT part of the appendicular skeleton?
   - a. clavicle
   - b. scapula
   - c. fibula
   - * d. ribs
   - e. patella

E 13. The bone in the upper arm is the
   - a. radius.
   - b. ulna.
   - c. tibia.
   - * d. humerus.
   - e. femur.

E 14. Bones in fingers or toes are called
   - a. hyoid.
   - b. patella.
   - c. scapula.
   - d. clavicle.
   - * e. phalanges.

E 15. The kneecap is the
   - a. hyoid.
   - * b. patella.
   - c. scapula.
   - d. clavicle.
   - e. phalanx.

E   16.   The collarbone is the
         a. hyoid.
         b. patella.
         c. scapula.
    *   d. clavicle.
         e. phalanx.

E   17.   The shoulder blade is the
         a. hyoid.
         b. patella.
    *   c. scapula.
         d. clavicle.
         e. phalanx.

E   18.   Bones such as the humerus and femur are examples of which kind of bones?
    *   a. long
         b. short
         c. flat
         d. irregular
         e. all of the above

M   19.   The nonmoving joints between skull bones are examples of what kind of joints?
         a. synovial
    *   b. fibrous
         c. cartilaginous
         d. hinge
         e. none of the above

M   20.   The vertebral discs with small amounts of movement are examples of what kind of joints?
         a. synovial
         b. fibrous
    *   c. cartilaginous
         d. hinge
         e. none of the above

M   21.   Growth of long bones
         a. follows the cartilage model.
         b. occurs in the middle at first, then at both ends.
         c. is characterized by bone tissue replacing calcified cartilage.
         d. is characterized by the persistence of cartilage at both ends of the shaft.
    *   e. all of the above

M   22.   Which statement is false?
         a. Calcium is the most important mineral involved with bone tissue turnover.
         b. Osteocytes and osteoclasts are involved with the reabsorption and repair of bones.
         c. Bone mass decreases with age.
    *   d. Males have greater problems with loss of bone tissue than females do.
         e. Marrow fills the cavities in the spaces of the spongy bone and in the center of the shaft of the bone almost as quickly as the spaces are formed.

MUSCULAR SYSTEM

E   23.   Each muscle fiber is also called a
    *   a. muscle.
         b. muscle cell.
         c. myofibril.
         d. sarcomere.
         e. all of the above

E 24. Smooth muscle is
  * a. involuntary and nonstriated.
   b. responsible for movement of the skeleton.
   c. involved in contraction of the heart.
   d. connected to bones by tendons.
   e. both a and c

M 25. The gastrocnemius muscle is located
   a. in the forelimb.
   b. on the back.
   c. in the hip area.
  * d. in the lower leg.
   e. in the neck.

E 26. The pectoralis major muscle is located
  * a. in the chest.
   b. on the back.
   c. near the hips.
   d. in the upper leg.
   e. in the lower leg.

M 27. Which of the following includes all the others?
   a. actin
   b. myofibril
   c. myosin
   d. myofilament
  * e. muscle cell

M 28. During muscle contractions
   a. the myofibrils shorten.
   b. the actin and myosin filaments slide over each other.
   c. the actin filaments move toward the middle of the sacromere during contraction and away on relaxation.
   d. the muscle thickens.
  * e. all of the above

D 29. During contraction
   a. cross-bridges of muscle filaments are broken and reformed.
   b. ATP is used to form cross-bridges.
   c. muscle cells use glycogen as their energy source.
   d. if there is a poor supply of oxygen, glycogen depletion by glycolysis will lead to fatigue.
  * e. all of the above

M 30. The element specifically associated with muscle contraction is
   a. phosphorus.
   b. potassium.
  * c. calcium.
   d. sodium.
   e. chlorine.

D 31. In their action, muscles would be most like
  * a. ropes.
   b. levers.
   c. push rods.
   d. screws.
   e. hammers.

M 32. In rigor mortis, the muscles of the body lose their ability to
    a. contract.
    b. flex.
*   c. relax.
    d. form cross-bridges.
    e. bend.

E 33. The most immediate, but necessarily limited, source of energy for reformation of ATP in muscle cells is
    a. aerobic respiration.
    b. mitochondrial pathways.
    c. electron transport phosphorylation.
*   d. creatine phosphate.
    e. anaerobic fermentation.

M 34. A motor neuron and all the muscles under its control is called what kind of unit?
    a. end
    b. movement
    c. muscle
*   d. motor
    e. coordination

Classification Questions

Answer questions 35–39 in reference to the five bones listed below:
    a. clavicle
    b. lumbar vertebrae
    c. tibia
    d. metatarsal
    e. metacarpal

E 35. All of the above are part of the appendicular skeleton EXCEPT _____.

M 36. Which bone is extremely subject to breakage in contact sports activity?

M 37. If one had a slipped disk, that disk might be next to which bone?

M 38. Which bone is an ankle bone in humans?

M 39. Which bone connects to the femur?

Answers: 35. b   36. a   37. b   38. d   39. c

Answer questions 40–44 in reference to the five muscles listed below:
    a. pectoralis major
    b. deltoid
    c. rectus femoris
    d. triceps
    e. gastrocnemius

D 40. Which muscle is a principal muscle of the upper leg?

M 41. Which muscle is located on the upper shoulder?

M 42. Which muscle is antagonistic to the action of the biceps?

D 43. The Achilles tendon attaches which muscle to the heel bones?

D   44. Which muscle is the principal flight muscle of birds?

Answers: 40. c   41. b   42. d   43. e   44. a

Selecting the Exception

M   45. Four of the five answers listed below are parts of the same anatomical area. Select
             the exception.
             a. humerus
        *   b. fibula
             c. radius
             d. clavicle
             e. scapula

M   46. Four of the five answers listed below are parts of the same skeletal division. Select
             the exception.
             a. cranium
             b. ribs
             c. sternum
             d. vertebrae
        *   e. phalanges

M   47. Four of the five answers listed below are regions of the vertebral column. Select
             the exception.
             a. cervical
        *   b. appendicular
             c. lumbar
             d. thoracic
             e. sacral

E   48. Four of the five answers listed below are types of bones. Select the exception.
        *   a. immovable
             b. long
             c. short
             d. flat
             e. irregular

E   49. Four of the five answers listed below are muscles. Select the exception.
             a. pectoralis
        *   b. patella
             c. gastrocnemius
             d. deltoid
             e. sartorius

D   50. Four of the five answers listed below are molecules that participate in muscle contraction.
             Select the exception.
        *   a. sarcolemma
             b. ATP
             c. calcium
             d. actin
             e. myosin

CHAPTER 25
DIGESTION AND HUMAN NUTRITION

Multiple-Choice Questions

FUNCTIONS OF DIGESTIVE SYSTEMS

E   1. Ruminants need special enzymes to digest
　　　　　a. starch.
　　　　　b. proteins.
　*　　c. cellulose.
　　　　　d. lignin.
　　　　　e. catin.

M   2. Which of the following possess an incomplete digestive system?
　　　　　a. annelids
　*　　b. planaria, or flatworms
　　　　　c. mollusks
　　　　　d. arthropods
　　　　　e. echinoderms

E   3. Chewing
　　　　　a. breaks food down into smaller pieces.
　　　　　b. physically and mechanically breaks up the food.
　　　　　c. increases the surface area of food exposed to digestive enzymes.
　　　　　d. actually mixes some enzymes with the food.
　*　　e. all of the above

M   4. The process that moves nutrients into the blood or lymph is
　*　　a. absorption.
　　　　　b. assimilation.
　　　　　c. digestion.
　　　　　d. ingestion.
　　　　　e. all of the above

HUMAN DIGESTIVE SYSTEM

E   5. Which of the following organs of the digestive system is different from the other four because it does NOT produce any secretions that aid in the digestive process?
　　　　　a. stomach
　　　　　b. liver
　*　　c. esophagus
　　　　　d. pancreas
　　　　　e. salivary gland

M   6. Which process propels the food down the esophagus into the stomach?
　　　　　a. glycolysis
　　　　　b. plasmolysis
　　　　　c. emulsion
　*　　d. peristalsis
　　　　　e. all of the above

M   7. Sphincters
- a. are circular muscles.
- b. prevent backflow.
- c. are smooth muscles.
- d. are found at the beginning and end of the stomach.
- * e. all of the above

E   8. The digestion of proteins begins in the
- * a. stomach.
- b. pancreas.
- c. small intestine.
- d. large intestine.
- e. esophagus.

E   9. Chyme is formed in the
- a. mouth.
- b. esophagus.
- * c. stomach.
- d. small intestine.
- e. large intestine.

E   10. The acid released in the stomach is
- a. carbonic acid.
- * b. hydrochloric acid.
- c. nitric acid.
- d. sulfuric acid.
- e. phosphoric acid.

D   11. Which of the following is NOT an active form of an enzyme?
- a. trypsin
- b. amylase
- c. pepsin
- * d. pepsinogen
- e. chymotrypsin

M   12. Which of the following factors does NOT stimulate the stomach to pass on its contents to the small intestine?
- * a. depression and fear
- b. stimulation of mechanoreceptors in the stomach wall following a large meal
- c. reduced fat or acid content of chyme in the duodenum
- d. elation and relaxation
- e. all of the above

E   13. The digestion of fats mostly occurs in the
- a. stomach.
- b. pancreas.
- * c. small intestine.
- d. lymph vascular system.
- e. liver.

E   14. Of the following the greatest amount of nutrient absorption takes place in the
- a. stomach.
- * b. small intestine.
- c. colon.
- d. pancreas.
- e. esophagus.

M   15. Which of the following are absorbed by the lymphatic system?
        a. monosaccharides
        b. amino acids
        c. monoglycerides
        d. fatty acids
    *   e. both c and d

M   16. Movement of glucose through the membranes of the small intestine is primarily by
        a. osmosis.
        b. bulk flow.
    *   c. active transport.
        d. diffusion.
        e. all of the above

M   17. Which of the following does NOT digest proteins?
        a. trypsin
        b. chymotrypsin
        c. aminopeptidase
        d. pepsin
    *   e. lipase

E   18. Ducts from the pancreas and liver enter the
        a. stomach.
        b. colon.
    *   c. small intestine.
        d. gall bladder.
        e. rectum.

M   19. Which of the following is NOT found in bile?
        a. salts
        b. cholesterol
        c. pigments
    *   d. digestive enzymes
        e. lecithin

M   20. Bile
        a. has no effect on digestion.
    *   b. helps in the digestion of fats.
        c. helps in the digestion of carbohydrates.
        d. helps in the digestion of proteins.
        e. both c and d

M   21. Bulk in the diet
        a. increases the length of time material is in the colon.
        b. increases the chance of cancer.
    *   c. prevents diarrhea and irritable colon syndrome.
        d. may increase the incidence of appendicitis in the people who eat too much bulk.
        e. is characteristic of people in urban areas.

D   22. Which of the following are tiny projections of the mucosal wall?
        a. microvilli
        b. mucins
    *   c. villi
        d. submucosa
        e. jejunum

E 23. Fats are digested by which of the following?
    a. aminopeptidase
    b. disaccharidases
    c. amylase
  * d. lipase
    e. trypsin

HUMAN NUTRITIONAL REQUIREMENTS

M 24. The ideal diet consists of all of the following EXCEPT
    a. bulk.
  * b. few complex carbohydrates.
    c. little salt and sugar.
    d. little red meat.
    e. fish, poultry, and legumes.

E 25. Body weight is controlled by
    a. caloric intake.
    b. energy utilization.
    c. level of metabolism.
    d. age and sex.
  * e. all of the above

E 26. Of the 20 amino acids, how many are considered to be essential in that the human body cannot synthesize them?
    a. 2
    b. 5
  * c. 8
    d. 10
    e. 12

M 27. Which of the following vitamins is fat-soluble and can be stored in the body?
  * a. A
    b. B_1 (thiamine)
    c. C (ascorbic acid)
    d. B_2 (riboflavin)
    e. niacin

E 28. Obesity is defined as what percent over the ideal weight?
    a. 10
    b. 15
    c. 20
  * d. 25
    e. 30

E 29. Obese people have a greater risk of
    a. diabetes.
    b. atherosclerosis.
    c. high blood pressure.
    d. death at all ages.
  * e. all of the above

E 30. Which vitamin functions in forming a blood clot?
    a. A
    b. E
  * c. K
    d. B
    e. all of the above

M   31. Which of the following statements is NOT true concerning mineral metabolism?
   a. Sodium and potassium are needed for maintaining osmotic balances.
   *   b. Zinc is important in building strong bones and teeth.
   c. Sodium and potassium are needed for muscle and nerve functioning.
   d. Iron is needed for building cytochromes and heme groups.
   e. All the statements are true.

E   32. Lack of which element can lead to thyroid problems?
   a. iron
   *   b. iodine
   c. calcium
   d. zinc
   e. magnesium

M   33. The element needed for blood clotting, nerve transmission, and bone and tooth formation is
   a. iron.
   b. iodine.
   *   c. calcium.
   d. zinc.
   e. magnesium.

M   34. The binge and purge abnormality is
   a. anorexia.
   b. characteristic of some women.
   c. a psychiatric disorder.
   *   d. bulimia.
   e. all of the above except a

NUTRITION AND METABOLISM

E   35. The organ that stores and detoxifies different organic compounds is the
   a. pancreas.
   b. small intestine.
   *   c. liver.
   d. spleen.
   e. gall bladder.

M   36. The liver is associated with all of the following functions EXCEPT
   a. formation of urea.
   b. formation of bile.
   c. detoxification of poisons.
   *   d. secretion of bicarbonate ions.
   e. carbohydrate metabolism.

M   37. The liver is associated with all of the following functions EXCEPT
   a. inactivation of drugs.
   b. assembly and storage of fats.
   c. assembly and disassembly of certain proteins.
   d. degradation of worn-out blood cells.
   *   e. formation of glucagon.

M   38. During, or shortly after a meal, most cells use which of the following as a source of energy?
   a. fat
   b. amino acids
   *   c. glucose
   d. glycogen
   e. any of the above, depending on the concentration of the particular organic compound

Matching Questions

D   39.   Choose the one most appropriate answer for each.

1 _____ amylase

2 _____ bile

3 _____ disaccharidase

4 _____ gastrin

5 _____ lipase

6 _____ monosaccharides

7 _____ pepsin

8 _____ amino- and carboxypeptidase

9 _____ sphincter

10 _____ trypsin

A. made in the small intestine and pancreas; acts on protein fragments

B. glucose, fructose, and galactose

C. made in the pancreas; acts on fats

D. made by the pancreas and salivary glands; acts on starch

E. made by the small intestine; acts on double sugars

F. made by the pancreas; acts on proteins and polypeptides

G. contains cholesterol; helps emulsify fats

H. made in the stomach; acts on proteins

I. stimulates hydrochloric acid secretion

J. separates the stomach from the small intestine

Answers: 1. D   2. G   3. E   4. I   5. C   6. B
                  7. H   8. A   9. J   10. F

Classification Questions

Answer questions 40–44 in reference to the five components of the gastrointestinal tract listed below:

a. stomach
b. gall bladder
c. small intestine
d. appendix
e. large intestine

D   40.   Many organisms, such as birds, have ceca (digestive pouches) in which bacteria break down difficult-to-digest plant materials. These ceca are homologous to which of the above in humans?

M   41.   Which organ absorbs about 95 percent of the water that enters the human body, either as fluids or as part of food being eaten?

M   42.   Enzymatic digestion of proteins occurs primarily in which organ?

E   43.   Bile salts, bile pigments, cholesterol, and lecithin are stored by which of the above?

E   44.   The digestion of cellulose occurs in what part of the digestive system of the cow?

Answers: 40. d   41. c   42. c   43. b   44. a

Answer questions 45–49 in reference to the four glands or structures of the mammalian gastrointestinal tract listed below:

a. salivary glands
b. stomach lining
c. intestinal lining
d. pancreas

M   45.   Where is the enzyme pepsin produced?

D   46. Where is the enzyme carboxypeptidase produced?

D   47. Where is the fat-digesting enzyme, lipase, formed?

D   48. Where is the peptide-digesting enzyme, aminopeptidase, produced?

M   49. Where is the protein-digesting enzyme, trypsin, produced?

Answers: 45. b   46. d   47. d   48. c   49. d

Answer questions 50–54 in reference to the five vitamins listed below:
- a. Vitamin B_1
- b. Vitamin B_2
- c. Niacin
- d. Vitamin B_6
- e. Vitamin B_{12}

D   50. Which vitamin is a coenzyme involved in amino acid metabolism and obtained from meat, potatoes, even spinach?

D   51. Which vitamin is a component of the coenzyme thiamine pyrophosphate?

M   52. Which vitamin is a constituent of the coenzymes NAD^+ and $NADP^+$?

M   53. Which vitamin is more commonly known as riboflavin?

D   54. Which vitamin acts as a coenzyme in nucleic acid metabolism?

Answers: 50. d   51. a   52. c   53. b   54. e

Selecting the Exception

E   55. Four of the five answers listed below are structures through which ingested foodstuffs travel. Select the exception.
- a. crop
- * b. liver
- c. gizzard
- d. rectum
- e. small intestine

M   56. Four of the five answers listed below are functions of the digestive organs. Select the exception.
- * a. excretion
- b. absorption
- c. motility
- d. secretion
- e. digestion

M   57. Four of the five answers listed below release secretions that assist digestion. Select the exception.
- a. salivary gland
- * b. esophagus
- c. pancreas
- d. gall bladder
- e. liver

M 58. Four of the five answers listed below increase HCl secretion. Select the exception.
    a. cola drinks
    b. coffee
  * c. beer
    d. chocolate
    e. tea

D 59. Four of the five answers listed below are end-products of digestion ready for intestinal absorption. Select the exception.
    a. monoglyceride
    b. nucleotides
  * c. disaccharides
    d. amino acids
    e. free fatty acids

M 60. Four of the five answers listed below digest the same class of foods. Select the exception.
    a. aminopeptidase
    b. pepsin
  * c. amylase
    d. trypsin
    e. chymotrypsin

M 61. Four of the five answers listed below perform their task in the same workplace. Select the exception.
  * a. pepsin
    b. lipase
    c. carboxypeptidase
    d. nuclease
    e. disaccharidase

M 62. Four of the five answers listed below are conditions related to diet. Select the exception.
    a. colon cancer
    b. kidney stones
    c. cardiovascular disorders
    d. obesity
  * e. Alzheimer's disease

M 63. Four of the five answers listed below are all of the same class of vitamins. Select the exception.
    a. Vitamin A
    b. Vitamin K
  * c. Vitamin C
    d. Vitamin D
    e. Vitamin E

D 64. Four of the five answers listed below are functions performed by the same organ. Select the exception.
  * a. regulates pH of body fluids
    b. removes toxic substances from the blood
    c. stores and interconverses carbohydrates, fats, and proteins
    d. inactivates hormones
    e. forms urea from nitrogenous waste

CHAPTER 26
CIRCULATION

Multiple-Choice Questions

CIRCULATORY SYSTEMS: AN OVERVIEW

M   1. Which of the following is usually NOT present in an open circulation system?
   * a. veins
   b. the heart
   c. arteries
   d. blood
   e. arterioles

E   2. Which of the following has a closed circulatory system?
   a. clam
   * b. earthworm
   c. spider
   d. snail
   e. insect

CHARACTERISTICS OF BLOOD

M   3. Which cell is NOT the same type as the others?
   * a. erythrocytes
   b. neutrophils
   c. lymphocytes
   d. eosinophils
   e. monocytes

M   4. Which cell is NOT involved with the defense response?
   * a. erythrocytes
   b. neutrophils
   c. lymphocytes
   d. eosinophils
   e. monocytes

M   5. Which cell is the most abundant in the human body?
   a. lymphocytes
   b. basophils
   * c. erythrocytes
   d. neutrophils
   e. platelets

M   6. Which cell produces the fibrin used in blood clots?
   a. lymphocytes
   b. basophils
   c. erythrocytes
   d. neutrophils
   * e. platelets

E   7. In humans, which cell does NOT have a nucleus when mature?
*   a. erythrocytes
     b. lymphocytes
     c. neutrophils
     d. eosinophils
     e. monocytes

E   8. Most of the oxygen in the blood is transported by
     a. plasma.
     b. serum.
     c. platelets.
*   d. hemoglobin.
     e. leukocytes.

E   9. Red blood cells originate in the
     a. liver.
     b. spleen.
     c. kidneys.
*   d. bone marrow.
     e. thymus gland.

M   10. How long does the average red blood cell live?
     a. 4 days
     b. 4 weeks
*   c. 4 months
     d. 1 year
     e. 4 years

E   11. About how many quarts of blood does a normal, 150-pound, human male have?
     a. 3
     b. 4
*   c. 5
     d. 6
     e. 7

E   12. What percent of the total blood volume does plasma normally amount to?
     a. 15 to 25
     b. 33 to 40
*   c. 50 to 60
     d. 66 to 75
     e. about 80

E   13. Hemoglobin contains which element?
     a. chlorine
     b. sodium
*   c. iron
     d. copper
     e. magnesium

M   14. Megakaryocytes fragment to produce
     a. red blood cells.
     b. lymphocytes.
*   c. platelets.
     d. eosinophils.
     e. neutrophils.

E   15. Blood rich in oxygen is what color?
              a. yellow
              b. pink
         *   c. bright red
              d. blue
              e. purple

HUMAN CARDIOVASCULAR SYSTEM

M   16. The pulmonary circulation
              a. involves the hepatic portal vein.
              b. moves oxygen-rich blood to the kidneys.
              c. includes the coronary arteries.
         *   d. leads to, through, and from the lungs.
              e. all of the above

E   17. The receiving zone of a vertebrate heart is
              a. a plaque.
              b. the aorta.
         *   c. an atrium.
              d. a capillary bed.
              e. all of the above

M   18. The aorta leaves the
              a. left atrium.
              b. right atrium.
         *   c. left ventricle.
              d. right ventricle.

M   19. The pulmonary artery carries blood away from the
              a. aorta.
              b. right atrium.
         *   c. right ventricle.
              d. left atrium.
              e. left ventricle.

E   20. Blood from the body is first received by the heart in the
              a. coronary vein.
              b. left atrium.
              c. right ventricle.
         *   d. right atrium.
              e. left ventricle.

M   21. The heart
         *   a. will contract as a result of stimuli from the sinoatrial node.
              b. contracts only as a result of nerve stimulation from the central nervous system.
              c. is activated primarily through the autonomic nervous system.
              d. pulse is primarily under the control of the atrioventricular node.
              e. is completely independent of all nervous control.

M   22. Blood pressure is highest in the
         *   a. aorta.
              b. pulmonary artery.
              c. capillary bed.
              d. subclavian vein.
              e. lower vena cava.

M 23. Heart excitation originates in the
    a. atrioventricular node.
    b. intercalated disk.
  * c. sinoatrial node.
    d. pericardium.
    e. all of the above

E 24. The greatest volume of blood is found in the
    a. aorta and arteries.
    b. capillaries.
  * c. veins.
    d. lungs.
    e. heart.

E 25. Which of the following has the highest blood pressure?
    a. right ventricle
    b. right atrium
  * c. left ventricle
    d. left atrium
    e. pulmonary circulation

M 26. Which of the following is NOT found in an arteriole?
    a. elastic layer
    b. basement membrane
    c. smooth muscle
  * d. valve
    e. endothelium

M 27. The diastolic pressure for a normal young adult would be
    a. 60 mmHg.
  * b. 80 mmHg.
    c. 100 mmHg.
    d. 120 mmHg.
    e. 140 mmHg.

E 28. A normal pulse pressure would be
    a. 20 mmHg.
  * b. 40 mmHg.
    c. 60 mmHg.
    d. 80 mmHg.
    e. 100 mmHg.

E 29. By controlling their musculature, which can vary the resistance to blood flow?
    a. arteries
    b. veins
    c. capillaries
  * d. arterioles
    e. all of the above

M 30. What occurs during systole?
    a. Oxygen-rich blood is pumped to the lungs.
  * b. The heart muscle tissues contract.
    c. The atrioventricular valves suddenly open.
    d. Oxygen-poor blood from all body regions except the lungs flows into the right atrium.
    e. all of the above

M   31. The most common vascular disease is
                a. phlebitis.
      *   b. hypertension.
                c. leukemia.
                d. sickle-cell anemia.
                e. a stroke.

E   32. A stroke is a rupture of a blood vessel in the
                a. leg.
      *   b. brain.
                c. heart.
                d. lung.
                e. internal organs.

M   33. In atherosclerosis
                a. abnormal multiplication of smooth muscle cells in blood vessels occurs.
                b. the arterial walls fill with connective tissue.
                c. the lipids in the bloodstream become embedded in the walls of the endothelial lining.
                d. a fibrous net covers the entire abnormal area.
      *   e. all of the above

M   34. Because of their great elasticity, which of the following can function as blood volume reservoirs during times of low metabolic output?
      *   a. veins and venules
                b. arteries
                c. arterioles
                d. capillaries
                e. all of the above

M   35. The mineral associated with atherosclerosis is
                a. iron.
                b. magnesium.
                c. cobalt.
      *   d. calcium.
                e. iodine.

M   36. Cholesterol is believed to be carried by
                a. albumin.
                b. high-density lipoproteins.
                c. low-density lipoproteins.
                d. triglycerides.
      *   e. both b and c

E   37. Which controls the distribution of blood?
                a. arteries
      *   b. arterioles
                c. capillaries
                d. venules
                e. veins

E   38. Which are pressure reservoirs with low resistance to flow?
      *   a. arteries
                b. arterioles
                c. capillaries
                d. venules
                e. veins

E 39. Which are highly distensible reservoirs for blood volume?
   a. arteries
   b. arterioles
   c. capillaries
   d. venules
 * e. veins

D 40. Hemostasis in vertebrates includes all of the following EXCEPT
   a. blood clot formation.
   b. vessel constriction.
 * c. release of iron to aid in the clumping of platelets.
   d. vessel spasms.
   e. platelets releasing substances that cause them to attract each other.

M 41. Type A blood will NOT agglutinate when mixed with
   a. type B blood.
   b. type A blood.
   c. type AB blood.
   d. type O blood.
 * e. both A and AB, but will clump with types B and O.

E 42. Which blood type is the universal donor?
   a. A+
   b. B
   c. AB+
   d. AB
 * e. O

E 43. Which blood type is the universal recipient?
   a. A
   b. B+
   c. AB+
 * d. AB
   e. O+

D 44. In the Rh disease
   a. the mother must be positive and her first and second children positive.
 * b. the mother must be negative and her first and second children positive.
   c. the mother must be negative and her first and second children negative.
   d. the mother must be positive and her first and second children negative.
   e. the mother and the father must both be negative and the child positive.

LYMPHATIC SYSTEM

M 45. Which of the following is transported in greater quantities in the lymphatic system than in the blood?
   a. red blood cells
   b. wastes
 * c. fats
   d. amino acids
   e. white blood cells

M 46. Which statement is NOT true of the lymph vascular system? The lymph vascular system
   a. transports lipids absorbed from the small intestine to the bloodstream.
   b. recovers and transports interstitial fluid back to the bloodstream.
 * c. absorbs glucose from the small intestine and transports it to the brain.
   d. serves the body's system of defenses against bacteria and other infectious agents.
   e. performs all of the above functions.

M   47. The lymphoid organs include all but the
   a. spleen.
   * b. stomach.
   c. thymus.
   d. tonsils and adenoids.
   e. appendix.

E   48. The system that reclaims fluids and proteins that have escaped from blood capillaries is the
   _____ system.
   a. cardiovascular.
   b. pulmonary.
   * c. lymphatic.
   d. sinoatrial.
   e. venous.

E   49. Areas where lumphocytes congregate as they cleanse the blood of foreign materials are called
   a. stem cells.
   b. SA nodes.
   c. capillary beds.
   * d. lymph nodes.
   e. antibodies.

Classification Questions

Answer questions 50–54 in reference to the five components of mammalian blood listed below:
   a. red blood cells
   b. basophils
   c. platelets
   d. serum albumin protein
   e. sodium and potassium chloride

E   50. Which blood component plays a central role in clotting blood following a wound?

E   51. Which blood component contains hemoglobin?

D   52. Which blood component plays a role in the inflammatory response and shows anticlotting activity?

E   53. Which blood component plays a role in maintaining the ionic balance of the body?

E   54. Oxygen is transported throughout the body by which blood component?

Answers: 50. c   51. a   52. b   53. e   54. a

Answer questions 55–59 in reference to the four structures of the heart listed below:
   a. right atrium
   b. left atrium
   c. left ventricle
   d. right ventricle

M   55. Blood from the upper and lower vena cavas enters the heart via which structure?

M   56. Blood passes to the lungs from which structure?

M   57. Deoxygenated blood exits the heart from which structure?

M   58. Oxygenated blood enters the heart via which structure?

M 59. Blood is pumped to the majority of the body by which structure?

Answers: 55. a 56. d 57. d 58. b 59. c

Selecting the Exception

M 60. Four of the five answers listed below designate organisms with open circulations. Select the exception.
- a. insects
- b. snails
- c. spiders
- d. clams
- * e. frogs

M 61. Four of the five answers listed below are related by a common property. Select the exception.
- a. neutrophil
- * b. erythrocyte
- c. lymphocytes
- d. monocyte
- e. basophil

M 62. Four of the five answers listed below are blood proteins. Select the exception.
- * a. epinephrine
- b. globulin
- c. hemoglobin
- d. fibrinogen
- e. albumin

M 63. Four of the five answers listed below are characteristics of most veins. Select the exception.
- a. blood volume reservoir
- b. contain valves
- c. low resistance-transport tubes
- * d. transport oxygen
- e. low blood pressure

M 64. Three of the four answers listed below are related by a common function. Select the exception.
- * a. gamma globulin
- b. prothrombin
- c. fibrin
- d. fibrinogen

D 65. Four of the five answers listed below are related by a common feature. Select the exception.
- a. A
- b. B
- c. AB
- * d. Rh+
- e. O

D 66. Four of the five answers listed below are related by a common function. Select the exception.
- * a. heart
- b. spleen
- c. thymus
- d. tonsils
- e. lymph node

CHAPTER 27
IMMUNITY

Multiple-Choice Questions

RUSSIAN ROULETTE, IMMUNOLOGICAL STYLE

E   1.   The first disease for which a successful vaccination was developed was
      a. the plague.
*   b. smallpox.
      c. rabies.
      d. chicken pox.
      e. diphtheria.

E   2.   The person who developed and demonstrated the first successful vaccine was
      a. Pasteur.
      b. Koch.
      c. Lister.
*   d. Jenner.
      e. Erhlich.

E   3.   The word *vaccination* comes from the Latin word for
      a. germ.
*   b. cow.
      c. chicken.
      d. rabbit.
      e. rat.

FIRST LINE OF DEFENSE—SURFACE BARRIERS TO INVASION

M   4.   The barrier to invasion by microbes involves
      a. stomach acids.
      b. the symbiotic microorganisms already in the body.
      c. ciliated mucous membranes.
      d. lysozyme and other enzymes.
*   e. all of the above

SECOND LINE OF DEFENSE—NONSPECIFIC RESPONSES

M   5.   Phagocytes are derived from stem cells in the
      a. spleen.
      b. thymus.
*   c. bone marrow.
      d. blood.
      e. liver.

M   6.   Which system involves plasma proteins activated when they contact a bacterial cell?
      a. infection
*   b. complement
      c. bodyguard
      d. enhancer
      e. defender

M   7.   Histamine causes
- a. blood vessels to contract.
- b. capillaries to lose their permeability.
- *   c. an outward flow of fluids from the capillaries.
- d. a destruction of mast cells.
- e. an opening of the area of infection, through which the body's defense system can enter.

M   8.   Which event does NOT occur in the inflammatory response?
- a. Tissue swells because of outflow from capillary beds.
- *   b. Blocking antibodies inactivate the resident mast cells.
- c. White blood cells are attracted to the area by chemotaxis.
- d. Complement proteins help identify invading material.
- e. The foreign invaders are engulfed and destroyed by phagocytosis.

THIRD LINE OF DEFENSE—THE IMMUNE SYSTEM

M   9.   Terms that describe the immune response include all of the following EXCEPT
- a. specific.
- b. rapid.
- c. memory.
- *   d. general.
- e. effective.

E   10.   Which cells are divided into two groups: T cells and B cells?
- a. macrophages
- *   b. lymphocytes
- c. complement cells
- d. platelets
- e. all of the above

M   11.   Which cells produce and secrete antibodies that set up bacterial invaders for subsequent destruction by macrophages?
- a. phagocytes
- b. macrophages
- *   c. B cells
- d. T cells
- e. all of the above

M   12.   Which of the following are NOT generally targets of T cells?
- a. transplants of foreign tissue
- b. cancer
- c. infections caused by viruses
- *   d. infections caused by bacteria
- e. all of the above

M   13.   Which cells produce antibodies?
- a. helper T
- b. suppressor T
- c. cytotoxic T
- d. natural killer
- *   e. B

M   14.   Which cells cause rapid division of the lymphocytes?
- *   a. helper T
- b. suppressor T
- c. cytotoxic T
- d. memory
- e. B

M 15. Which cells are held in reserve to be used for a rapid response to subsequent intruders of the same type?
    a. helper T
    b. suppressor T
    c. cytotoxic T
  * d. memory
    e. B

M 16. Which cells are similar to cytotoxic cells in their mode of action?
    a. helper T
  * b. natural killer
    c. cytotoxic T
    d. memory
    e. B

M 17. Which cells directly destroy body cells infected by viral or fungal parasites?
    a. helper T
    b. suppressor T
  * c. cytotoxic T
    d. memory
    e. B

M 18. Mutant and cancerous cells are destroyed by which cells?
    a. helper T
    b. suppressor T
  * c. cytotoxic T
    d. memory
    e. B

E 19. Antibodies are shaped like the letter
    a. C.
    b. E.
    c. H.
    d. K.
  * e. Y.

E 20. The antibody molecule consists of how many polypeptide chains, including light and heavy chains?
    a. 2
    b. 3
  * c. 4
    d. 5
    e. 6

M 21. Body cells have self-markers located
    a. in their nuclei.
    b. in the endoplasmic reticulum.
    c. in the mitochondria.
  * d. on the plasma membrane.
    e. inside the Golgi bodies.

M 22. The markers for each cell in a body are referred to by the letters
  * a. MHC.
    b. HTC.
    c. ADS.
    d. RSW.
    e. AKA.

E 23. Antibodies are
*   a. proteins.
    b. steroids.
    c. polysaccharides.
    d. lipoproteins.
    e. all of the above

E 24. Antibodies belong to a group of compounds known as
    a. self-recognizing compounds.
*   b. immunoglobulins.
    c. histosaccharides.
    d. antisteroids.
    e. virulent bases.

D 25. Which statement is NOT true?
    a. When an invading bacterium is destroyed by a macrophage, its antigens are preserved.
*   b. Antibodies attack and destroy invading antigens.
    c. Helper T cells recognize the major histocompatibility complex and antigens on the surface of macrophages.
    d. Self cells have major histocompatibility complex markers or antigens.
    e. Helper T cells secrete lymphokines, which help the cells of the immune system communicate with each other.

M 26. Clones of B or T cells are
    a. being produced continually.
    b. interchangeable.
*   c. produced only when their surface proteins recognize specific protein.
    d. known as memory cells.
    e. produced and mature in the bone marrow.

M 27. Effector (plasma) cells
    a. die within a week of production.
    b. manufacture and secrete antibodies.
    c. do not divide and form clones.
    d. develop from B cells.
*   e. all of the above

M 28. Cell-mediated response
*   a. involves cytotoxic T cells.
    b. involves the action of antibodies to destroy invaders.
    c. acts only on extracellular clues.
    d. results in the production of clones of plasma cells.
    e. all of the above

M 29. Most organ transplants fail because
    a. of poor vascular connection between host and donor tissue.
    b. the migrating leukocytes attack the tissue adjacent to the transplant.
*   c. cytotoxic T cells enter the transplant through the connecting blood vessels and kill the individual transplant tissue.
    d. introduced tissues produce antibodies that cause a massive reaction.
    e. all of the above

M   30. The primary immune response
            a. is shorter in duration than a secondary response.
            b. is quicker than a secondary response.
            c. depends on random construction of appropriate antibodies.
            d. is the result of a reproduction of an appropriate lymphocyte resulting in a sensitive clone.
       *   e. both c and d

D   31. After a primary immune response
            a. a clone of sensitive lymphocytes is ready for any subsequent invasion of the same antigen.
            b. some of the clone cells will remain alive for decades.
            c. clone cells may be modified to attack new invaders.
            d. clone cells are continually reproduced to confer immunity against subsequent invasion.
       *   e. both a and b

E   32. Organ transplants are safest between
            a. two brothers.
            b. father and daughter.
            c. fraternal twins.
       *   d. identical twins.
            e. unrelated individuals.

IMMUNIZATION

E   33. A vaccine contains
            a. killed pathogen.
            b. weakened pathogen.
            c. noninfective fragments of a pathogen.
            d. full-strength pathogen.
       *   e. All except d may be used.

M   34. Passive immunity can be obtained by
            a. having the disease.
            b. receiving a vaccination against the disease.
            c. receiving antibodies by injection.
            d. receiving antibodies from the mother at birth.
       *   e. either c or d

M   35. Whenever the body is reexposed to a sensitizing agent, the IgE antibodies cause
       *   a. the production of prostaglandins and histamine.
            b. the release of antihistamines.
            c. the suppression of the inflammatory response.
            d. the production of clonal cells.
            e. all of the above

M   36. A person sensitive to bee stings might die minutes after a sting due to
            a. a collapse of the immune system.
            b. a clogging of the capillaries.
       *   c. a release of excessive fluids from the capillary beds.
            d. respiratory distress caused by excessive mucus.
            e. the extremely sharp rise in blood pressure.

ABNORMAL OR DEFICIENT IMMUNE RESPONSES

E   37.   The reason AIDS is so serious is that
       a.   the excessive immune reaction leads to death.
       b.   it is so highly contagious.
   *   c.   it is fatal.
       d.   it is caused by a retrovirus.
       e.   many natural reservoirs may spread the disease at any time.

E   38.   Kaposi's sarcoma is characteristic of people who have
   *   a.   AIDS.
       b.   allergic reactions.
       c.   a hypersensitive immune system.
       d.   ancestors who come from Cyprus.
       e.   herpes.

E   39.   Of the following, AIDS is usually transferred by
       a.   casual contact.
       b.   food.
       c.   water.
   *   d.   sexual intercourse.
       e.   insect bites.

M   40.   The human immunodeficiency virus (HIV-1) primarily destroys which cells?
       a.   B
       b.   M
       c.   T1
   *   d.   CD4
       e.   suppressor T

E   41.   Rheumatoid arthritis is
       a.   sexually transmitted.
   *   b.   an autoimmune disease.
       c.   one of the diseases associated with AIDS.
       d.   caused by a bacterial infection.
       e.   preventable by vaccination.

Matching Questions

D   42.   Choose the most appropriate answer for each.

1 _____ antigens

2 _____ B lymphocytes

3 _____ blocking antibodies

4 _____ clone

5 _____ histamine

6 _____ cytotoxic T lymphocytes

7 _____ interleukins

8 _____ macrophages

9 _____ memory cells

10 _____ effector (plasma) cells

11 _____ retroviruses

12 _____ stem cells

13 _____ natural killer cells

A. cells that do not divide, die in less than a week, and secrete large quantities of antibodies

B. cells that directly destroy body cells already infected by viral or fungal parasites, as well as mutant and cancerous cells

C. lymphocytes that are held in reserve, circulate in the bloodstream, and enable a rapid response to subsequent encounters with the same type of invader

D. chemical that causes capillaries to become "leaky"

E. cells that are produced in the bone marrow and are never changed by the thymus; these cells produce antibodies

F. destroy cells coated with complement proteins

G. a class of proteins that help cells of the immune system communicate with each other

H. "big eaters" that alert other lymphocytes to the invasion of specific antigens

I. immature cells that may or may not be committed to develop into one of several mature cell types

J. a group of cells that are all produced asexually from one original parent cell

K. surface patterns of nonself molecules or particles

L. Y-shaped recognition proteins for allergy victims; can be injected into a victim's body in increasing amounts to provoke production of IgG

M. one of this group has been identified as the causative agent of AIDS

Answers: 1. K   2. E   3. L   4. J   5. D   6. B
              7. G   8. H   9. C   10. A   11. M   12. I
             13. F

Classification Questions

Answer questions 43–47 in reference to the five types of white cells listed below:

    a. macrophages
    b. helper T cells
    c. B cells
    d. cytotoxic T cells
    e. natural killer cells

D   43.   Which cells attack cells marked with coatings of complement proteins?

M   44.   These cells scavenge dead cells and attack bacteria directly.

D   45.   These cells destroy cells infected by viruses.

D   46.   These cells recognize cell surface antigens and initiate the proliferation of lymphocytes.

M   47.   Antibody production occurs in which of the above?

Answers: 43. e   44. a   45. d   46. b   47. c

Answer questions 48–52 in reference to the five items listed below:

      a. antigens
      b. antibodies
      c. helper T cells
      d. cytotoxic T cells
      e. memory B cells

E   48.   Which of the above bind, as in a lock-and-key mechanism, to foreign proteins?

M   49.   Which of the above produce immunoglobulins in response to the reinvasion by a virus?

D   50.   Which of the above directly attack the foreign cells of an incompatible skin graft?

M   51.   An Rh^+ molecule in the body of an Rh^- woman is an example of what?

D   52.   Bacteria and viruses in the blood are attacked by proteins produced by what?

Answers: 48. b   49. e   50. d   51. a   52. e

Selecting the Exception

M   53.   Four of the five answers listed below are barriers to invasion. Select the exception.
      a. intact skin
      b. mucous membrane
      c. gastric juices
  * d. blood plasma
      e. lysosyme

D   54.   Four of the five answers listed below are characteristic reactions of the complement system to invaders. Select the exception.
      a. causes an amplifying cascade of reactions to invaders
  * b. triggers the secretion of histamines
      c. causes invading cells to lyse
      d. enhances the recognition of invaders by phagocytes
      e. creates gradients that attract phagocytes

D   55.   Four of the five answers listed below are events of the inflammatory response. Select the exception.
      a. increases capillary permeability
      b. release of histamine
      c. blood vessels dilate
  * d. temperature of the affected areas drops
      e. phagocytes migrate toward the affected area

E   56.   Four of the five answers listed below are targets of the immune system. Select the exception.
      a. virus
  * b. normal cells
      c. cancer cells
      d. bacteria
      e. debris and dead cells

CHAPTER 28
RESPIRATION

Multiple-Choice Questions

THE NATURE OF RESPIRATION

E 1. For the surface of an animal to function in the integumentary exchange of gases it must
    a. be thin and soft.
    b. have a high number of blood vessels.
    c. have mucus or moist covering.
*   d. all of the above

M 2. Blood and water flowing in opposite directions, in conjunction with respiratory systems, is a mechanism that explains how
*   a. oxygen uptake by blood capillaries in fish gills occurs.
    b. ventilation occurs.
    c. sounds originating in the vocal cords of the larynx are formed.
    d. intrapleural pressure is established.
    e. all of the above

E 3. External gills are characteristic of
    a. larval insects.
    b. larval amphibians.
    c. most fish.
    d. all of the above
*   e. only a and b

E 4. The oxygen content of air is approximately
*   a. 21 percent.
    b. 78 percent.
    c. 0.04 percent.
    d. 0.96 percent.
    e. 100 percent.

M 5. Adult insects exchange respiratory gases primarily by means of
    a. spiracles.
*   b. tracheae.
    c. lungs.
    d. gills.
    e. body surface.

E 6. The group of animals with the most efficient respiratory system is the
    a. amphibians.
*   b. birds.
    c. mammals.
    d. reptiles.
    e. fish.

M 7. Birds
    a. breathe through air sacs.
    b. exchange gas with their lungs as they breathe in or out.
    c. have exceptionally large and flexible lungs.
    d. have four air sacs for each lung that behave like bellows.
*   e. both b and d

M   8. Ventilation is defined as
        a. bailing water over the gills.
        b. movement of water past cells by using flagella.
        c. moving air in and out of lungs.
        d. tracheal exchanges.
    *   e. all of the above

HUMAN RESPIRATORY SYSTEM

M   9. What is the proper sequence in the flow of air in mammals?
        a. nasal cavities, larynx, pharynx, bronchi, trachea
        b. nasal cavities, pharynx, bronchi, larynx, trachea
    *   c. nasal cavities, pharynx, larynx, trachea, bronchi
        d. nasal cavities, larynx, pharynx, trachea, bronchi
        e. nasal cavities, bronchi, larynx, trachea, pharynx

M   10. The last mammalian structure that air moves through before the alveoli is the
        a. larynx.
        b. glottis.
    *   c. bronchioles.
        d. trachea.
        e. pharynx.

D   11. During inhalation,
        a. the pressure in the thoracic cavity is greater than the pressure within the lungs.
    *   b. the pressure in the thoracic cavity is less than the pressure within the lungs.
        c. the diaphragm moves upward and becomes more curved.
        d. the chest cavity volume decreases.
        e. all of the above

M   12. Food and drink are prevented from entering the respiratory passageways during swallowing
        by means of the
        a. glottis.
        b. pharynx.
    *   c. epiglottis.
        d. larynx.
        e. trachea.

M   13. When you swallow, the epiglottis covers the opening to the
        a. pharynx.
        b. esophagus.
    *   c. larynx.
        d. bronchus.
        e. alveoli.

E   14. The human vocal cords are located in the
        a. glottis.
        b. pharynx.
        c. trachea.
    *   d. larynx.
        e. bronchus.

M   15. In pleurisy,
        a. some of the alveoli fill with fluid.
    *   b. the pleural membrane becomes inflamed and swollen and causes painful breathing.
        c. the diaphragm develops muscular cramps.
        d. the vagus nerve is irritated.
        e. the intercostal muscles become inflamed and cause pain during deep breathing.

GAS EXCHANGE AND TRANSPORT

M   16. Oxygen moves from alveoli to the bloodstream
  *   a. because the concentration of oxygen is greater in alveoli than in the blood.
        b. mainly due to the activity of carbonic anhydrase in the red blood cells.
        c. by using the assistance of carbaminohemoglobin.
        d. through active transport.
        e. all of the above

E   17. Actual exchange of gases in the lungs occurs in the
        a. bronchi.
  *   b. alveoli.
        c. bronchioles.
        d. tracheas.
        e. glottis.

M   18. Hemoglobin
        a. tends to give up oxygen in regions where partial pressure of oxygen exceeds that in the lungs.
        b. tends to hold onto oxygen when the pH of the blood drops.
        c. tends to release oxygen where the temperature is lower.
  *   d. releases oxygen more readily in highly active tissues.
        e. all of the above

M   19. Which statement is NOT true?
        a. Carbon dioxide is more soluble in fluid than in oxygen.
        b. Carbon dioxide diffuses more rapidly across the respiratory surface than does oxygen.
        c. The major muscle involved in breathing is the diaphragm.
  *   d. Oxygen is carried primarily by blood plasma.
        e. Carbon dioxide is carried by the blood plasma.

M   20. Hemoglobin gives up O_2 when
  *   a. carbon dioxide concentrations are high.
        b. body temperature is lowered.
        c. pH values are high.
        d. CO_2 concentrations are low.
        e. all of the above

M   21. Most of the carbon dioxide produced by the body is transported to the lungs in
        a. a gaseous form.
        b. blood plasma.
        c. potassium carbonate ions.
  *   d. bicarbonate ions.
        e. carbonic acid.

M   22. The enzyme responsible for converting free carbon dioxide in the blood into forms in which it can be transported in the blood is
  *   a. carbonic anhydrase.
        b. carboxypeptidase.
        c. carbonase.
        d. decarboxylase.
        e. dehydrogenase.

M 23. Which statement is true?
   a. Breathing rate and depth are completely under voluntary control.
   b. A person can commit suicide by holding one's breath.
   c. The contraction of the diaphragm and muscle of the rib cage are under the control of areas of the brain.
   d. There are chemoreceptors in the brain that monitor carbon dioxide content in the blood and control breathing.
 * e. both c and d

RESPIRATION IN UNUSUAL ENVIRONMENTS

M 24. Hypoxia
   a. causes hyperventilation.
   b. may cause headaches, nausea, and lethargy.
   c. can lead to loss of consciousness and death.
   d. may be the result of changes in altitude.
 * e. all of the above

M 25. The enzyme responsible for converting free carbon dioxide in the blood into forms in which it can be transported in the blood is
 * a. carbonic anhydrase.
   b. carboxypeptidase.
   c. carbonase.
   d. decarboxylase.
   e. dehydrogenase.

E 26. Carbon monoxide
   a. has a very low affinity or attraction to hemoglobin.
   b. is unlikely to be transported by the circulatory system.
   c. is not the cause of death of people who breathe excessive amounts of automobile exhausts.
 * d. can arise from cigarette smoke.
   e. both c and d

E 27. The cessation of smoking
   a. can reduce the risk of stillbirth.
   b. reduces the chances of cancer.
   c. reduces the chances of coronary disease.
   d. improves lung functioning.
 * e. all of the above

M 28. Life-long nonsmokers live an average of how much longer than those who, in their mid-twenties, smoked two packs of cigarettes a day?
   a. 6 months
   b. 1–2 years
   c. 3–5 years
 * d. 7–9 years
   e. over 12 years

E 29. Smoking has been shown to cause
   a. bronchitis.
   b. emphysema.
   c. lung cancer.
   d. coronary disease.
 * e. all of the above

Matching Questions

D   30.   Choose the one most appropriate answer for each.

1 _____ alveoli   A.   flexible windpipe reinforced with cartridges

2 _____ bronchi   B.   contains two true vocal cords

3 _____ diaphragm   C.   move the ribs

4 _____ epiglottis   D.   throat cavity behind the mouth

5 _____ intercostal rib muscles   E.   connect trachea to lungs

6 _____ larynx   F.   flaplike structure that points upward and allows air to enter trachea; closed during swallowing

7 _____ pharynx

8 _____ trachea   G.   contraction moves it downward

H.   microscopically small pockets lined with moist epithelium

Answers: 1. H   2. E   3. G   4. F   5. C   6. B
                 7. D   8. A

Classification Questions

Answer questions 31–35 in reference to the five components of respiratory systems listed below:

    a.   pharynx
    b.   larynx
    c.   trachea
    d.   bronchiole
    e.   alveolus

E   31.   Where is the voice box located?

M   32.   Which is the last component of the human lung that air flows into?

M   33.   Where does gas exchange between the air in the lungs and their blood supply occur?

E   34.   Air moves from the nasal cavity into which component?

M   35.   Spent air moves from the bronchial tubes back to which component?

Answers: 31. b   32. e   33. e   34. a   35. c

Selecting the Exception

E   36.   Four of the five answers listed below are parts of the same body system. Select the exception.
       a.   trachea
  *   b.   esophagus
       c.   alveoli
       d.   bronchiole
       e.   glottis

M   37. Four of the five answers listed below are components of the human respiratory system. Select the exception.
    a. thoracic cavity
    b. trachea
    c. diaphragm
*   d. spiracle
    e. larynx

CHAPTER 29
WATER-SOLUTE BALANCE

Multiple-Choice Questions

TALE OF THE DESERT RAT

E   1. Animals began invading land how many million years ago?
- a. 800
- b. 600
- *   c. 375
- d. 250
- e. 150

MAINTAINING EXTRACELLULAR FLUID

E   2. The most abundant waste product of metabolism is
- *   a. carbon dioxide.
- b. ammonia.
- c. urea.
- d. uric acid.
- e. water.

M   3. All but which of the following are significant routes for water loss from the body?
- a. excretion in urine
- *   b. sneezing
- c. sweating
- d. elimination in feces
- e. evaporation from respiratory surfaces

E   4. The process that normally exerts the greatest control over the water balance of an individual is
- a. sweating.
- b. elimination in feces.
- *   c. kidney function.
- d. evaporation through the skin.
- e. respiratory loss.

D   5. Which of the following does NOT dispose of a type of waste directly to the environment?
- a. digestive system
- b. respiratory system
- c. integumentary system
- *   d. circulatory system
- e. urinary system

D   6. Humans gain the least amounts of water by what route?
- *   a. metabolism
- b. ingestion of liquids
- c. ingestion of solids
- d. All of the above contribute equal amounts of water.

D   7. The most toxic substances routinely found in the blood are metabolites of
             a. carbohydrates.
   *   b. proteins.
             c. lipids.
             d. minerals.
             e. vitamins.

URINARY SYSTEM OF MAMMALS

E   8. The subunit of a kidney that purifies blood and restores solute and water balance is called a
             a. glomerulus.
             b. loop of Henle.
   *   c. nephron.
             d. ureter.
             e. all of the above

M   9. In the kidney, the ducts from the nephrons empty immediately into the
             a. renal cortex.
             b. renal medulla.
   *   c. renal pelvis.
             d. ureter.
             e. urethra.

E   10. The last portion of the excretory system through which urine passes before it is eliminated
             from the body is the
             a. glomerulus.
             b. ureter.
   *   c. urethra.
             d. bladder.
             e. rectum.

E   11. The functional unit of the kidney is the
             a. Bowman's capsule.
   *   b. nephron.
             c. glomerulus.
             d. urinary bladder.

M   12. Which of the following processes is under voluntary control?
             a. filtration
             b. reabsorption
   *   c. urination
             d. secretion
             e. excretion

D   13. Kidney stones form in the
   *   a. renal pelvis.
             b. ureters.
             c. urethra.
             d. urinary bladder.
             e. glomerulus.

URINE FORMATION

M   14.   In mammals, which of the following governs both the thirst mechanism and the hormonal action that affects the amount of water and solutes excreted in the urine?
- a. adrenal cortex
- b. adrenal medulla
- c. anterior pituitary
- * d. hypothalamus
- e. none of the above

M   15.   Filtration occurs in which section of mammalian nephrons?
- * a. glomerulus
- b. loops of Henle
- c. proximal tubules
- d. distal tubules
- e. peritubular capillaries

M   16.   The process during which potassium and hydrogen ions, penicillin, and some toxic substances are put into the urine by active transport is called
- * a. tubular secretion.
- b. reabsorption.
- c. filtration.
- d. countercurrent multiplication.

E   17.   Which of the following substances is NOT filtered from the bloodstream?
- a. water
- * b. plasma proteins
- c. urea
- d. glucose
- e. sodium

M   18.   What is the name given to the fluid removed from the blood but not yet processed by the nephron tubules?
- a. urine
- b. water
- c. uretrial fluid
- * d. filtrate
- e. renal plasma

E   19.   A kidney machine removes solutes from the blood by means of
- a. osmosis.
- b. diffusion.
- * c. dialysis.
- d. active transport.
- e. bulk flow.

M   20.   The antidiuretic hormone
- a. promotes processes that lead to an increase in the volume of urine.
- * b. promotes processes that lead to a decrease in the volume of urine.
- c. acts on the proximal tubules of nephrons in the kidney.
- d. is produced by the adrenal cortex.
- e. all of the above

M   21. Reabsorption is the movement of water and solutes from the _____ to the _____.
     a. interstitial fluid; tubules
     b. glomerular capillaries; Bowman's capsule
     c. Bowman's capsule; nephron tubules
   * d. nephron tubules; capillaries
     e. glomerular capillaries; peritubular capillaries

E   22. In reabsorption,
     a. plasma proteins are returned to the blood.
     b. excess hydrogen ions are removed from the blood.
     c. excess water is passed on to the urine.
   * d. nutrients and salts are selectively returned to the blood.
     e. drugs and foreign substances are passed into the urine.

E   23. About what percent of the fluid removed from the blood is eventually returned to the blood?
     a. 59
     b. 90
   * c. 98
     d. 0.9
     e. 9

D   24. Most of the water and sodium is reabsorbed in the
     a. glomerulus.
   * b. proximal tubule.
     c. distal tubule.
     d. loop of Henle.
     e. collecting duct.

D   25. The reabsorption of solutes is the result of active transport of
     a. potassium.
   * b. sodium.
     c. carbonate.
     d. chloride.
     e. all of the above

M   26. The hormone that influences sodium reabsorption in the kidney is
     a. antidiuretic hormone.
     b. cortisone.
   * c. aldosterone.
     d. corticotropic hormone.
     e. adrenalin.

E   27. The hormone that controls the concentration of urine is
     a. insulin.
     b. glucagon.
   * c. the antidiuretic hormone.
     d. thyroxine.
     e. epinephrine.

D   28. A rise in sodium levels and extracellular volume leads to a rise in blood pressure. As a result
     a. renin levels rise, but aldosterone levels fall.
     b. renin levels fall, but aldosterone levels rise.
     c. renin and aldosterone levels rise.
   * d. renin and aldosterone levels drop.

M   29. The hormonal control over excretion occurs in the
        a. Bowman's capsule.
        b. proximal tubule.
    *   c. distal tubule.
        d. loop of Henle.
        e. urinary bladder.

ACID-BASE BALANCE

M   30. The longer this structure is, the greater is an animal's capacity to conserve water and to concentrate solutes for excretion in the urine.
        a. Bowman's capsule
    *   b. loop of Henle
        c. proximal tubule
        d. ureter

D   31. The urinary system helps to maintain the extracellular fluid pH by
        a. synthesizing buffers.
        b. retaining carbon dioxide in the filtrate.
    *   c. excreting hydrogen ions as water.
        d. combining hydrogen ions with urea.

D   32. Which of the following features would tend to promote water retention by the kidney?
        a. many nephridia
    *   b. a long loop of Henle
        c. a long proximal tubule
        d. a short distal tubule
        e. a high filtration rate

Matching Questions

D   33. Choose the one most appropriate answer for each.

1 _____ nephron

2 _____ aldosterone

3 _____ renin

4 _____ ADH

5 _____ glomerular filtration

6 _____ hemodialysis

7 _____ tubular reabsorption

A. flow of protein-free fluid from capillaries into Bowman's capsule

B. substance that acts on the adrenal glands to release aldosterone

C. a long, slender tubular unit in the vertebrate kidney that forms urine

D. secreted by adrenal glands; influences sodium reabsorption

E. passive transport of water; active and passive transport of solutes out of the nephron into peritubular capillaries

F. released from the posterior lobe of the pituitary in response to hypothalmic signals

G. toxic substances are extracted from blood circulating in cellophane tubes suspended in a warm-water bath

Answers: 1. C   2. D   3. B   4. F   5. A   6. G
           7. E

Classification Questions

Answer questions 34–38 in reference to the four regions of a nephron listed below:

        a. Bowman's capsule
        b. proximal tubule
        c. descending portion of loop of Henle
        d. distal tubule

M   34. What portion precedes the loop of Henle?

M   35. Filtration of the blood occurs in association with which structure?

D   36. Antibiotics are secreted from which structure?

M   37. Permeability to water is regulated by antidiuretic hormone in which structure?

E   38. The glomerular capillaries are intimately associated with which structure?

Answers: 34. b   35. a   36. d   37. d   38. a

Selecting the Exception

D   39. Four of the five answers listed below are potentially toxic waste products of metabolism. Select the exception.
        a. urea
   *   b. water
        c. uric acid
        d. carbon dioxide
        e. ammonia

M   40. Four of the five answers listed below are parts of the same organ. Select the exception.
        a. distal tubule
        b. loop of Henle
   *   c. ureter
        d. proximal tubule
        e. Bowman's capsule

M   41. Four of the five answers listed below are functions of the nephron. Select the exception.
        a. filtration
   *   b. dilution
        c. excretion
        d. reabsorption
        e. secretion

D   42. Four of the five answers listed below are the result of ADH (antidiuretic hormone) secretion. Select the exception.
        a. Water is reabsorbed in the distal tubule.
        b. The fluid volume of blood increases.
   *   c. There is a rise in solute concentration in blood.
        d. The distal tubule and collecting duct become more permeable to water.
        e. Solutes concentration decreases.

CHAPTER 30
NEURAL CONTROL AND THE SENSES

Multiple-Choice Questions

CELLS OF THE NERVOUS SYSTEM

E   1.   The single long process that extends from a typical motor nerve cell is the
  *   a.   axon.
      b.   neuron.
      c.   synapse.
      d.   dendrite.
      e.   both a and d, but not b or c

M   2.   Neuroglial cells
      a.   metabolically support other neurons.
      b.   form sheaths around neurons and control the rate of impulse transmission.
      c.   form more than half of the volume of the brain.
      d.   provide physical support.
  *   e.   all of the above

M   3.   Neurons and other cells that produce action potentials are said to show
      a.   polarity.
      b.   saltatory conduction.
  *   c.   excitability.
      d.   capacitance.
      e.   voltage.

M   4.   When a neuron is at rest,
      a.   there is a voltage difference across the membrane of about 70 millivolts.
      b.   the interior is negatively charged.
      c.   it is not responding to a stimulus.
      d.   the fluid outside the membrane has more sodium and less potassium than the cytoplasm.
  *   e.   all of the above

M   5.   The membrane-bound enzyme system that restores and maintains the resting membrane potential is which of the following pumps?
      a.   sodium-phosphorus
  *   b.   sodium-potassium
      c.   sodium-chlorine
      d.   phosphorus-calcium
      e.   phosphorus-chlorine

D   6.   The term that best describes what happens to a neuron as an impulse passes along it is
      a.   polarization-depolarization.
  *   b.   depolarization-repolarization.
      c.   ionization-depolarization.
      d.   repolarization-depolarization.
      e.   ionization-repolarization.

D   7.   Which of the following is the first response a neuron makes to a stimulus?
  *   a.   Sodium ions enter the cell.
      b.   Sodium ions leave the cell.
      c.   Potassium ions enter the cell.
      d.   Potassium ions leave the cell.
      e.   a and c above

D   8. An action potential is brought about by
  - a. a sudden membrane impermeability.
  - b. the movement of negatively charged proteins through the neuronal membrane.
  - c. the movement of lipoproteins to the outer membrane.
  - * d. a local change in membrane permeability caused by a greater-than-threshold stimulus.
  - e. all of the above

D   9. During the passage of a nerve impulse
  - a. sodium ions pass through gated channels.
  - b. positive feedback causes more sodium ions to enter the cell.
  - c. the interior of the cell becomes positive.
  - d. changing voltage increases the number of open gates.
  - * e. all of the above

D   10. During the refractory period
  - a. the threshold value is increased.
  - b. the threshold value is reduced.
  - * c. the sodium gates are shut and the potassium gates are opened.
  - d. both sodium and potassium gates are shut.
  - e. the nerve is said to be at the resting potential.

D   11. The phrase "all or none," used in conjunction with discussion about an action potential, means that
  - a. a resting membrane potential has been received by the cell.
  - * b. nothing can stop the action potential once the threshold is reached.
  - c. the membrane either achieves total equilibrium or remains as far from equilibrium as possible.
  - d. propagation along the neuron is saltatory.
  - e. none of the above

M   12. The recovery time from the passage of a nerve impulse is called the
  - a. polarized response.
  - b. wave of depolarization.
  - c. action potential propagation.
  - * d. refractory period.
  - e. saltatory period.

M   13. The myelin sheath
  - a. is formed by the Schwann cell.
  - b. speeds up the transmission of impulses.
  - c. does not surround all nerves.
  - d. extends from node to node.
  - * e. all of the above

M   14. The spaces that separate adjacent Schwann cells are called
  - a. neuroglia.
  - b. myelin sheaths.
  - * c. nodes of Ranvier.
  - d. dendrites.
  - e. synapses.

M   15. Saltatory ("jumping") conduction
  - a. occurs only in the central nervous system.
  - b. is a quicker type of nerve conduction.
  - c. occurs between nerves and muscles.
  - d. involves the movement of impulses from node of Ranvier to node of Ranvier.
  - * e. both b and d

M   16.   Transmitter substances
- a.   are expelled from the presynaptic cells.
- b.   tend to destroy acetylcholine.
- c.   enter the presynaptic cell to continue the passage of the impulse.
- d.   interact with membrane receptors of the postsynaptic cells.
- *   e.   both a and d

E   17.   Which is a junction between two neurons?
- a.   Schwann cell
- *   b.   chemical synapse
- c.   node of Ranvier
- d.   sodium gate
- e.   all of the above

M   18.   Which bridges the gap between a neuron sending a message and the neuron receiving it?
- a.   threshold value
- b.   action potential
- *   c.   transmitter substance
- d.   neurohormone
- e.   all of the above

M   19.   Transmitter substances
- a.   include acetylcholine.
- b.   change the permeability of postsynaptic cells.
- c.   may be excitatory or stimulatory.
- d.   may participate in synaptic integration.
- *   e.   all of the above

M   20.   *Clostridium tetani*
- a.   causes lockjaw.
- b.   produces a nerve toxin.
- c.   is an anaerobic bacterium.
- d.   interferes with the inhibitory synapses on motor neurons.
- *   e.   all of the above

M   21.   In lockjaw
- *   a.   a muscle cannot relax.
- b.   nerve impulses in involuntary muscles are blocked.
- c.   nerve impulses cannot be propagated along a neuron.
- d.   acetylcholine is destroyed.
- e.   the impulse cannot pass across a synapse.

D   22.   At an inhibitory synapse
- a.   no transmitter substances are released by the sending cell.
- *   b.   a transmitter substance produces changes in the receiving cell that drive the membrane potential away from threshold.
- c.   no transmitter substance can bind to the receiving cell.
- d.   a transmitter substance produces changes in the receiving cell that drive the membrane potential closer to threshold.
- e.   a and c above

M   23.   Synaptic integration means that
- a.   all positive or excitatory stimuli are added together.
- *   b.   the positive and negative ions neutralize each other.
- c.   excitatory and inhibitory signals are combined in a neuron.
- d.   adjacent neurons interact so that excitatory and inhibitory stimuli cancel each other.
- e.   all of the above

E   24.   The simplest nerve pathway
          a.   is located in the midbrain.
   *   b.   is the reflex pathway.
          c.   is found in the lower part of the brain.
          d.   is found in the autonomic nervous system.
          e.   is in the flow of information from a sense receptor to the brain.

M   25.   One example of a simple reflex involves the
   *   a.   contraction of a muscle when it is stretched.
          b.   conscious message to move part of the body.
          c.   receptor, the brain, and the effector.
          d.   muscle action in a salute when a noncommissioned serviceman sees an officer.
          e.   contraction of an antagonistic muscle when its opposite muscle relaxes.

M   26.   The stretch reflex
          a.   is an adaptation that enables humans to stand upright.
          b.   is activated by stretch-sensitive receptors inside the muscle spindles.
          c.   is a simple, stereotyped, and repeatable motor action.
          d.   is elicited by a sensory stimulus.
   *   e.   all of the above

D   27.   Which statement is false?
          a.   A nerve will not fire unless a stimulus exceeds the threshold.
          b.   An action potential is an all-or-nothing event.
   *   c.   An action potential continues indefinitely until a quenching signal is released.
          d.   An action potential is self-propagating.
          e.   An action potential transmission depends on activities at the membrane.

M   28.   Which statement is false?
          a.   Reflexes are the simplest of all nervous reactions.
          b.   The nervous system required sense organs before organisms could perceive their environment.
   *   c.   Motor neurons lead toward the brain or central nervous system.
          d.   Reflex actions are stereotyped and repeatable.
          e.   All of the above statements are true.

E   29.   Clusters of cell bodies of neurons outside the central nervous system are known as
          a.   nerve cords.
   *   b.   ganglia.
          c.   a plexus.
          d.   notochords.
          e.   nerves.

M   30.   The two MAJOR divisions of the vertebral nervous system are the
          a.   autonomic and peripheral systems.
          b.   sympathetic and parasympathetic systems.
          c.   cranial and spinal nerves.
   *   d.   central and peripheral nervous systems.
          e.   brain and spinal cord.

M   31.   The two principal divisions of the efferent nervous system are the
   *   a.   somatic and autonomic systems.
          b.   sympathetic and parasympathetic systems.
          c.   peripheral and central systems.
          d.   afferent and autonomic systems.
          e.   cranial and skeletal nerves.

E   32.   The autonomic subdivision consists specifically of
             a. central and peripheral nerves.
       *   b. parasympathetic and sympathetic.
             c. somatic and involuntary.
             d. brain and spinal cord.
             e. spinal and cranial nerves.

M   33.   Which nerves generally dominate internal events when environmental conditions permit
             normal body functioning?
             a. ganglia
             b. pacemaker
             c. sympathetic
       *   d. parasympathetic
             e. all of the above

M   34.   The process of biofeedback attempts to influence the response of the
             a. peripheral nervous system.
       *   b. autonomic nervous system.
             c. central nervous system.
             d. motor nervous system.
             e. both a and c

D   35.   Which statement is true?
             a. Both the parasympathetic and sympathetic nervous systems send nerves to all organs.
             b. The sympathetic nervous system that supplies an organ will also provide
                 parasympathetic nerves to it.
             c. Both the sympathetic and parasympathetic have either excitatory or inhibitory effects.
       *   d. The sympathetic branch of the autonomic system usually speeds up the activities of
                 the body.
             e. The parasympathetic system usually speeds up the activities of the body.

E   36.   Signals from the parasympathetic nervous system cause which of the following?
             a. rise in blood pressure
             b. increase in pulse rate
       *   c. increase in digestive system movements
             d. rise in blood sugar level
             e. rise in metabolic rate

M   37.   The parasympathetic nervous system includes the
             a. cranial and thoracic nerves.
             b. thoracic and lumbar nerves.
             c. lumbar and sacral nerves.
             d. cervical and lumbar nerves.
       *   e. cranial and sacral nerves.

M   38.   The sympathetic nervous system includes the
             a. cranial and thoracic nerves.
       *   b. thoracic and lumbar nerves.
             c. lumbar and sacral nerves.
             d. cervical and lumbar nerves.
             e. cranial and sacral nerves.

M   39.   Activation of the sympathetic nervous system
       *   a. causes the pupils of the eye to dilate.
             b. increases the flow of watery saliva.
             c. stimulates peristaltic contractions of the intestinal system.
             d. slows heartbeat and lowers blood pressure.
             e. allows the body to relax rather than prepare for fight or flight.

E   40.   Interneurons are found in the
           a.   dorsal root.
   *   b.   spinal cord.
           c.   sensory neurons.
           d.   motor neurons.
           e.   autonomic nervous system.

M   41.   The ascending and descending tracts
           a.   are found in the gray matter of the spinal cord.
           b.   are found in the white matter of the spinal cord.
           c.   are covered with myelin sheaths.
           d.   are both sensory and motor.
   *   e.   All except a are correct.

E   42.   The midbrain includes the
           a.   thalamus.
           b.   pineal gland.
   *   c.   tectum.
           d.   medulla.
           e.   olfactory lobes.

E   43.   The hindbrain includes the
           a.   thalamus.
           b.   pineal gland.
           c.   cerebellum.
           d.   medulla.
   *   e.   both c and d

E   44.   The pituitary gland is controlled by the
           a.   pineal gland.
           b.   medulla.
   *   c.   hypothalamus.
           d.   thalamus.
           e.   cerebrum.

E   45.   The center of consciousness and intelligence is the
           a.   medulla.
           b.   thalamus.
           c.   pons.
           d.   cerebellum.
   *   e.   cerebrum.

E   46.   Which part of the mammalian brain is disproportionately larger than the corresponding part of a fish brain?
           a.   medulla
           b.   thalamus
           c.   pons
           d.   cerebellum
   *   e.   cerebrum

E   47.   The protective covering of the brain is the
           a.   ventricles.
   *   b.   meninges.
           c.   tectum.
           d.   olfactory and optic bulbs.
           e.   pineal gland.

E   48.   Which structure forms the roof of the midbrain where visual and auditory signals are integrated?
   a. ventricles
   b. meninges
 * c. tectum
   d. olfactory and optic bulbs
   e. pineal gland

E   49.   The part of the brain that connects one brain center with another is the
   a. cerebrum.
 * b. pons.
   c. cerebellum.
   d. fissure of Rolando.
   e. hypothalamus.

E   50.   The part of the brain that deals with the basic drives such as hunger, sex, and thirst is the
   a. cerebrum.
   b. pons.
   c. cerebellum.
   d. thalamus.
 * e. hypothalamus.

E   51.   The major relay center of the brain is the
   a. cerebrum.
   b. olfactory area.
   c. cerebellum.
 * d. thalamus.
   e. hypothalamus.

E   52.   The center for balance and coordination is the
   a. cerebrum.
   b. pons.
 * c. cerebellum.
   d. thalamus.
   e. hypothalamus.

E   53.   The gray matter of the brain is associated with the
 * a. cerebral cortex.
   b. pons.
   c. optic chiasm.
   d. corpus callosum.
   e. thalamus.

M   54.   Broca's area is concerned with
   a. coordination of hands and fingers.
 * b. speech.
   c. memory.
   d. sense of taste and smell.
   e. vision.

E   55.   The part of the brain that controls the basic responses necessary to maintain life processes (breathing, heartbeat) is the
 * a. medulla.
   b. corpus callosum.
   c. fissure of Rolando.
   d. cerebellum.
   e. cerebral cortex.

E   56. Active chemicals found in chocolate, tea, coffee, and soft drinks are examples of which of the following?
        a. depressant
    *   b. stimulant
        c. narcotic analgesic
        d. hallucinogen or psychedelic
        e. antipsychotic

E   57. Pain relievers such as endorphins and enkephalins are
        a. depressants.
        b. stimulants.
    *   c. analgesics.
        d. hallucinogens or psychedelics.
        e. antipsychotics.

E   58. Substances that lower the activity of the brain and inhibit transmission at a synapse are
    *   a. depressants.
        b. stimulants.
        c. narcotic analgesics.
        d. hallucinogens or psychedelics.
        e. antipsychotics.

E   59. Substances that could be called hypnotics and that induce sleep are
    *   a. depressants.
        b. stimulants.
        c. narcotic analgesics.
        d. hallucinogens or psychedelics.
        e. antipsychotics.

M   60. A chemical substance that behaves as a natural analgesic is
        a. an amphetamine.
        b. LSD.
        c. epinephrine.
    *   d. endorphin.
        e. none of the above

M   61. A group of chemicals that at low doses reduce fatigue and heighten awareness but at high doses elicit anxiety and irritability while mimicking the effect of norepinephrine are
        a. depressants.
        b. stimulants.
        c. narcotic analgesics.
    *   d. hallucinogens or psychedelics.
        e. antipsychotics.

E   62. Substances that alter sensory perception, cause disorientation, and inhibit the ability to perform complex tasks are
        a. depressants.
        b. stimulants.
        c. narcotic analgesics.
    *   d. hallucinogens or psychedelics.
        e. antipsychotics.

E   63. Barbiturates are
    *   a. depressants.
        b. stimulants.
        c. narcotic analgesics.
        d. hallucinogens or psychedelics.
        e. antipsychotics.

E   64.   Substances that sedate the body and relieve pain are
         a. depressants.
         b. stimulants.
    *   c. narcotic analgesics.
         d. hallucinogens or psychedelics.
         e. antipsychotics.

E   65.   The sleep center of the brain is the
         a. pons.
         b. thalamus.
         c. hypothalamus.
    *   d. reticular activating system.
         e. medulla.

M   66.   High levels of which chemical in the sleep centers of the brain induce drowsiness and sleep?
         a. norepinephrine
    *   b. serotonin
         c. adrenalin
         d. enkephalin
         e. cyclic AMP

SENSORY SYSTEMS

M   67.   In order for snakes such as pythons to capture prey at night, they are equipped with
         a. extra-sensitive hearing.
         b. extraordinary sight.
    *   c. pits that are sensitive to heat.
         d. a strong sense of smell located in the tongue.
         e. special organs that detect vibrations so that they can detect nearby movement.

M   68.   Differences in intensity of a stimulus
         a. do not affect the impulse transmitted.
         b. are indicated by the number of nerves activated.
         c. control the part of the brain that receives the stimulus.
         d. are encoded in the frequency of action potentials on a single axon.
    *   e. both b and d, but not a or c

E   69.   Which sense uses mechanical energy?
         a. sense of touch
         b. acceleration
         c. sense of pain
         d. sense of balance
    *   e. all of the above

E   70.   Olfactory centers are responsive to
         a. touch.
    *   b. smell.
         c. taste.
         d. sound.
         e. sight.

E   71.   The Pacinian corpuscle is used in detecting
         a. sound.
    *   b. pressure.
         c. chemicals.
         d. sight.
         e. chemical differences.

E   72.   Mechanoreceptors are located in
       a. internal organs.
       b. skin.
       c. joints.
       d. tendons.
    *   e. all of the above

E   73.   A stretch receptor is classified as a
       a. chemoreceptor.
    *   b. mechanoreceptor.
       c. photoreceptor.
       d. thermoreceptor.
       e. all of the above

E   74.   Infrared receptors are classified as
       a. chemoreceptors.
       b. mechanoreceptors.
       c. photoreceptors.
    *   d. thermoreceptors.
       e. none of the above

M   75.   Which of the following has receptors for ultraviolet light?
       a. bears
    *   b. bees
       c. birds
       d. reptiles
       e. amphibians

M   76.   Which statement is true?
       a. All action potentials for the same nerve are alike.
       b. Receptors respond by graded potential.
       c. Different nerves convey different information by going to different areas of the brain.
       d. Differences in intensities may be due to the number of receptors and nerves involved in response.
    *   e. all of the above

E   77.   The organ of Corti is a
       a. chemoreceptor.
    *   b. mechanoreceptor.
       c. photoreceptor.
       d. nocireceptor.
       e. all of the above

E   78.   Receptors in the human nose are
    *   a. chemoreceptors.
       b. mechanoreceptors.
       c. photoreceptors.
       d. nocireceptors.
       e. none of the above

E   79.   Eyes are
       a. chemoreceptors.
       b. mechanoreceptors.
    *   c. photoreceptors.
       d. nocireceptors.
       e. none of the above

M   80. Invertebrates may not perceive pain the same way as vertebrates because the invertebrate brain does NOT have
- a. olfactory bulbs.
* b. a limbic system.
- c. a cerebral cortex.
- d. ganglia.
- e. sensory neurons.

E   81. Sense receptors are located on
- a. insect legs.
- b. octopus tentacles.
- c. antennae.
- d. fish fins.
* e. all of the above

E   82. The pain produced in an internal organ may be perceived as occurring somewhere else. This is called
- a. mixed nerve messages.
* b. referred pain.
- c. phantom pain.
- d. psychosomatic pain.
- e. hypochondria.

M   83. Pheromones
- a. are social signals.
- b. identify individuals who belong to a group in case they get separated.
- c. may serve as sex attractants.
- d. may be used for an alarm signal.
* e. all of the above

E   84. Female silk moths secrete bombykol as a(n)
- a. way to gather young when they scatter.
- b. message to stay close to the cocoon.
- c. alarm signal.
* d. sexual attractant.
- e. territory marker.

M   85. The somatic senses include all but which one of the following sensations?
* a. balance
- b. pain near the body surface
- c. temperature
- d. touch
- e. pressure

E   86. Hair cells are important in the sense of
- a. equilibrium.
- b. hearing.
- c. taste.
- d. smell.
* e. both a and b

E   87. The sense of equilibrium can detect
- a. motion.
- b. acceleration.
- c. gravity.
- d. position.
* e. all of the above

E   88.   The semicircular canals are
             a. empty.
             b. filled with gas.
    *   c. filled with a liquid.
             d. filled with bones or stones.
             e. filled with sand grains.

M   89.   An otolith is one of the functional parts of the
             a. eye.
             b. Pacinian corpuscle.
    *   c. semicircular canal.
             d. taste bud.
             e. pits, or heat-sensing devices, of snakes.

E   90.   How many semicircular canals are in each organ of balance?
             a. 2
    *   b. 3
             c. 4
             d. 5
             e. more than 6

E   91.   The principal place in the human ear where sound waves are amplified by means of the vibrations of tiny bones is the
             a. pinna.
             b. ear canal.
    *   c. middle ear.
             d. organ of Corti.
             e. all of the above

M   92.   The place where vibrations are translated into patterns of nerve impulses is the
             a. pinna.
             b. ear canal.
             c. middle ear.
    *   d. organ of Corti.
             e. none of the above

E   93.   The organ of Corti is located in the
             a. thoracic cavity.
    *   b. inner ear.
             c. abdominal cavity.
             d. brain stem.
             e. semicircular canals.

D   94.   In hearing, the last place that pressure or sound waves pass through is the
             a. bones of the middle ear.
             b. tympanic membrane.
             c. oval window.
    *   d. round window.
             e. tectorial membrane.

E   95.   How many coiled and fluid-filled ducts are found in each cochlea?
             a. 1
             b. 2
    *   c. 3
             d. 4
             e. 5 or more

E   96.   The layer of the eye where photoreceptors are located is the
         a.   lens.
         b.   cornea.
         c.   pupil.
         d.   iris.
    *   e.   retina.

D   97.   According to the mosaic theory,
         a.   the basement membrane's pigment molecules prevent the scattering of light.
         b.   light falling on the inner area of an "on center" field activates firing of the cells.
         c.   hair cells in the semicircular canals cooperate to detect rotational acceleration.
    *   d.   each unit of the compound eye detects information about only one small region of the visual field; many units contribute "bits" to the total image.
         e.   all of the above

E   98.   The repeating units of a compound eye are called
         a.   ocelli.
         b.   lenses.
         c.   rhabdomeres.
    *   d.   ommatidia.
         e.   pupils.

E   99.   The adjustable ring of contractile and connective tissues that controls the amount of light entering the eye is the
         a.   lens.
         b.   cornea.
         c.   pupil.
    *   d.   iris.
         e.   retina.

E   100.   The white protective fibrous tissue of the eye, often called the white of the eye, is the
         a.   lens.
    *   b.   sclera.
         c.   pupil.
         d.   iris.
         e.   retina.

E   101.   Rods and cones are located in the
         a.   lens.
         b.   cornea.
         c.   pupil.
         d.   iris.
    *   e.   retina.

E   102.   The highest concentration of cones is in the
    *   a.   fovea.
         b.   blind spot.
         c.   sclera.
         d.   ommatidium.
         e.   choroid.

E   103.   The dark middle layer of the eye that prevents the scattering of light is the
         a.   fovea.
         b.   retina.
         c.   sclera.
    *   d.   choroid.
         e.   cornea.

M 104. In the human eye, what provides the greatest visual acuity (the precise discrimination between adjacent points in space)?
    a. photoreceptors in the sclera
   * b. photoreceptors in the fovea
    c. protein filaments in the lens
    d. photoreceptors in the optic nerve
    e. none of the above

M 105. Accommodation involves the ability to
    a. change the sensitivity of the rods and cones by means of neurotransmitters.
    b. change the curvature of the cornea.
   * c. change the width of the lens by contracting or relaxing certain muscles.
    d. adapt to large changes in light intensity.
    e. all of the above

E 106. The outer transparent protective cover of the eyeball is the
    a. fovea.
    b. retina.
    c. sclera.
    d. choroid.
   * e. cornea.

E 107. The part of the eye that may be colored (for example, brown, blue, green, or gray) is the
    a. retina.
    b. sclera.
    c. choroid.
    d. cornea.
   * e. iris.

E 108. Nearsightedness is caused by
   * a. eye structure that focuses an image in front of the retina.
    b. uneven curvature of the cornea.
    c. uneven curvature of the lens.
    d. eye structure that focuses an image posterior to the retina.
    e. all of the above

E 109. Cones are
    a. sensitive to red light.
    b. sensitive to green light.
    c. sensitive to blue light.
    d. relatively insensitive to dim light.
   * e. all of the above

M 110. Where are bipolar, amacrine, and ganglion cells located?
    a. sclera
    b. thalamus
    c. organ of Corti
   * d. retina
    e. all of the above

Matching Questions

D   111.   Matching I. Choose the BEST response.

1 _____ effector	A.	cells that nurture and support neurons
2 _____ ganglion	B.	a neuron cannot propagate an action potential during this time
3 _____ integrator		
4 _____ stretch receptor	C.	ACh
5 _____ myelin sheath	D.	interneuron in brain or spinal cord
6 _____ neuroglia	E.	establishes basis of resting membrane potential
7 _____ receptor	F.	sheathed muscle cells that contain receptors
8 _____ refractory period	G.	input
9 _____ response	H.	modified dendrite of a neuron
10 _____ sodium-potassium pump	I.	output
11 _____ stimulus	J.	muscle or gland
12 _____ transmitter substance	K.	produced by a specific kind of Schwann cell
	L.	cluster of cell bodies from different neurons

Answers: 1. J   2. L   3. D   4. F   5. K   6. A
          7. H   8. B   9. I   10. E   11. G   12. C

D   112.   Matching II. Choose the one most appropriate answer for each.

1 _____ autonomic nervous system	A.	integrates body position, motions, balance
2 _____ Broca's area	B.	messages from here arouse the brain and maintain wakefulness
3 _____ cerebellum		
4 _____ ganglion	C.	the cortical region that coordinates muscles required for speech
5 _____ hypothalamus		
6 _____ limbic system	D.	all parts of nerve cells outside the brain and spinal cord
7 _____ medulla oblongata		
8 _____ midbrain	E.	as, for example, acetylcholine
9 _____ peripheral nervous system	F.	reflex control center for breathing, heart rate, and blood pressure
10 _____ reticular activating system		
11 _____ transmitter substances	G.	axons of the central nervous system that are sheathed with fatty myelin
12 _____ white matter		

H.   at top of the brain stem bordering the cerebral hemispheres; influences learning and emotional behavior

I.   motor neurons that are divided into sympathetic and parasympathetic divisions

J.   contains the optic lobes; receives and integrates sensory information that is largely sent on to the forebrain for further neural processing

K.   groups of nerve cell bodies encased in connective tissue; form integrative centers

L.   contains centers concerned with body temperature regulation and with salt and water balance

Answers: 1. I   2. C   3. A   4. K   5. L   6. H
            7. F   8. J   9. D   10. B   11. E   12. G

D   113. Matching III. Choose the one most appropriate answer for each.

1 _____ amplitude

2 _____ cochlea

3 _____ eardrum

4 _____ iris

5 _____ oval window

6 _____ pheromone

7 _____ pitch

8 _____ retina

9 _____ round window

10 _____ semicircular canals

A. dissipates excess vibrational energy to the middle ear

B. contains the organ of Corti

C. separates the outer and middle ears

D. membrane-covered gateway to inner ear

E. consists of tissue containing rods and cones

F. peak height and valley depth of sound waves are its basis

G. maintain balance and position; detect acceleration

H. depends on how many wave changes per second occur

I. a substance that elicits a response in members of the same species

J. regulates size of pupil and amount of incoming light

Answers: 1. F   2. B   3. C   4. J   5. D   6. I

            7. H   8. E   9. A   10. G

Classification Questions

Answer questions 114–118 in reference to the four cell types listed below:

a. sensory neurons
b. interneurons
c. motor neurons
d. Schwann cells

M   114. Which nerve cells transmit signals to muscle cells?

M   115. Which cell type are neuroglial cells?

E   116. Myelin is formed by which of the above?

E   117. An animal brain is composed mostly of which cell type?

E   118. Which cell type picks up environmental signals?

Answers: 114. c   115. d   116. d   117. b   118. a

Answer questions 119–123 in reference to the autonomic nervous system associated with the five regions of the human vertebral column listed below:

a. cervical
b. thoracic
c. lumbar
d. sacral
e. coccygeal

D   119. Sympathetic nerves from this region innervate the bladder, uterus, and genitals.

D   120. Sympathetic nerves from this region innervate the kidney.

D   121. Parasympathetic nerves from this region innervate the rectum.

D   122. Sympathetic nerves from this region innervate the heart.

D   123. Sympathetic nerves from this region pass through the celiac ganglion.

Answers: 119. c   120. b   121. d   122. b   123. b

Answer questions 124–128 in reference to the five regions of the vertebrate brain listed below:

    a. cerebrum
    b. hypothalamus
    c. pons
    d. cerebellum
    e. medulla oblongata

D   124. Which region of the brain contains the reflex centers involved in respiration?

D   125. Which region of the brain controls neural-endocrine activities such as temperature control?

D   126. Which region of the brain controls carbohydrate metabolism?

M   127. Which part of the brain controls the complex coordination of motor activity and limb movement?

D   128. Which region of the brain contains parasympathetic nerves that innervate the heart and lungs?

Answers: 124. e   125. b   126. b   127. d   128. e

Answer questions 129–133 in reference to the five kinds of energy listed below:

    a. chemical
    b. mechanical
    c. thermal
    d. light
    e. wavelike form of mechanical energy

E   129. Receptors on the tongue detect variation in which kind of energy?

M   130. Which kind of energy do olfactory receptors detect?

D   131. Which kind of energy do ears monitor?

E   132. Ultraviolet radiation detected by insects is in which category?

E   133. The pain you feel from a pebble in your shoe is a result of detecting which kind of energy?

Answers: 129. a   130. a   131. e   132. d   133. b

Answer questions 134–138 in reference to the five eye structures listed below:

    a. cornea
    b. lens
    c. retina
    d. ommatidium
    e. vitreous body

D   134. Which structure is found in the compound eyes of insects but not in the eyes of octopi?

M   135. Which structure is composed of photoreceptor cells?

E   136.   Which structure primarily acts to focus light waves?

M   137.   Which structure is composed of rod- and cone-shaped cells in mammals and birds?

M   138.   Which structure acts to maintain the shape of the eye and to transmit light to other structures?

Answers: 134. d   135. c   136. b   137. c   138. e

Selecting the Exception

M   139.   Four of the five answers listed below are actively involved in nerve impulse transmission. Select the exception.
*   a. neuroglia
     b. neuron
     c. ganglia
     d. nerves
     e. tracts

M   140.   Four of the five answers listed below are true of a neuron at resting potential. Select the exception.
*   a. interior of neuron is positive
     b. interior of neuron has negative charge
     c. more sodium ions outside neuron
     d. more potassium ions inside neuron
     e. membrane of neuron is polarized

M   141.   Four of the five answers listed below are used in descriptions of neuron membranes. Select the exception.
     a. gate
     b. pump
     c. wave of depolarization
     d. channel
*   e. synaptic cleft

M   142.   Four of the five answers listed below are used in descriptions of the nerve sheath. Select the exception.
     a. Schwann cell
*   b. threshold
     c. myelin sheath
     d. saltatory conduction
     e. node of Ranvier

M   143.   Four of the five answers listed below are participants in a common function. Select the exception.
     a. sensory neuron
*   b. medulla
     c. interneuron
     d. effector
     e. receptor

D   144.   Four of the five answers listed below are related by the same theory. Select the exception.
     a. Reflex pathways are the basic operating machines of the nervous system.
     b. Nervous systems evolved through accretion.
     c. The oldest part of the brain dealt with reflex actions.
     d. More recent layering of nervous tissue allows nonstereotypic action.
*   e. The nervous system exerts control over the endocrine system.

D 145. Four of the five answers listed below are characteristic of bilaterally symmetrical forms. Select the exception.
* a. sessile, nonmoving
b. segmentation
c. cephalization
d. paired nerves, muscles, sensory structures
e. right and left halves of the body

M 146. Four of the five answers listed below are parts of the central nervous system. Select the exception.
a. spinal cord
b. medulla
* c. ganglia
d. cerebellum
e. cerebrum

M 147. Four of the five answers listed below are parts of the same nerve grouping. Select the exception.
* a. cranial nerve
b. thoracic nerve
c. lumbar nerve
d. cervical nerve
e. sacral nerve

E 148. Four of the five answers listed below are innervated by the autonomic nervous system. Select the exception.
* a. skeletal muscles
b. smooth muscles
c. heart
d. endocrine glands
e. exocrine glands

D 149. Four of the five answers listed below are actions mediated by the sympathetic nervous system. Select the exception.
a. pulse increase
* b. blood glucose levels drop
c. metabolism increases
d. digestion slows down
e. dilates pupils of the eye

D 150. Four of the five answers listed below are located within the spinal cord. Select the exception.
* a. dorsal root ganglion
b. interneurons between sensory input motor outputs
c. major ascending and descending nerve tracts
d. interneurons connecting with other neurons
e. direct reflex connections between sensory and motor neurons

M 151. Four of the five answers listed below are parts of the forebrain. Select the exception.
a. limbic system
b. thalamus
c. olfactory lobes
* d. cerebellum
e. cerebrum

E 152. Four of the five answers listed below are lobes of the brain. Select the exception.
   a. parietal
   * b. squamosal
   c. frontal
   d. occipital
   e. temporal

D 153. Four of the five answers listed below are classified as white matter. Select the exception.
   a. myelin sheath
   b. descending tracts
   c. corpus callosum
   * d. cerebrum
   e. ascending tract

M 154. Four of the five answers listed below are stimulants. Select the exception.
   * a. heroin
   b. caffeine
   c. nicotine
   d. cocaine
   e. amphetamine

M 155. Four of the five answers listed below are depressants. Select the exception.
   a. alcohol
   b. barbiturates
   c. Valium
   * d. marijuana
   e. Quaalude

D 156. Four of the five answers listed below are analgesics. Select the exception.
   a. endorphin
   b. opium
   c. heroin
   d. enkephalin
   * e. lithium

M 157. Four of the five answers listed below are related by a similar sense receptor. Select the exception.
   a. touch or pressure
   * b. olfaction
   c. balance (equilibrium)
   d. hearing
   e. pain

M 158. Four of the five answers listed below are related by a similar sensation. Select the exception.
   * a. papillae
   b. Meissner corpuscle
   c. Ruffini ending
   d. free nerve endings
   e. Pacinian corpuscle

M 159. Four of the five answers listed below are somatic senses. Select the exception.
   * a. light
   b. pressure
   c. touch
   d. temperature
   e. pain

D   160. Four of the five answers listed below are related by a similar receptor. Select the exception.
         a. otolith
         b. vestibular apparatus
         c. semicircular canal
     * d. cochlea
         e. saccule

M   161. Four of the five answers listed below are parts of the inner ear. Select the exception.
     * a. eardrum
         b. oval window
         c. scala tympani
         d. basilar membrane
         e. cochlea

M   162. Three of the four answers listed below are functionally connected to each other. Select the exception.
         a. hammer
     * b. pinna
         c. stirrup
         d. anvil

M   163. Four of the five answers listed below are parts of the same sense organ. Select the exception.
         a. choroid
         b. retina
         c. vitreous humor
     * d. ampulla
         e. sclera

M   164. Four of the five answers listed below are parts of the same sense organ. Select the exception.
     * a. cochlea
         b. cornea
         c. sclera
         d. choroid
         e. fovea

D   165. Three of the four answers listed below are colors for which the cone cells have pigments. Select the exception.
         a. red
     * b. yellow
         c. blue
         d. green

M   166. Four of the five answers listed below are receptors. Select the exception.
     * a. muscle
         b. Pacinian corpuscle
         c. ommatidium
         d. organ of Corti
         e. eyespots

CHAPTER 31
ENDOCRINE CONTROL

Multiple-Choice Questions

"THE ENDOCRINE SYSTEM"

E   1.   The first hormone to be discovered was
- a. insulin.
- b. gastrin.
- *   c. secretin.
- d. thyroxine.
- e. estrogen.

E   2.   The word *hormone* comes from the Greek word meaning
- a. target.
- b. response.
- c. secretion.
- *   d. set in motion.
- e. internal gland.

HORMONES AND OTHER SIGNALING MOLECULES

M   3.   Target cells
- a. are found only in specific endocrine glands.
- b. are equipped with specific receptor molecules.
- c. are muscle cells.
- d. may occur in any part of the body.
- *   e. both b and d, but not a or c

E   4.   Which glands secrete pheromones?
- *   a. exocrine
- b. ductless
- c. sebaceous
- d. endocrine
- e. digestive

THE HYPOTHALAMUS AND PITUITARY GLAND

E   5.   Which gland is often called the master gland?
- a. pineal
- *   b. pituitary
- c. thyroid
- d. adrenal
- e. pancreas

E   6.   The pituitary gland is controlled by the
- a. pons.
- b. corpus callosum.
- c. medulla.
- d. thalamus.
- *   e. hypothalamus.

M   7. Which is an example of an organ that is nervous in origin, structure, and function but secretes substances into the bloodstream?
         a. anterior pituitary
 *   b. posterior pituitary
         c. pancreas
         d. adrenal cortex
         e. testis

D   8. The hypothalamus and pituitary link the activities of the endocrine system and nervous system by
 *   a. neurohormones being secreted in response to the summation of neural messages that enter the hypothalamus.
         b. shifts in hormonal concentrations being detected by the anterior pituitary.
         c. pheromones being secreted as a response to photoperiodic stimuli.
         d. the nervous tissue of the anterior lobe of the pituitary sending stimuli to the glandular tissue of the posterior pituitary to produce hormones that will be secreted by the hypothalamus.
         e. all of the above

M   9. Which statement is true?
         a. The anterior pituitary gland is essentially nervous tissue.
         b. The anterior pituitary gland secretes only two hormones.
         c. The posterior pituitary gland is the master gland.
 *   d. The posterior pituitary gland only stores hormones produced by the hypothalamus.
         e. all of the above

E   10. If you were cast up on a desert island with no fresh water to drink, the level of which of the following would rise in your bloodstream in an effort to conserve water?
         a. erythropoietin
         b. oxytocin
         c. insulin
 *   d. antidiuretic hormone
         e. glucose

M   11. The antidiuretic hormone
         a. controls water balance.
         b. controls the concentration of urea in the urine.
         c. influences blood pressure.
         d. changes the permeability of the urine-conducting tubules so that the interstitial fluid increases.
 *   e. all of the above

E   12. Oxytocin affects the
 *   a. uterine wall.
         b. voluntary muscles throughout the body.
         c. nervous tissue.
         d. target cells in the brain.
         e. target cells in the digestive tract.

E   13. The anterior pituitary secretions produce their effects in the
         a. gonads.
         b. thyroid glands.
         c. adrenal glands.
         d. mammary glands.
 *   e. all of the above

M   14. The pituitary hormone associated most directly with metabolic rate and with growth and
          development is
          a. ACTH.
      *   b. TSH.
          c. FSH.
          d. LH.
          e. ADH.

M   15. The most general of the pituitary hormones, in that it may affect almost any cell in the body, is
          a. the adrenocorticotropic hormone.
          b. the thyroid-stimulating hormone.
          c. gonadotropin.
      *   d. somatotropin.
          e. prolactin.

M   16. Prolactin
      *   a. stimulates the mammary glands to produce milk.
          b. causes the development of breasts and other secondary sexual characteristics in the male.
          c. acts in concert with FSH to produce milk.
          d. has secondary effects on reducing the size of the uterus after birth.

E   17. The growth hormone is
          a. prolactin.
          b. adrenalin.
          c. thyroxine.
          d. ACTH.
      *   e. somatotropin.

E   18. Dwarfism may be due to insufficient production of
          a. mineralocorticoid.
          b. glucocorticoid.
          c. calcitonin.
      *   d. somatotropin.
          e. the parathyroid hormone.

E   19. Acromegaly is the result of excessive secretion of which of the following by adults?
          a. mineralocorticoid
          b. glucocorticoid
          c. thyroxine
          d. testosterone
      *   e. somatotropin

SELECTED EXAMPLES OF HORMONAL CONTROL

M   20. Which hormone prepares and maintains the uterine lining for pregnancy?
          a. estrogen
          b. progesterone
          c. follicle-stimulating hormone
          d. luteinizing hormone
      *   e. both a and b

E   21. Which hormone is produced by the liver?
          a. calcitonin
          b. norepinephrine
      *   c. somatomedin
          d. erythropoietin
          e. angiotensin

M   22.   The hormone that is antagonistic in action to glucagon is
           a.   norepinephrine.
       *   b.   insulin.
           c.   thyroxine.
           d.   epinephrine.
           e.   mineralocorticoids.

M   23.   Which of the following does NOT affect blood sugar levels?
           a.   glucagon
           b.   epinephrine
       *   c.   parathyroid hormones
           d.   glucocorticoids
           e.   insulin

E   24.   Which gland secretes sex hormones?
       *   a.   testis
           b.   adrenal medulla
           c.   thyroid
           d.   kidney
           e.   pancreas

M   25.   The melanocyte-stimulating hormone
           a.   affects kidney functions.
           b.   causes melanoma if there is excess secretion.
           c.   is found only in humans.
       *   d.   controls pigmentation in the external protective tissue.
           e.   maintains normal reproductive or estrus cycle.

M   26.   ACTH
           a.   is secreted by the posterior pituitary.
           b.   has target cells in the autonomic nervous system.
       *   c.   has target cells in the adrenal cortex.
           d.   has target cells in the adrenal medulla.
           e.   initiates the autoimmune response.

M   27.   The luteinizing hormone
       *   a.   stimulates ovulation.
           b.   has no function in males.
           c.   is produced by the corpus luteum.
           d.   stimulates milk production.
           e.   promotes sperm formation.

M   28.   Calcitonin acts in opposition to
       *   a.   the parathyroid hormone.
           b.   thyroxine.
           c.   glucagon.
           d.   the adrenal medulla.
           e.   all of the above

M   29.   Glucocorticoids
           a.   are secreted by the adrenal cortex.
           b.   influence carbohydrate, fat, and protein metabolism.
           c.   function during infection and injury as part of the defense response.
           d.   are exemplified by cortisol.
       *   e.   all of the above

E   30.   Angiotensin is produced in the
- a. bloodstream.
- b. adrenal cortex.
- c. adrenal medulla.
- * d. kidneys.
- e. heart.

D   31.   You have just moved from Norfolk, Virginia (sea level), to Taos, New Mexico (high in the mountains), and you find yourself out of breath climbing a small hill. Three months later, climbing the same hill, you have no difficulty. In the interim you have not altered your level of activity or diet. Which hormone has been at work?
- a. angiotensin
- * b. erythropoietin
- c. aldosterone
- d. estrogen
- e. none of the above

M   32.   Which gland is associated with biological clocks or biorhythms?
- * a. pineal
- b. parathyroid
- c. hypothalamus
- d. pituitary
- e. thymus

M   33.   Which gland promotes body immune response as its primary function?
- a. pineal
- * b. thymus
- c. thyroid
- d. gonads
- e. adrenal

E   34.   Glucagon is produced by the
- a. adrenal cortex.
- b. adrenal medulla.
- c. thyroid.
- d. kidneys.
- * e. pancreas.

D   35.   A friend tells you that her husband has been feeling guilty and stressed for the past month. During the same time interval he has felt fatigued most of the time and many foods now seem to upset his stomach. Doctors have already checked for ulcers, cancer, blood pressure changes, and other blood irregularities, but these apparently are normal. You are an endocrinologist, so you suggest that he be tested for the most likely endocrine malfunction, which would be
- a. androgen/estrogen levels in the bloodstream.
- * b. glucocorticoid levels in the bloodstream.
- c. calcitonin level in the bloodstream.
- d. melatonin level in the bloodstream.
- e. none of the above

E   36.   The adrenal medulla produces
- a. mineralocorticoids.
- * b. epinephrine.
- c. cortisol.
- d. testosterone.
- e. glucocorticoids.

M   37. If you eliminated all sources of calcium (dairy products, some vegetables) from your diet, the level of which of the following would rise in an attempt to supply calcium stored in your body to the tissues that need it?
             a. aldosterone
             b. calcitonin
             c. mineralocorticoids
         *   d. parathyroid hormone
             e. all of the above

E   38. A goiter is an enlarged form of which gland?
             a. adrenal
             b. pancreas
         *   c. thyroid
             d. parathyroid
             e. thymus

E   39. The normal individual has how many parathyroid glands?
             a. 2
             b. 3
         *   c. 4
             d. 5
             e. 6

M   40. A group of hormones that are believed to affect the membrane surface receptors of lymphocytes are
         *   a. thymosins.
             b. prostaglandins.
             c. erythropoietin.
             d. secretin.
             e. none of the above

M   41. Which gland is both an exocrine and endocrine gland?
         *   a. pancreas
             b. adrenal
             c. ovary
             d. thyroid
             e. pituitary

E   42. Excess glucose is converted into glycogen in the
             a. pancreas.
         *   b. liver.
             c. thymus.
             d. thyroid.
             e. none of the above

M   43. Specialized islet cells that secrete hormones are found scattered throughout the
             a. adrenal cortex.
             b. liver.
             c. thymus.
             d. adrenal medulla.
         *   e. pancreas.

M   44. Which gland is involved in the maturation of lymphocytes?
             a. thyroid
             b. adrenal
             c. kidney
         *   d. thymus
             e. parathyroid

E   45. Which gland is the remnant of the third eye?
   *   a. pineal
         b. pituitary
         c. thyroid
         d. parathyroid
         e. thymus

E   46. The gonads are another name for the
         a. parathyroid and thyroid.
   *   b. ovary and testis.
         c. adrenal cortex and medulla.
         d. anterior and posterior pituitary.
         e. none of the above

E   47. The gland that functions in controlling the reproductive cycle is the
         a. thyroid.
   *   b. pineal.
         c. thymus.
         d. pancreas.
         e. kidney.

SIGNALING MECHANISMS

M   48. Which is the predominant second messenger involved in regulating glucose metabolism?
         a. insulin
         b. glucagon
         c. adenyl cyclase
   *   d. cyclic AMP
         e. all of the above

M   49. Second messengers are molecules of
         a. steroid compounds.
   *   b. cyclic AMP.
         c. ADP.
         d. prostaglandin.
         e. intermedin.

M   50. In the testicular feminization syndrome
         a. no testosterone is produced.
         b. chemicals circulating in the blood deactivate the male hormone.
   *   c. the cellular receptor for testosterone in the target cells is defective.
         d. the male with this defect is normal in all respects except that he is sterile.
         e. all of the above

M   51. Water-soluble hormones
         a. have to be transported by specific carriers in the blood.
         b. have no trouble entering the target cells.
         c. find and react with the surface receptor molecules.
         d. sometimes elicit the production of a second messenger.
   *   e. all except b

Matching Questions

D   52.   Choose the one most appropriate answer for each.

1 _____ adrenal cortex

2 _____ adrenal medulla

3 _____ anterior lobe of pituitary

4 _____ exocrine glands

5 _____ endocrine cells in gastrointestinal tract

6 _____ gonad

7 _____ hypothalamus

8 _____ intermediate lobe of pituitary

9 _____ kidneys

10 _____ pancreatic islets

11 _____ parathyroid gland

12 _____ pineal gland

13 _____ posterior lobe of pituitary

14 _____ thymus gland

15 _____ thyroid gland

A. secretes one hormone that increases the metabolic rate and another that inhibits calcium release from bone storage sites

B. secrete insulin and glucagon

C. secretes hormones that prepare accessory reproductive structures for reproduction

D. involved in lymphocyte maturation

E. secretes tropic hormones, growth hormone, and prolactin

F. secretes mineralocorticoids and glucocorticoids

G. in many vertebrates, helps to determine the amount and distribution of dark pigments in the skin

H. secrete enzymes that help to form angiotensin and erythropoietin

I. participates in reproductive physiology and senses photoperiods

J. secretes (releases into bloodstream) oxytocin and antidiuretic hormone

K. secretes a hormone that promotes calcium release from bone storage sites

L. produces oxytocin and antidiuretic hormone

M. secrete secretin and gastrin

N. secretes epinephrine and norepinephrine

O. secrete pheromones, milk, tears, sweat, and mucus

Answers: 1. F.   2. N   3. E   4. O   5. M   6. C
               7. L   8. G   9. H   10. B   11. K   12. I
               13. J   14. D   15. A

Classification Questions

Answer questions 53–57 in reference to the five endocrine glands listed below:

    a. pituitary
    b. adrenal
    c. pancreas
    d. thyroid
    e. thymus

M   53.   Which gland is the target for corticotropin (ACTH)?

E   54.   In which gland is oxytocin produced?

M   55.   In which gland is antidiuretic hormone produced?

M   56.   Which gland produces a hormone that controls metabolism most directly?

E   57.   Insulin is produced in which gland?

Answers: 53. b   54. a   55. a   56. d   57. c

Answer questions 58–62 in reference to the five pituitary hormones listed below:

    a. estrogen
    b. luteinizing hormone
    c. somatotropin
    d. oxytocin
    e. antidiuretic hormone

M   58.   Which hormone controls water retention and loss?

M   59.   The mammary glands are the target for which hormone?

D   60.   Which hormone induces protein synthesis and cell division in young animals?

D   61.   The kidneys are the target for which hormone?

M   62.   Uterine contractions are induced by which hormone?

Answers: 58. e   59. d   60. c   61. e   62. d

Answer questions 63–67 in reference to the five endocrine glands listed below:

    a. adrenal cortex
    b. ovary
    c. pineal
    d. thyroid
    e. thymus

D   63.   Which gland controls circadian rhythms?

M   64.   Which gland plays a central role in the immune response?

D   65.   Which gland secretes a hormone that prepares and maintains the uterus for pregnancy?

M   66.   Progesterone is produced by which of the above?

M   67.   Calcium concentration in the blood is controlled by which of the above glands?

Answers: 63. c   64. e   65. b   66. b   67. d

Selecting the Exception

E   68.   Four of the five answers listed below are endocrine glands. Select the exception.
        a. thymus gland
   * b. salivary gland
        c. parathyroid gland
        d. thyroid gland
        e. pituitary gland

D   69.   Four of the five answers listed below are produced by the same lobe of the pituitary. Select the exception.
   * a. antidiuretic hormone
        b. prolactin
        c. corticotropin
        d. somatotropin
        e. luteinizing hormone

M 70. Four of the five answers listed below are related by a common source. Select the exception.
   a. glucocorticoids
   b. sex hormones
   c. cortisol
 * d. adrenaline
   e. mineralocorticoid

M 71. Four of the five answers listed below affect blood glucose level. Select the exception.
 * a. calcitonin
   b. glucagon
   c. glucocorticoid
   d. insulin
   e. epinephrine

D 72. Four of the five answers listed below directly affect another endocrine gland. Select the exception.
 * a. cortisol
   b. corticotropin
   c. luteinizing hormone
   d. follicle-stimulating hormone
   e. angiotensin

D 73. Four of the five answers listed below are characteristic of hyperthyroidism. Select the exception.
   a. excessive weight loss
 * b. excessive water loss through urination
   c. intolerance of heat
   d. increased heart rate and blood pressure
   e. excessive sweating

M 74. Four of the five answers listed below are related by a similar source. Select the exception.
 * a. prolactin
   b. progesterone
   c. androgen
   d. estrogen
   e. testosterone

D 75. Four of the five answers listed below are related by a similar gland. Select the exception.
   a. goiter
   b. deficiency of iodine in the diet
   c. hypothyroidism
 * d. rickets
   e. excessive stimulation of the thyroid gland

D 76. Four of the five answers listed below are related by the same action. Select the exception.
   a. activates vitamin D
   b. induces resorption of calcium by the kidney
   c. removes calcium and phosphate from bones
 * d. regulates blood volume
   e. involved in the biofeedback control of extracellular calcium

CHAPTER 32
REPRODUCTION AND DEVELOPMENT

Multiple-Choice Questions

BASIC PATTERNS OF DEVELOPMENT

M   1. At the end of gastrulation, which of the following are produced?
- a. hollow balls of cells
- * b. embryos with germ layers
- c. solid balls of cells
- d. maternal messages
- e. all of the above

E   2. Which stage in development occurs first?
- a. cleavage
- b. morula
- c. gastrula
- * d. zygote
- e. blastula

E   3. Which of the following is a single-layered, hollow ball of cells?
- a. cleavage
- b. morula
- c. gastrula
- d. zygote
- * e. blastula

E   4. The germ layers are formed in which of the following stages?
- a. cleavage
- b. morula
- * c. gastrula
- d. zygote
- e. blastula

D   5. Before gastrulation the future phenotype of cell lineages is largely established by which of the following acquired during cleavage?
- a. the genotype
- * b. the portion of egg cytoplasm
- c. surface recognition factors on the plasma membrane
- d. the number and type of organelles
- e. all of the above

E   6. The heart, muscles, bones, and blood develop primarily from
- a. ectoderm.
- * b. mesoderm.
- c. endoderm.
- d. the placenta.
- e. the gray crescent.

M 7. Which of the following affects the developmental pathways that different embryonic cells eventually will follow?
   a. sperm nucleus
   b. egg nucleus
   c. sperm cytoplasm
   * d. egg cytoplasm
   e. both b and c

E 8. The process of cleavage most commonly produces a
   a. zygote.
   * b. blastula.
   c. gastrula.
   d. puff.
   e. third germ layer.

M 9. Which embryonic tissue is incorrectly associated with its derivative?
   * a. skin from mesoderm
   b. nervous system from ectoderm
   c. liver from endoderm
   d. circulatory system from mesoderm

E 10. Muscles differentiate from which tissue?
   a. ectoderm
   b. endoderm
   * c. mesoderm
   d. all of the above

E 11. Shortly after fertilization, successive cell divisions convert the zygote into a multicellular embryo during a process known as
   a. meiosis.
   b. parthenogenesis.
   c. embryonic induction.
   * d. cleavage.
   e. invagination.

M 12. The mesoderm is responsible for the formation of all of the following adult tissues EXCEPT
   a. reproductive system.
   b. circulatory system.
   * c. nervous system.
   d. muscle system.
   e. excretory system.

M 13. If an optic cup is transplanted to an area where ectoderm is available,
   a. the optic cup will be reabsorbed.
   b. the optic cup will develop into a fully functional eye.
   * c. the epidermis will be induced to form a lens.
   d. the eye fails to differentiate any further.

M 14. During which of the following stages do cells of identical genetic makeup become structurally and functionally different from one another according to the genetically controlled developmental program of the species?
   a. cleavage
   * b. differentiation
   c. morphogenesis
   d. metamorphosis
   e. ovulation

M   15. In the process of differentiation,
          a. some daughter cells usually receive varying assortments of genes.
     *   b. cells with identical assortments of genes come to have different individual genes expressed.
          c. cells become specialized as a result of meiosis.
          d. daughter cells acquire different characteristics as a result of mutations that have occurred.
          e. all of the above

HUMAN REPRODUCTIVE SYSTEM

E   16. The female reproductive system includes all the following EXCEPT
          a. clitoris.
          b. vagina.
          c. oviduct.
          d. ovary.
     *   e. mammary gland.

E   17. The primary reproductive organ in the human female is the
          a. uterus.
     *   b. ovary.
          c. vagina.
          d. clitoris.
          e. vulva.

E   18. In the human male several hundred million sperm are produced by spermatogenesis occurring in
          a. interstitial cells.
          b. the prostate.
     *   c. seminiferous tubules.
          d. the vas deferens.
          e. epididymis.

M   19. Which mammal does NOT exhibit seasonal sexual activities?
          a. whale
          b. cats
     *   c. primates
          d. horses
          e. dogs

M   20. Which cells are diploid?
          a. spermatids
          b. primary spermatocytes
          c. secondary spermatocytes
          d. spermatogonia
     *   e. both b and d

M   21. Which cells are produced during meiosis I?
          a. spermatids
          b. primary spermatocytes
     *   c. secondary spermatocytes
          d. spermatids
          e. sperm

M   22. Sperm become fully developed in the
          a. vas deferens.
          b. epididymis.
          c. seminiferous tubules.
     *   d. vagina.
          e. seminal fluid.

E   23. Sperm are produced in the
*   a. testes.
      b. vas deferens.
      c. epididymis.
      d. prostate gland.
      e. penis.

M   24. Seminal fluid is produced by the
      a. prostate gland.
      b. seminal vesicle.
      c. bulbourethral gland.
      d. urinary bladder.
*   e. all except d

M   25. Testosterone
      a. stimulates sperm production.
      b. promotes the normal development and maintenance of sexual behavior.
      c. is responsible for secondary sexual characteristics.
      d. is responsible for the development of the male genitalia.
*   e. all of the above

E   26. The passageway that channels ova from the ovary into the uterus is known as
      a. a vagina.
      b. a uterus.
*   c. an oviduct.
      d. an endometrium.
      e. all of the above

M   27. The surface of which of the following is covered with fingerlike projections that produce a sweeping action?
      a. ovary
      b. uterus
      c. vagina
*   d. oviduct
      e. follicle

E   28. The cervix is part of the
      a. vulva.
      b. ovary.
*   c. uterus.
      d. oviduct.
      e. vagina.

E   29. In most mammals a predictably recurring time when the female becomes sexually receptive to the male is called
*   a. estrus.
      b. endometrium.
      c. menstruation.
      d. coitus.
      e. parturition.

M   30. Which of the following statements is NOT true of the human female?
      a. She produces all the eggs that she ever will before she is born.
      b. The process of meiosis may take thirty to fifty years to complete.
      c. The primary oocytes lay dormant until puberty.
*   d. She will produce more gametes than her male counterpart.
      e. It is possible that more than one egg will be released at ovulation.

M 31. FSH and LH are secreted by the
   a. hypothalamus.
   b. ovaries.
*   c. anterior pituitary.
   d. testes.
   e. uterus.

M 32. Ovulation is triggered by
*   a. high levels of LH.
   b. low levels of LH.
   c. high levels of chorionic gonadotropin.
   d. high levels of estrogen.
   e. high levels of progesterone.

E 33. Menstrual flow results in the discharge of
   a. the follicle.
   b. the corpus luteum.
*   c. the endometrial lining.
   d. surface cells from the vagina.
   e. blood from the blood vessels on the outer surface of the uterus.

E 34. Ovulation is triggered primarily by
*   a. a surge of LH that occurs halfway through the menstrual cycle.
   b. the falling levels of estrogen and progesterone.
   c. the rising levels of progesterone.
   d. both a and c

M 35. Destruction of the corpus luteum, if pregnancy does NOT occur, results from the action of
   a. chorionic gonadotropism.
   b. the luteinizing hormone.
   c. progesterone.
*   d. prostaglandins.
   e. estrogen.

E 36. Menstrual flow begins in response to
   a. rising levels of FSH and LH.
   b. falling levels of estrogen.
   c. falling levels of progesterone.
*   d. both b and c

FROM FERTILIZATION TO BIRTH

E 37. Fertilization in mammals occurs in the
   a. ovary.
   b. uterus.
   c. vagina.
*   d. oviduct.
   e. follicle.

M 38. During a human pregnancy, implantation occurs at which stage?
   a. zygote
   b. early cleavage
*   c. blastocyst
   d. gastrula
   e. morula

E   39. The average number of sperm that are deposited in the vagina during an ejaculation is between
       a. 150,000 and 350,000.
       b. 1.5 and 3.5 million.
       c. 15 and 35 million.
    *   d. 150 and 350 million.
       e. 1.5 and 3.5 billion.

E   40. Implantation occurs in the
       a. ovary.
    *   b. uterus.
       c. vagina.
       d. oviduct.
       e. follicle.

M   41. In the eggs of birds and reptiles, the waste products are stored in the
    *   a. allantois.
       b. placenta.
       c. chorion.
       d. amnion.
       e. yolk sac.

M   42. In humans, the fluid immediately surrounding the embryo is contained in the
       a. allantois.
       b. placenta.
       c. chorion.
    *   d. amnion.
       e. yolk sac.

M   43. The outermost membrane that forms the majority of the placenta is the
       a. amnion.
       b. allantois.
    *   c. chorion.
       d. yolk sac.
       e. umbilical cord.

E   44. Which drug, if taken during pregnancy, results in the production of infants without arms or legs?
       a. tetracycline
    *   b. thalidomide
       c. streptomycin
       d. salicylic acid
       e. codeine

M   45. Which disease may produce a malformed embryo if the mother develops the disease early in pregnancy?
    *   a. German measles
       b. chicken pox
       c. red measles
       d. hepatitis
       e. mumps

CONTROL OF HUMAN FERTILITY

E   46. Which of the following is the most effective in helping prevent venereal disease?
   * a. condoms
     b. the Pill
     c. douching
     d. the IUD
     e. rhythm

E   47. Of the following, which is the least successful method of birth control?
     a. early withdrawal
     b. a condom alone
     c. a spermicidal jelly or foam alone
   * d. douching
     e. the Pill

M   48. A contraceptive pill contains
     a. estrogen.
     b. progesterone.
     c. the follicle-stimulating hormone.
     d. the luteinizing hormone.
   * e. both a and b

Matching Questions

D   49. Matching I. Choose the one most appropriate answer for each.

1 _____ abortion	A. the production and secretion of milk
2 _____ abstention	B. sloughing off of endometrium stops permanently
3 _____ coitus	C. birth control exercised after development begins
4 _____ douching	
5 _____ ejaculation	D. an abortion that occurs spontaneously
6 _____ implantation	E. the burrowing of the blastocyst into the uterus
7 _____ lactation	F. the release of an egg from the ovary
8 _____ menopause	G. the release of seminal fluid from the male reproductive tract
9 _____ menstruation	
10 _____ miscarriage	H. a 100-percent effective method of preventing conception
11 _____ orgasm	I. a highly unreliable form of birth control
12 _____ ovulation	J. the periodic elimination of the uterine lining
13 _____ tubal ligation	K. characterized by involuntary muscle contractions, release of tension, and warmth
14 _____ vasectomy	
	L. sexual intercourse
	M. sperm and egg cannot meet because section of oviduct is missing
	N. cutting and tying of vas deferens

Answers:
1. C	2. H	3. L	4. I	5. G	6. E
7. A	8. B	9. J	10. D	11. K	12. F
13. M	14. N				

D   50. Matching II. Choose the one most appropriate answer for each.

1 _____ acrosome

2 _____ allantois

3 _____ blastocyst

4 _____ cervix

5 _____ clitoris

6 _____ endometrium

7 _____ epididymis

8 _____ FSH

9 _____ Leydig cells of testis

10 _____ LH

11 _____ placenta

12 _____ seminal vesicles

13 _____ vas deferens

A. in females, acts on ruptured follicle to produce corpus luteum

B. structures that secrete mucus and nutrients absorbable by sperm; open into the ejaculatory duct

C. forms as an outgrowth of the embryonic gut; becomes part of umbilical cord and placenta

D. two of these connect seminiferous tubules with vasa deferentia

E. opening between uterus and vagina

F. organ that supplies the embryo/fetus with nutrients and removes waste products

G. connect epididymides with ejaculatory duct

H. cap over the head of a sperm; contains lytic enzymes that help penetrate egg membrane

I. inner cell mass plus trophoblast; attaches to uterine wall

J. testosterone produced here

K. part of vulva; develops from same embryonic tissues as does the penis in males

L. the uterine lining

M. acts on gonad to help mature gametes; released from anterior lobe of pituitary

Answers: 1. H   2. C   3. I   4. E   5. K   6. L

               7. D   8. M   9. J   10. A   11. F   12. B

               13. G

Classification Questions

Answer questions 51–55 in reference to the five stages of development listed below:

     a. zygote

     b. blastula

     c. morula

     d. gastrula

     e. embryo

M   51. Which stage appears as a multicellular, hollow ball?

E   52. Which is the fertilized egg?

M   53. Which stage might be described as a "solid ball"?

D   54. The gut cavity of an animal forms during which stage?

D   55. The major germ layers are formed during which stage?

Answers: 51. b   52. a   53. c   54. d   55. d

Answer questions 56–60 in reference to the five stages of sperm development listed below:

    a. spermatogonia
    b. secondary spermatocyte
    c. primary spermatocyte
    d. spermatid
    e. sperm

D   56. At which stage of development is the male sex cell first in the haploid condition?

M   57. What continues to undergo mitosis throughout the reproductive life of the male?

D   58. What represents the product of the first meiotic division?

D   59. What is a mitotic product, but then undergoes meiosis?

M   60. At which stage of development is the male sex cell fully motile?

Answers: 56. b   57. a   58. b   59. c   60. e

Answer questions 61–65 in reference to the five stages and structures involved in the development of the human egg:

    a. oogonium
    b. primary oocyte
    c. secondary oocyte
    d. polar body
    e. secondary follicle

M   61. Which structure becomes the mature egg only after fertilization is begun?

D   62. Which structure contains the first sex cell stage to be in the haploid state?

M   63. Which structure contains a full haploid set of chromosomes, but will never be fertilized?

M   64. Which structure divides by mitosis during the fetal stages of development until all of the approximately 2 million potential eggs have been formed?

D   65. Which stage lies dormant between birth and puberty?

Answers: 61. c   62. c   63. d   64. a   65. b

Selecting the Exception

M   66. Four of the five answers listed below are events occurring after fertilization. Select the exception.
    a. cleavage
    * b. gametogenesis
    c. blastula
    d. gastrulation
    e. organogenesis

M   67. Four of the five answers listed below are produced by the same germ layer. Select the exception.
    * a. nervous system
    b. muscle system
    c. circulatory system
    d. reproductive system
    e. excretory system

M 68. Three of the four answers listed below produce portions of the seminal fluid. Select the exception.
* a. epididymis
   b. prostate
   c. seminal vesicle
   d. bulbourethral gland

M 69. Three of the four answers listed below are related by the number of chromosomes present. Select the exception.
   a. sperm
* b. spermatogonia
   c. secondary spermatocyte
   d. spermatids

E 70. Three of the four answers listed below are all parts of a sperm. Select the exception.
   a. flagella
   b. midpiece
   c. acrosome
* d. polar body

D 71. Four of the five answers listed below are related by a common quantity. Select the exception.
* a. urethra
   b. testis
   c. ejaculatory duct
   d. vas deferens
   e. epididymis

D 72. Four of the five answers listed below are true of testosterone. Select the exception.
   a. promotes secondary sex characteristics
   b. controls sexual behavior
   c. necessary for growth and function of male reproductive tract
   d. stimulates spermatogenesis
* e. produced by spermatogonia cells

M 73. Four of the five answers listed below are related by a common location. Select the exception.
   a. follicle
   b. corpus luteum
* c. cervix
   d. oogonium
   e. primary oocyte

D 74. Four of the five answers listed below are related by a matching feature. Select the exception.
* a. blastocyst
   b. amnion
   c. allantois
   d. yolk sac
   e. chorion

M 75. Four of the five answers listed below are related by a common theme. Select the exception.
   a. alcohol
   b. thalidomide
   c. German measles
* d. vitamins
   e. antibiotics

M 76. Four of the five answers listed below are related by a similar effectiveness. Select the exception.
  a. the Pill
  b. tubal ligation
  c. vasectomy
* d. douching
  e. IUD

CHAPTER 33
POPULATION ECOLOGY

Multiple-Choice Questions

FROM POPULATIONS TO THE BIOSPHERE

E   1.   Which of the following includes all the others?
       a. ecosystem
*   b. biosphere
       c. community
       d. individual
       e. population

E   2.   A group of individuals of the same species occupying a given area defines a
       a. community
       b. ecosystem
*   c. population
       d. biosphere
       e. habitat

M   3.   By definition, which of the following is NOT part of a community?
       a. bacteria
       b. populations
       c. animals
*   d. soil
       e. plants

POPULATION DYNAMICS

E   4.   The total number of individuals of the same species that occupy a given area at a given time is the
       a. population distribution.
       b. population growth.
       c. population birth rate.
*   d. population size.
       e. carrying capacity.

M   5.   The average number of individuals of the same species per unit of surface area at a given time is the
*   a. population density.
       b. population growth.
       c. population birth rate.
       d. population size.
       e. carrying capacity.

M   6.   The maximum rate of increase of a population is its
*   a. biotic potential.
       b. carrying capacity.
       c. exponential growth.
       d. distribution.
       e. reproductive base.

M   7. What distribution pattern is the most common in the natural world?
- a. random
- b. uniform
- * c. clumped
- d. stratified or layered
- e. bimodal

E   8. Population size depends on
- a. deaths.
- b. births.
- c. migration.
- d. immigration.
- * e. all of the above

M   9. A situation in which the birth rate equals the death rate is called
- a. an intrinsic limiting factor.
- b. exponential growth.
- c. saturation.
- * d. zero population growth.
- e. geometric growth.

D   10. The rate of increase for a population (r) refers to what kind of relationship between birth rate and death rate?
- a. their sum
- b. their product
- c. the doubling time between them
- * d. the difference between them
- e. reduction in each of them

E   11. Which characteristic of a population is a convenient way to express the rate of change within a population?
- a. size
- * b. growth
- c. density
- d. carrying capacity
- e. age

E   12. A population that is growing exponentially in the absence of limiting factors can be illustrated by which curve?
- a. S-shaped
- * b. J-shaped
- c. one that terminates in a plateau phase
- d. bimodal
- e. binomial

M   13. Which concept is a way to express the growth rate of a given population?
- * a. doubling time
- b. population density
- c. population size
- d. carrying capacity
- e. all of the above

D 14. In a population growing exponentially,
   a. the number of individuals added to the population next year is greater than the number added this year.
   b. the population growth rate increases year after year.
   c. net reproduction per individual increases year after year.
   * d. a and b
   e. a, b, and c

M 15. Interaction between resource availability and a population's tolerance to prevailing environmental conditions defines
   * a. the carrying capacity of the environment.
   b. exponential growth.
   c. the doubling time of a population.
   d. density-independent factors.
   e. all of the above

D 16. In natural communities some feedback mechanisms operate whenever populations change in size; they are
   * a. density-dependent factors.
   b. density-independent factors.
   c. always within the individuals of the community.
   d. always outside the individuals of the community.
   e. none of the above

M 17. A change in a population that is NOT related strictly to the size of the population is best described as
   a. density-dependent.
   * b. density-independent.
   c. within.
   d. an S-shaped curve.
   e. a J-shaped curve.

M 18. In itself, a flood that washes away an entire population of rabbits is
   a. a density-dependent factor.
   b. a limiting factor dependent on the individuals.
   c. a consequence of exponential growth.
   * d. density-independent.
   e. all of the above

M 19. Which density-dependent factor controls the size of a population?
   a. wind velocity
   b. light intensity
   * c. nutrient supply
   d. rainfall
   e. wave action in an intertidal zone

E 20. Which is NOT a density-dependent, growth-limiting factor?
   a. predation
   * b. drought
   c. parasitism
   d. competition

M 21. As population density increases, the chance of _____ also increases.
   a. parasitism
   b. pathogens
   c. predation
   d. competition
   * e. all of the above

LIFE HISTORY PATTERNS

M   22. A type III survivorship curve is characteristic of
    a. monkeys.
    b. horses.
    c. eagles.
  * d. sea urchins.

M   23. Organisms that demonstrate a type I survivorship curve are characterized by
    a. high r, small offspring.
    b. low r, small offspring.
  * c. low r, large offspring.
    d. high r, large offspring.

M   24. A type III survivorship curve (mortality high at birth and decreasing with age) is characteristic of all but which species?
    a. flies
  * b. humans
    c. frogs
    d. reptiles
    e. fish

M   25. A cohort is
  * a. a group of newborn individuals of the same species.
    b. any member of the same species.
    c. any member of the same species and sex within a population.
    d. a sexual mate.
    e. a litter mate or sibling within a large population.

E   26. Life tables provide data concerning
    a. expected life span.
    b. reproductive age.
    c. death rate.
    d. birth rate.
  * e. all of the above

D   27. Type II survivorship curves
    a. are characteristic of humans and elephants.
  * b. typify a population in which all ages have an equal chance of surviving.
    c. indicate a high mortality rate in the very young.
    d. show that very few young are produced, that each is given parental support, and that most individuals live a relatively long life and die of old age.
    e. are typical of annual plants.

HUMAN POPULATION GROWTH

D   28. All of the following are reasons for the rapid population explosion of humans EXCEPT
    a. increases in carrying capacity.
    b. expansion into new habitats.
    c. removal of limiting factors.
    d. reproduction occurring earlier in the life cycle.
  * e. longer generation times.

M 29. The tremendous increase in the number of human beings over the course of the past 100 years is attributable to
  a. immunization and vaccination programs.
  b. colonization of previously underutilized habitat.
  c. more equal distribution of scattered resources.
  d. a and b
  * e. a, b, and c

M 30. The age structure diagram for rapidly growing populations
  a. is in the form of a pyramid.
  b. is characterized by a large percentage of the population in the postreproductive years.
  c. has a very broad base showing a large number of young.
  d. has about equal distribution between all age groups.
  * e. both a and c

D 31. If reproduction occurs early in the life cycle, what results?
  * a. population growth rate increases
  b. population size declines
  c. population size is not affected
  d. generation time increases
  e. growth rate remains unchanged

M 32. As the twenty-first century draws near, the continent with the highest potential for human population growth rate is _____ and that with the lowest is _____.
  a. North America, Asia
  b. Asia, North America
  * c. Africa, Europe
  d. Africa, Asia

M 33. If the reproductive rate drops to the maintenance level (zero population growth), how many year(s) would it take for world population to stop growing?
  a. 1
  b. 20
  c. 50
  * d. 60
  e. 150

Matching Questions

D 34. Choose the one most appropriate answer for each.

1 _____ age structure

2 _____ population growth rate

3 _____ J-shaped curve

4 _____ limiting factor

A. describes a population that is experiencing unrestrained growth

B. the birth rate minus the death rate plus any inward or minus any outward migration

C. how individuals are distributed at each age level for a population

D. the amount of glucose in a culture flask containing bacteria

Answers: 1. C   2. B   3. A   4. D

Classification Questions

Answer questions 35–39 in reference to the four levels of organization listed below:

    a. population
    b. community
    c. ecosystem
    d. biosphere

E   35. Which of the above is composed of living organisms (biotic) and the abiotic environment?

E   36. All of the individuals of a single species living in a region constitute _____.

M   37. A group of different species living together in a single habitat is _____.

M   38. Which is the basic functional unit of ecology?

E   39. Which contains all of the others?

Answers: 35. c   36. a   37. b   38. c   39. d

Selecting the Exception

E   40. Four of the five answers listed below are components of the abiotic environment. Select the exception.
    a. soil
    b. rainfall
   * c. predator
    d. temperature
    e. sunlight

E   41. Four of the five answers listed below are factors that affect population size. Select the exception.
    a. births
   * b. distribution
    c. emigration
    d. immigration
    e. deaths

D   42. Four of the five answers listed below follow a type II survivorship curve. Select the exception.
    a. songbirds
   * b. large mammals with extended parental care
    c. small mammals
    d. lizards
    e. seed prior to germination

D   43. Four of the five answers listed below follow a type III survivorship curve. Select the exception.
    a. most insects
    b. most reptiles
    c. many fish
   * d. humans
    e. most marine invertebrates

M   44. Four of the five answers listed below are density-independent factors. Select the exception.
   * a. nutrient supply
    b. temperature drop
    c. drought
    d. volcanic eruption
    e. hard freeze

CHAPTER 34
COMMUNITY INTERACTIONS

Multiple-Choice Questions

CHARACTERISTICS OF COMMUNITIES

E   1.   Which is a habitat?
- a. predator
- *   b. intestinal tract
- c. parasite
- d. producer
- e. decomposer

M   2.   All of the populations of different species that occupy and are adapted to a given area are referred to by which term?
- a. biosphere
- *   b. community
- c. ecosystem
- d. niche
- e. habitat

M   3.   What term denotes the range of all factors that influence whether a species can obtain resources essential for survival and reproduction?
- a. habitat
- *   b. niche
- c. carrying capacity
- d. ecosystem
- e. community

E   4.   A relationship in which two species are dependent on each other for survival is
- a. neutral interaction.
- b. commensalism.
- c. competitive exclusion.
- *   d. mutualism.
- e. parasitism.

E   5.   A one-way relationship in which one species benefits at the expense of another is called
- a. commensalism.
- b. symbiosis.
- *   c. parasitism.
- d. mutualism.
- e. all of the above

D   6.   The relationship between the brown-headed cowbird and another bird such as a warbler is an example of
- a. commensalism.
- b. competitive exclusion.
- c. mutualism.
- *   d. social parasitism.
- e. none of the above

M   7.   The weakest symbiotic attachment, in which one species simply lives better in the presence
          of another species that is relatively unaffected, is called
     *   a. commensalism.
          b. competitive exclusion.
          c. mutualism.
          d. predation.
          e. parasitism.

M   8.   Fruit flies probably have what type of relationship with humans?
          a. parasitic
          b. mutualistic
          c. predatory
     *   d. commensal
          e. neutral interaction

E   9.   In the food chain grass → rabbit → eagle, the reaction between the grass and eagle is
          a. predation.
          b. commensalism.
          c. competition.
     *   d. neutral.
          e. mutualism.

E   10. The interaction in which one species benefits and the second species is neither harmed nor
          benefited is
          a. mutualism.
          b. parasitism.
     *   c. commensalism.
          d. competition.
          e. predation.

E   11. An interaction between two species in which both species benefit is known as
     *   a. mutualism.
          b. parasitism.
          c. commensalism.
          d. competition.
          e. predation.

M   12. The interaction between two species in which both species are harmed is known as
          a. mutualism.
          b. parasitism.
          c. commensalism.
     *   d. competition.
          e. predation.

E   13. The interaction between two species in which one species benefits and the other species is
          harmed is
          a. mutualism.
          b. commensalism.
          c. competition.
     *   d. predation.
          e. none of the above

MUTUALLY BENEFICIAL INTERACTIONS

M 14. The relationship between an insect and the plants it pollinates is best described as
  * a. mutualism.
    b. competitive exclusion.
    c. parasitism.
    d. commensalism.
    e. all of the above

E 15. The relationship between the yucca plant and the yucca moth that pollinates it is best described as
    a. camouflage.
    b. commensalism.
    c. competitive exclusion.
  * d. mutualism.
    e. all of the above

M 16. In mixed assemblages, baboons sometimes see predators that impala do not hear, and impala sometimes hear predators that baboons do not see. In both cases, the flight of one species alerts the other to danger. This interaction is an example of
    a. a neutral relationship.
    b. commensalism.
  * c. mutualism.
    d. competition.

COMPETITIVE INTERACTIONS

M 17. Niche overlap initially leads to
    a. mutualism.
    b. commensalism.
  * c. competition.
    d. predation.
    e. parasitism.

M 18. Competitive exclusion is the result of
    a. mutualism.
    b. commensalism.
  * c. competition.
    d. predation.
    e. parasitism.

M 19. A male wolf who is courting a female bares his teeth when a second male approaches the same female. The second male retreats. This series of events provides an example of
    a. a neutral interaction.
    b. exploitation competition.
  * c. interference competition.
    d. competitive exclusion.

M 20. The construction of a fence around your yard would establish a relationship with the neighbor's dog that would be described as
    a. succession.
  * b. interference competition.
    c. commensalism.
    d. mutualism.
    e. niche.

M 21. In Gause's experiments with *Paramecium* growing in test tubes, he demonstrated that
    a. organisms with similar niches will evolve enough to survive in different niches.
    b. organisms with slightly different feeding habits will change to become exclusive competitors.
  * c. organisms with similar feeding habits may compete to the point of extinction.
    d. both b and c
    e. both a and c

M 22. Gause's exclusion principle refers to
    a. isolation.
  * b. competition.
    c. habitat preference.
    d. physiological adaptation.

M 23. The concept of competitive exclusion is based on the idea that
    a. one species will hold some sort of advantage over the other one.
    b. no two species can completely occupy the same niche.
  * c. both of the above
    d. neither of the above

CONSUMER-VICTIM INTERACTIONS

E 24. A goat eating by pulling a plant out of the ground is an example of
    a. parasitism.
  * b. predation.
    c. competition.
    d. commensalism.
    e. mutualism.

M 25. Conditions of stable coexistence between predator and prey include
    a. high predator reproductive rate relative to that of the prey.
    b. a carrying capacity for prey that is not high.
    c. large predator size relative to that of the prey.
  * d. a and b
    e. a, b, and c

M 26. Humans hunt the black rhinoceros, which is rapidly approaching extinction as a result of this predation. What accounts for the absence of stable coexistence between the two species?
    a. Predator and prey have not coevolved.
    b. Human predation is not necessarily density-dependent.
    c. The prey reproductive rate is greater than that of the predator.
  * d. a and b
    e. a, b, and c

M 27. Which is an adaptation against predation?
    a. thorns
    b. camouflage
    c. mimicry
    d. a and b
  * e. a, b, and c

E 28. Chemicals in both plants and animals serve as which of the following to predators?
    a. warnings
    b. repellants
    c. poisons
    d. bad tastes
  * e. all of the above

M   29. Which is an example of warning coloration?
        a. the dark brown mane of a lion
        b. the bright green and blue feathers of a peacock
      * c. the black and yellow bands of a wasp
        d. the black and white stripes of a zebra

M   30. Parasitoids
        a. can be an alternative to pesticides.
        b. usually kill rather than only damage those they infect.
        c. are biotic or natural controls.
        d. are better than pesticides in that they are target-specific (they affect a limited number
           and type of organisms).
      * e. all of the above

E   31. Which is a social parasite and lays its eggs in the nests of other birds?
        a. catbird
      * b. cowbird
        c. magpie
        d. Kirtland warbler
        e. bluejay

COMMUNITY ORGANIZATION, DEVELOPMENT, AND DIVERSITY

D   32. During the process of community succession,
        a. the total mass of living things remains constant.
      * b. there are increasing possibilities for resource partitioning.
        c. the pioneer community gives way quickly to the climax community, followed by a
           succession of more diverse arrays of organisms.
        d. nutrients cycle more rapidly with time.
        e. all of the above

E   33. Populations are held in check by
        a. resource partitioning.
        b. predation.
        c. social parasitism.
        d. competition.
      * e. all of the above

M   34. Which exotic organism was NOT intentionally introduced to this country?
      * a. Japanese beetle
        b. English house sparrow
        c. carp
        d. water hyacinth
        e. starling

M   35. Many introduced species have had deleterious effects on communities and ecosystems because
      * a. coevolved parasites and competitors are absent.
        b. the introduced species are long-lived.
        c. predators prefer the introduced species, and the local prey therefore proliferate to
           dangerously high levels.
        d. the communities from which they came lose an important predator, competitor,
           or parasite.

M   36. Most dominant plant species in a climax community
     a. become quickly reestablished in a cleared area because they are adapted specifically to that geographic region.
*   b. cannot grow or develop fully except as part of a certain integrated community structure.
     c. grow faster in areas exposed to sunlight by clear-cutting.
     d. both a and c
     e. all of the above

M   37. Which statement is false?
     a. Succession is highly predictable.
     b. Pioneer species have wide ranges of tolerances.
     c. Pioneer plant species are usually small annuals with an abundance of easily dispersed seeds.
*   d. The succession that occurs after a large fire is primary succession.
     e. Climax species are those that are best adapted to the specific climate where the succession occurs.

M   38. Secondary succession is likely to occur
     a. in a deciduous forest.
     b. on an eroded, bare hillside.
     c. in an abandoned field.
     d. a and b
*   e. a, b, and c

M   39. Pioneer plant species are usually characterized by
     a. small size.
     b. efficient dispersal mechanisms.
     c. long life cycles.
*   d. a and b
     e. a, b, and c

M   40. In 1882, the tropical volcanic island Krakatoa exploded and was reduced to an abiotic island covered by a thick layer of volcanic ash. By 1933, populations of all of the following organisms were present. Which population was probably established after all the others?
     a. ferns
     b. bacteria
     c. insects
*   d. rodents

M   41. Of the following four islands at the same latitude, the one that possesses the fewest number of species is
     a. 1,000 square kilometers and 300 km from the mainland.
     b. 3,000 square kilometers and 100 km from the mainland.
*   c. 100 square kilometers and 3,000 km from the mainland.
     d. 300 square kilometers and 1,000 km from the mainland.

M   42. Stable coexistence between predator and prey is least likely to occur on an island that is
*   a. small and distant from the mainland.
     b. small and close to the mainland.
     c. large and close to the mainland.
     d. large and distant from the mainland.

D   43. There are more insect species per square kilometer in a Brazilian rain forest than there are in a redwood forest of the Pacific Northwest of the United States. According to contemporary ecological hypotheses, an explanation for this finding is
   a. the tropics have been climatically stable for a longer period of time than have temperate areas.
   b. niches in the tropics are smaller than those in temperate areas.
   c. on average, insects are smaller in the tropics than they are in temperate areas.
 * d. a and b
   e. a, b, and c

M   44. An equilibrium population of 5 individuals on an island is more likely to go extinct than an equilibrium population of 50 individuals because
   a. intraspecific competition is more intense in smaller groups.
 * b. density-independent factors are more likely to eliminate smaller rather than larger groups.
   c. there is more ecological space for predators if there are fewer numbers of prey.
   d. predation pressure increases as prey populations decrease.

Matching Questions

D   45. Choose the one most appropriate answer for each.

1 _____ camouflage	A.	blending in and being hidden by the background
2 _____ commensalism		
3 _____ competitive exclusion	B.	where an organism is generally located in an environment
4 _____ habitat		
5 _____ mimicry	C.	organism benefits at another organism's expense
6 _____ mutualism		
7 _____ parasitism	D.	a self-sustaining array of interacting organisms that is best suited for a particular environment
8 _____ primary succession		
9 _____ climax community	E.	lichens on newly hardened, newly cooled lava
10 _____ secondary succession	F.	robins and human populations
11 _____ succession	G.	the yucca moth and the yucca
	H.	one species is forced from an area of niche overlap
	I.	a tasty viceroy butterfly resembles a bad-tasting monarch butterfly
	J.	the process that converts a pioneer community to a climax community
	K.	natural reforestation of burned over forest

Answers: 1. A   2. F   3. H   4. B   5. I   6. G
             7. C   8. E   9. D   10. K   11. J

Classification Questions

Answer questions 46–50 in reference to the five kinds of species interactions listed below:

        a. competition
        b. predation
        c. mutualism
        d. commensalism
        e. parasitism

E   46. In which interaction does one species benefit while the other is neither harmed nor benefits?

M   47. In which interaction between two species are both species harmed in some way?

M   48. In which interaction do both species benefit?

E   49. In which interaction is one individual or species usually killed while the other benefits by eating the first?

E   50. In which interaction is one species harmed, but usually not killed, to the benefit of the other that lives on or in the first?

Answers: 46. d   47. a   48. c   49. b   50. e

Answer questions 51–55 in reference to the five kinds of species interactions listed below:

        a. competition
        b. predation
        c. mutualism
        d. commensalism
        e. parasitism

E   51. The relationship between a dog and a wood tick is which kind of relationship?

M   52. The interaction between termites and the cellulose-digesting protozoans in the termite gut is which kind of relationship?

M   53. What is the likely interaction between two closely related species of woodpeckers that live in a temperate forest?

M   54. If a wasp lays its eggs inside the larva of a fly, what type of interaction is this a form of?

M   55. When a tropical bird places its nest in association with a wasp nest on the same tree, what type of interaction is this?

Answers: 51. e   52. c   53. a   54. e   55. d

Selecting the Exception

M   56. Four of the five answers listed below are relationships in which at least one of the interactants benefits. Select the exception.
    * a. competition
       b. parasitism
       c. mutualism
       d. commensalism
       e. predation

D   57. Four of the five answers listed below are examples of mutualism. Select the exception.
          a. plants and pollinators
          b. plants and seed dispersal by seed-eating animals
          c. mycorrhiza
      *   d. antibiotic
          e. lichen

E   58. Four of the five answers listed below are examples of prey defense. Select the exception.
          a. display behavior
          b. chemicals
          c. camouflage
      *   d. albinism
          e. mimicry

E   59. Four of the five answers listed below are defense chemicals. Select the exception.
      *   a. perfume
          b. warning odors
          c. poisons
          d. alarm substances
          e. repellants

M   60. Four of the five answers listed below are exotic or introduced species. Select the exception.
          a. Argentine fire ant
      *   b. cockroach
          c. starling
          d. water hyacinth
          e. chestnut blight

M   61. Four of the five answers listed below are events that lead to secondary succession. Select
          the exception.
          a. opening the canopy in a tropical rain forest
          b. abandoning a cotton field
      *   c. retreat of a glacier in Alaska
          d. following a fire
          e. growth of weeds in an unmowed lawn

CHAPTER 35
ECOSYSTEMS

Multiple-Choice Questions

CHARACTERISTICS OF ECOSYSTEMS

M   1. Which statement about ecosystems is false?
  - a. The rate of energy flow depends on the ratio of producers to consumers.
  - b. The requirements of an ecosystem change with age.
  - c. The larger the ecosystem, the more flexible it is.
  - * d. The smaller the ecosystem, the more stable it is.
  - e. The more efficient the producers are, the more energy must be put in and the more energy is available for the next trophic level.

M   2. A network of interactions that involve the cycling of materials and the flow of energy between a community and its physical environment is which of the following?
  - a. population
  - b. community
  - * c. ecosystem
  - d. biosphere
  - e. species

M   3. A community differs from an ecosystem in that the former does NOT include
  - a. unicellular organisms.
  - b. decomposers.
  - * c. abiotic (nonliving) factors.
  - d. a and b
  - e. a, b, and c

E   4. In a natural community, the primary consumers are
  - * a. herbivores.
  - b. carnivores.
  - c. scavengers.
  - d. decomposers.
  - e. all of the above

E   5. Which is usually a primary carnivore?
  - a. chicken
  - b. cow
  - c. rabbit
  - * d. wolf
  - e. squirrel

M   6. Which is a primary consumer?
  - * a. cow
  - b. dog
  - c. hawk
  - d. fox
  - e. snake

E · 7. Herbivores represent the
  * a. primary consumers.
  b. secondary consumers.
  c. tertiary consumers.
  d. primary producers.
  e. secondary producers.

STRUCTURE OF ECOSYSTEMS

M 8. Chemosynthetic organisms are
  a. primary consumers.
  b. secondary consumers.
  c. tertiary consumers.
  * d. primary producers.
  e. secondary producers.

E 9. The ultimate source of all energy in a terrestrial ecosystem is
  a. the organic matter in all the organisms of the ecosystem.
  b. water.
  * c. sunlight.
  d. carbon dioxide.

M 10. Primary carnivores are
  a. tertiary consumers in the third trophic level.
  * b. secondary consumers in the third trophic level.
  c. secondary consumers in the second trophic level.
  d. tertiary consumers in the fourth trophic level.

E 11. In the Antarctic, blue whales feed mainly on
  a. petrels.
  * b. krill.
  c. seals.
  d. fish and small squid.
  e. penguins.

M 12. Which cannot be placed in a single trophic level?
  a. oak tree
  b. zebra
  * c. mushroom
  d. rabbit

ENERGY FLOW THROUGH ECOSYSTEMS

D 13. Net primary productivity is the
  a. rate of photosynthesis.
  b. rate of energy flow.
  c. amount of energy stored in the ecosystem.
  d. amount of energy utilized.
  * e. amount of energy stored in the plant tissue in excess of that used by autotrophs in respiration.

E 14. Most of the energy within an ecosystem is lost
  a. when organisms disperse.
  b. when organisms die.
  * c. as a result of metabolism.
  d. by organisms at the top of the food web.

M   15. The percentage of incident light energy that is normally stored in the organic matter of terrestrial ecosystems is approximately
   a. 100.
   b. 10.
 * c. 1.
   d. 0.1.
   e. 0.01.

E   16. Of the energy that enters one trophic level, approximately what percent (average) becomes available for the next trophic level?
   a. 100
 * b. 10
   c. 1
   d. 0.1
   e. 0.01

M   17. The difference between gross primary productivity and net primary productivity is
   a. the amount of sunlight reflected by plants.
   b. the rate of photosynthesis of autotrophs.
 * c. the rate of respiration of autotrophs.
   d. the rate of herbivorous consumption of autotrophs.

M   18. Detritivores are
   a. bacteria.
   b. plants.
   c. fungi.
 * d. animals.
   e. a and c

M   19. About what percent of the solar energy reaching the earth's surface is stored as organic material?
 * a. 1–2
   b. 5–6
   c. 10–12
   d. 15–18
   e. 25

M   20. The simple food chain, grass → zebra → lion, provides a good example of a pyramid of
   a. energy.
   b. height.
   c. biomass.
   d. a and b
 * e. a and c

M   21. Detritus specifically includes
   a. organic wastes.
   b. toxic materials.
   c. dead and partially decayed material.
   d. living bacteria and fungi.
 * e. both a and c

E   22. At the bottom or base of a pyramid of energy are the
 * a. primary producers.
   b. secondary producers.
   c. primary consumers.
   d. secondary consumers.
   e. tertiary consumers.

E   23. At the top of a pyramid of biomass are the
          a. primary producers.
          b. secondary producers.
          c. primary consumers.
          d. secondary consumers.
  *   e. tertiary consumers.

M   24. The biomass of a community is the weight of the
          a. material decomposed in a year.
          b. producers.
  *   c. living organisms.
          d. consumers.
          e. decomposers.

M   25. Of the following, which must always have a base larger than the other components?
          a. pyramid of numbers
  *   b. pyramid of energy
          c. pyramid of biomass
          d. a and b
          e. a, b, and c

BIOGEOCHEMICAL CYCLES

M   26. The Hubbard Brook watershed studies revealed the importance of tree roots in preventing loss of calcium from an ecosystem. Calculation of calcium loss is performed by sampling
          a. the roots of the trees.
          b. the soil of the watershed.
  *   c. the stream exiting the watershed.
          d. a and b
          e. a, b, and c

M   27. Which gas is increasing in the atmosphere and threatening the world with the greenhouse effect?
  *   a. carbon dioxide
          b. carbon monoxide
          c. ozone
          d. fluorocarbons
          e. oxygen

E   28. Carbon is stored in what form?
          a. biomass
          b. fossil fuels
          c. limestone rocks
          d. shells of animals
  *   e. all of the above

M   29. Which is NOT part of the nitrogen cycle?
          a. denitrification
  *   b. deammonification
          c. nitrogen fixation
          d. ammonification
          e. assimilation and biosynthesis

M 30. Carbon is introduced into the atmosphere by all of the following means EXCEPT
  a. respiration.
  b. volcanic eruptions.
  c. burning of fossil fuels.
  * d. wind erosion.

M 31. Some nitrogenous waste products or organic remains of organisms are decomposed by soil bacteria and fungi. The bacteria and fungi use the amino acids for their own growth and, in turn, release the excess as NH_3 or NH_4^+. This process is
  a. nitrification.
  * b. ammonification.
  c. denitrification.
  d. nitrogen fixation.
  e. hydrogenation.

E 32. The greatest concentration of nitrogen on the planet Earth is found in
  a. living organisms, including bacteria.
  * b. the atmosphere.
  c. soil minerals.
  d. fossil fuels.
  e. oceans.

E 33. Nitrogen is released into the atmosphere by
  a. nitrogen fixation.
  * b. denitrification.
  c. nitrification.
  d. ammonification.
  e. decomposition.

E 34. Which plants are planted to increase the amount of nitrogen in the soil?
  a. watermelon and cantaloupe vines
  * b. legumes
  c. mints
  d. grasses
  e. heaths

M 35. Plant cells assimilate nitrogen in the form of
  a. ammonia and N_2.
  b. N_2 and nitrite.
  * c. nitrate and ammonia.
  d. urea and nitrate.

M 36. Nitrifying bacteria convert
  * a. NH_3 to NO_2^- and NO_3^-
  b. NO_3^- to NO_2^- to N_2.
  c. NO_3^- to NH_3.
  d. urea to NH_3.

E 37. In biological magnification
  * a. poisons build up in food chains and webs so that the concentration is highest at the high end of the food chain.
  b. there is a tendency for an environment to change when organisms first invade.
  c. more highly evolved forms are able to build large populations under favorable conditions.
  d. parasites spread rapidly through congested populations.
  e. sediments fill in aquatic environments so that succession will occur if organisms disturb the aquatic habitat.

M   38. Which substance is magnified during transfers in ecosystems?
*   a. fat-soluble pesticides
     b. carbohydrates
     c. inorganic phosphates
     d. a and b
     e. a, b, and c

Matching Questions

D   39. Choose the one most appropriate answer for each.

1 _____ biological magnification
2 _____ detritus
3 _____ legumes
4 _____ net primary production
5 _____ primary productivity
6 _____ webs
7 _____ gross primary production

A. rate at which energy becomes stored in organic compounds through photosynthesis
B. total amount of solar energy stored in organic compounds during photosynthesis
C. interconnected food chains
D. the potential chemical energy remaining (after aerobic respiration by autotrophs) that can still be passed on to other trophic levels
E. DDT spraying program in Borneo
F. a kind of plant that often harbors symbiotic nitrogen fixers in its roots
G. particles of organic waste products, dead or partly decomposed tissues

Answers: 1. E   2. G   3. F   4. D   5. A   6. C
              7. B

Classification Questions

Answer questions 40–44 in reference to the five trophic categories of an ecosystem listed below:

a. producer
b. herbivore
c. primary carnivore
d. secondary carnivore
e. decomposer

M   40. What is a primary consumer?

M   41. A Venus flytrap plant obtains its nitrogen when it functions as what?

M   42. What do most mushrooms function as?

D   43. What is a bear feeding on a salmon functioning as?

E   44. What is a bear feeding on blueberries functioning as?

Answers: 40. b   41. c   42. e   43. d   44. b

Answer questions 45–49 in reference to the four steps of the nitrogen cycles listed below:

     a. nitrogen fixation
     b. nitrification
     c. denitrification
     d. ammonification

M   45. The action of bacteria on urea occurs during which process?

M   46. The action of bacteria on ammonia, ultimately converting it to nitrate, occurs during which process?

E   47. The action of bacteria on nitrates, converting them to gaseous nitrogen, occurs during which process?

E   48. What is the process whereby gaseous nitrogen is first converted to ammonia and then to other nitrogenous compounds?

M   49. The process whereby nitrite is converted to nitrate is an important part of which process?

Answers: 45. d   46. b   47. c   48. a   49. b

Selecting the Exception

E   50. Three of the four answers listed below are related by a common theme. Select the exception.
      a. numbers
  * b. nutrients
      c. biomass
      d. energy

M   51. Four of the five answers listed below are related by a common action. Select the exception.
      a. volcanic eruption
  * b. photosynthesis
      c. respiration
      d. fire
      e. decomposition

D   52. Four of the five answers listed below are related by a common action that retains nitrogen in the biomass. Select the exception.
      a. decomposition
      b. ammonification
      c. nitrification
      d. nitrogen fixation
  * e. denitrification

CHAPTER 36
THE BIOSPHERE

Multiple-Choice Questions

CHARACTERISTICS OF THE BIOSPHERE

E   1. The amount of ultraviolet radiation hitting the earth's surface is greatly reduced by which gas in the atmosphere?
  *   a. ozone
       b. oxygen
       c. water vapor
       d. carbon dioxide
       e. nitrogen

E   2. An important gas in the absorption of ultraviolet radiation is
       a. N_2.
  *   b. O_3.
       c. CO_2.
       d. SO_2.

M   3. The amount of solar energy that any spot on the surface of the earth receives is controlled by the
       a. photoperiod or duration of light.
       b. angle at which the sun strikes the earth.
       c. amount of atmosphere above the spot.
       d. particulate matter and pollution in the atmosphere.
  *   e. all of the above

M   4. At how many degrees north and south of the equator does air rise as a result of differential heating and cooling?
       a. 10
       b. 30
       c. 40
  *   d. 60
       e. 75

M   5. The tradewinds in the zone from 0 to 30 degrees north latitude are generally from the
       a. north.
       b. northwest.
  *   c. northeast.
       d. southeast.
       e. southwest.

M   6. Major air masses rise from the earth's surface at
       a. the equator and 30 degree latitudes.
       b. 30 degree and 60 degree latitudes.
  *   c. the equator and 60 degree latitudes.
       d. 30 degree latitudes and the poles.

M   7. Which factor has the least effect on the amount of incoming light that strikes an area?
       a. latitude
  *   b. temperature
       c. the degree that a slope is exposed to the incoming light
       d. the amount of recurring cloud cover
       e. all of the above

M   8. A mountain rain shadow is the
      a. arid area on the windward slope.
      b. wet area on the windward slope.
  *   c. arid area on the leeward slope.
      d. wet area on the leeward slope.

M   9. Temperature variations during the course of a year tend to increase with
  *   a. increasing distance from the equator and increasing distance from the oceans.
      b. increasing distance from the equator and decreasing distance from the oceans.
      c. decreasing distance from the equator and decreasing distance from the oceans.
      d. decreasing distance from the equator and increasing distance from the oceans.

THE WORLD'S BIOMES

M   10. In general, which list places the terms in order of increasing size?
      a. ecosystem, biogeographical realm, biome, biosphere
      b. ecosystem, biome, biosphere, biogeographical realm
      c. biome, ecosystem, biogeographical realm, biosphere
  *   d. ecosystem, biome, biogeographical realm, biosphere

E   11. Productivity of a biome increases as
      a. water availability increases and elevation increases.
      b. water availability decreases and elevation increases.
  *   c. water availability increases and elevation decreases.
      d. water availability decreases and elevation decreases.

M   12. Which is NOT a biogeographical realm?
      a. Palearctic
      b. Ethiopian
  *   c. Pantropical
      d. Neotropical
      e. Nearctic

M   13. Mountains produce
      a. rain shadows on the windward sides.
      b. precipitation on the leeward sides.
  *   c. deserts on the leeward sides.
      d. extensive grasslands on the windward sides.
      e. all of the above

D   14. The first two scientists to divide the world into biogeographical realms were
      a. Lamarck and Cuvier.
      b. Linnaeus and Ray.
      c. Darwin and Huxley.
      d. Elowitz and Whipple.
  *   e. Sclater and Wallace.

E   15. The first widely accepted attempt at an analysis of biogeographical distribution of life used six
      a. biomes.
  *   b. realms.
      c. ecosystems.
      d. biotas.
      e. life zones.

M   16. The biome at the top of a very tall mountain at the equator would be
  *   a. alpine tundra.
        b. taiga (boreal forest).
        c. tropical rain forest.
        d. temperate deciduous forest.
        e. chaparral (shrublands).

E   17. The largest biome in North America is the
  *   a. taiga (evergreen coniferous).
        b. tundra.
        c. temperate grassland.
        d. temperate deciduous forest.
        e. chaparral (shrublands).

E   18. Most desert biomes are in close proximity to what other biome?
        a. tundra
  *   b. grasslands
        c. deciduous forests
        d. evergreen forests

E   19. The soil described as a mixture of sand, silt, clay, and humus is
        a. humus.
        b. sand.
        c. soil.
  *   d. loam.
        e. silt.

M   20. At which latitudes are deserts usually found?
        a. 0–15
        b. 15–25
  *   c. 25–40
        d. 40–60
        e. 60–90

M   21. In shrublands,
  *   a. cool winters are followed by prolonged drought.
        b. primary production is abundant throughout the year.
        c. there are constant cool temperatures throughout the year.
        d. winters are mild and summers are wet.
        e. precipitation occurs evenly year round.

M   22. The biome with the greatest range of daily temperature extremes is the
        a. tundra.
        b. taiga.
        c. tropical rain forest.
  *   d. desert.
        e. grassland.

M   23. The biome that is currently increasing in size most rapidly is
        a. tundra.
        b. taiga.
        c. tropical rain forest.
  *   d. desert.
        e. grassland.

E   24. The biome with the greatest diversity of life forms is
       a. tundra.
       b. taiga.
   *   c. tropical rain forest.
       d. desert.
       e. grassland.

E   25. The biome with the greatest amount of topsoil and the richest, most fertile soil is
       a. tundra.
       b. taiga.
       c. tropical rain forest.
       d. desert.
   *   e. grassland.

M   26. A biome with grasses as primary producers and scattered trees adapted to prolonged dry spells is known as a
       a. warm desert.
   *   b. savanna.
       c. tundra.
       d. taiga.
       e. chaparral.

E   27. In tropical rain forests,
   *   a. competition for available sunlight is intense.
       b. diversity is limited because the tall forest canopy shuts out most of the incoming light.
       c. conditions are extremely favorable for growing luxuriant food crops.
       d. there is little competition for resources.
       e. habitat partitioning is minimal.

M   28. The biome most closely associated with fire (and later, mudslides) is the
       a. desert.
       b. tropical rain forest.
   *   c. chaparral (dry shrublands).
       d. temperate deciduous forest.
       e. taiga.

E   29. In which biome is plant and animal life greatly "layered"?
       a. tundra
       b. taiga
   *   c. tropical rain forest
       d. desert
       e. grassland

M   30. A wind system that influences large climatic regions and reverses direction seasonally, producing dry and wet seasons, is referred to as
       a. a geothermal ecosystem.
       b. an upwelling.
       c. a taiga.
   *   d. a monsoon.
       e. a hurricane.

E   31. Which biome is characterized by plants whose leaves drop off in the wintertime?
       a. coniferous forest
       b. tundra
   *   c. temperate deciduous forest
       d. tropical rain forest
       e. all of the above

M 32. Concerning biomes where maple and beech trees are the dominant vegetation, which statement is true?
     a. Winters are mild.
     b. Rainfall is low.
     c. Rate of evaporation is low.
   * d. Soil nutrient concentration is high.

E 33. Which biome is a treeless plain that occurs around the Arctic Circle?
     a. chaparral
     b. taiga
     c. desert
     d. grassland
   * e. tundra

M 34. Permafrost and low rainfall are characteristic of which biome?
     a. boreal forest
     b. montane coniferous forest
   * c. tundra
     d. evergreen coniferous forest

M 35. Low temperature, short growing seasons, limited rainfall, dwarf trees, and herbaceous plants characterize the
   * a. tundra.
     b. taiga.
     c. temperate deciduous forest.
     d. grassland.
     e. tropical montane forests.

E 36. The taiga could best be described as what type of forest?
     a. deciduous
     b. thorn
   * c. evergreen coniferous
     d. broad-leafed
     e. shrub

E 37. The word *permafrost* is associated with which biome?
   * a. tundra
     b. taiga
     c. temperate deciduous forest
     d. grassland
     e. montane forest

D 38. Which is NOT true of a mature temperate deciduous forest?
     a. Larger predators and herbivores use the forest more for shelter than for food; they tend to feed in clearings.
     b. Extensive tree roots prevent a great deal of soil erosion.
   * c. The principal producers are the bushes and low-lying grasses.
     d. The mature trees are the primary energy foundation for the entire community and play a key role in recycling nutrients.
     e. All of the above are not true.

THE WATER PROVINCES

M 39. The greatest diversity of organisms in lake ecosystems is found in what zone?
     a. profundal
     b. limnetic
     c. thermocline
   * d. littoral

E   40. Freshwater lakes will turn over in the
        a. fall.
        b. winter.
        c. spring.
        d. summer.
    *   e. both a and c

M   41. In a lake, the open sunlit water with its suspended phytoplankton is referred to as
        which zone?
        a. epipelagic
    *   b. limnetic
        c. littoral
        d. profundal
        e. benthic

M   42. The profundal zone is characterized by
        a. plankton.
        b. algae.
        c. plants and animals.
    *   d. decomposers.
        e. all of the above

M   43. Thorough mixing of oxygen and nutrients within a lake occurs in
        a. winter and summer.
        b. winter and spring.
        c. spring and summer.
    *   d. spring and autumn.
        e. summer and autumn.

E   44. The upper and lower levels of a lake are separated by the
        a. limnetic zone.
    *   b. thermocline.
        c. littoral zone.
        d. lentic zone.
        e. eutrophic zone.

E   45. A lake in which minerals are scarce is
        a. profundal.
    *   b. oligotrophic.
        c. eutrophic.
        d. benthic.
        e. pelagic.

M   46. Oligotrophic lakes are characterized by all but which of the following?
        a. deep water
        b. steep banks
        c. abundant oxygen
        d. low nutrients
    *   e. high production of fish

M   47. Eutrophication refers to which change in a lake?
        a. decrease in depth
    *   b. increase in dissolved nitrogen and phosphorus
        c. increase in species diversity
        d. decrease in nutrient concentrations

M   48. Because thermal stratification is _____ prevalent in tropical oceans, they exhibit _____ productivity when compared to oceans in temperate regions.
             a. more; higher
        *   b. more; lower
             c. less; higher
             d. less; lower

M   49. Which zone of the ocean is found above the continental shelf?
             a. abyssal
             b. benthic
             c. pelagic
        *   d. neritic
             e. oceanic

M   50. Estuaries often exhibit a great degree of species diversity because
             a. saltwater and freshwater species are present.
             b. many species of the open ocean spend a portion of their life cycles in estuarine waters.
             c. there is a continued upwelling of nutrients.
        *   d. a and b
             e. a, b, and c

M   51. Water draining from the land mixes with seawater carried in on tides in which of the following?
             a. abyssal zone
             b. rift zone
             c. upwelling
        *   d. estuary
             e. pelagic zone

M   52. Differences in which factor determine the distribution of producer organisms in marine ecosystems?
             a. the intensity of incoming solar radiation
             b. the salinity of surface waters
             c. the availability of nutrients
        *   d. all of the above

M   53. Which are nursery grounds for shrimp and many marine forms?
             a. photic zones
             b. benthic zones
        *   c. estuaries
             d. pelagic zones
             e. limnetic areas

E   54. Which zone is characterized by organisms adapted to great pressures and continental darkness?
        *   a. abyssal
             b. benthic
             c. pelagic
             d. neritic
             e. eutrophic

E   55. The region where fresh water and salt water mix is the
             a. neteric zone.
        *   b. estuary.
             c. lotic zone.
             d. littoral region.
             e. pelagic zone.

M 56. The organisms that occupy the first trophic level near hydrothermal vents are
  a. detritivores.
* b. chemosynthetic bacteria.
  c. decomposers.
  d. photosynthetic bacteria.

Matching Questions

D 57. Choose the one most appropriate answer for each.

1 _____ bathyl zone
2 _____ biome
3 _____ cold deserts
4 _____ hydrothermal vents
5 _____ estuary
6 _____ savanna
7 _____ shortgrass prairie
8 _____ taiga
9 _____ tallgrass prairie
10 _____ deciduous forest
11 _____ littoral zone
12 _____ tropical rain forest
13 _____ tundra
14 _____ upwellings
15 _____ warm deserts

A. northern coniferous forest
B. strong vertical currents
C. Steinbeck and Michener lamented their disruption
D. mosaics of tall, coarse grasses, shrubs, and low trees, even humid forests; rainfall varies
E. shallow area near lakeshores
F. buffalo, Indians, and future fields of corn and wheat
G. has little variation in temperature and salinity; no light penetrates from surface
H. sagebrush communities of the western United States; frost and arid conditions
I. stratified communities with vines, orchids, and monkeys
J. where hot water spews from fissures
K. large daily temperature fluctuations; prickly pear cacti, ocotillo
L. dwarf willows, mosses, lichens, caribou, and lemmings
M. *Spartina*, eelgrass, and diatoms
N. a large region characterized by its large array of dominant primary producers
O. Southern Appalachian mountains; moderate rain, cold snowy winters; deer kept in check by hunters

Answers: 1. G   2. N   3. H   4. J   5. M   6. D
             7. C   8. A   9. F   10. O   11. E   12. I
            13. L   14. B   15. K

Classification Questions

Answer questions 58–62 in reference to the five biomes listed below:

    a. tundra
    b. grassland
    c. desert
    d. taiga (boreal forest)
    e. savanna

M   58. A tropical plant community composed primarily of shrubby trees widely spaced and surrounded by grasses is which biome?

M   59. A community composed of herbaceous plants, no trees, a very short growing season, and relatively few animal species is likely to be which biome?

E   60. Which biome is characterized by variable daily temperatures and plants that are highly resistant to desiccation?

M   61. Which biome has the richest soils?

E   62. In which biome are conifers most likely to be found?

Answers: 58. e   59. a   60. c   61. b   62. d

Answer questions 63–67 in reference to the five biomes listed below:

    a. tundra
    b. chaparral
    c. desert
    d. taiga (coniferous forest)
    e. deciduous forest

M   63. In which biome could you find a black spruce?

E   64. In which biome are you most likely to find sagebrush?

M   65. In which biome would you expect to find caribou?

E   66. Which biome would be most likely to have a black oak?

M   67. Which biome is most likely to have a population of moose?

Answers: 63. d   64. b   65. a   66. e   67. d

Selecting the Exception

E   68. Four of the five answers listed below are characteristics of the tropical rain forest. Select the exception.
    a. slash and burn
    b. great diversity
    c. highly stratified
    d. lack of nutrients
  * e. large herds of herbivores

E 69. Four of the five answers listed below are related by a common biome. Select the exception.
   a. no trees
   b. permafrost
   c. short growing seasons
* d. found in the rain shadows
   e. may be found above Arctic Circle or at top of mountains

D 70. Four of the five answers listed below are related by a similar habitat. Select the exception.
   a. neritic zone
* b. littoral zone
   c. benthic province
   d. pelagic province
   e. abyssal zone

CHAPTER 37
HUMAN IMPACT ON THE BIOSPHERE

Multiple-Choice Questions

ENVIRONMENTAL EFFECTS OF HUMAN POPULATION GROWTH

M   1. Carbon dioxide is a pollutant because it
       a. is absorbed by the ocean and converted into insoluble carbonates.
       b. is liberated when fossil fuel is burned.
       c. is a waste product of respiration.
   *   d. cannot be recycled at a rate equal to its present production.

M   2. The foundation for rapid population growth in the world occurred about 10,000 years ago with improvements in
       a. recycling.
       b. medicine.
       c. science.
   *   d. agriculture.
       e. forestry.

CHANGES IN THE ATMOSPHERE

M   3. In the United States, how many metric tons of pollutants are discharged into the atmosphere each day?
       a. 1,000
       b. 100,000
   *   c. 700,000
       d. 5 million
       e. 15 to 30 million

E   4. Air pollution
       a. reduces visibility.
       b. corrodes buildings.
       c. causes various human diseases.
       d. damages plants.
   *   e. all of the above

E   5. Air pollution may cause
       a. lung cancer.
       b. emphysema.
       c. bronchitis.
       d. burning eyes.
   *   e. all of the above

M   6. Chlorofluorocarbons (CFCs) are pollutants because
   *   a. biogeochemical mechanisms for their removal have not yet appeared in the biosphere.
       b. they combine with water to form hydrochloric and hydrofluoric acids.
       c. they are found in smog.
       d. they are photochemical oxidants.

M   7. The atmosphere above which region is known to have a hole in the ozone layer?
   *   a. Antarctica
       b. Eastern North America
       c. Northern Europe
       d. the western Pacific

M   8. Each factor appears to be correlated with a decrease in atmospheric ozone EXCEPT
        a. suppression of the immune system.
        b. decreased rates of photosynthesis.
        c. increased incidence of skin cancers.
    *   d. decreased levels of atmospheric carbon dioxide.

M   9. Uses of chlorofluorocarbons include each of the following EXCEPT
    *   a. gasoline additives.
        b. aerosol propellants.
        c. refrigeration coolants.
        d. plastic packaging.

M   10. Which acid is a severe air pollutant?
        a. carbonic acid
    *   b. nitric acid
        c. hydrofluoric acid
        d. hydrochloric acid
        e. boric acid

E   11. Acid rain
        a. attacks nylons.
        b. attacks marble statues.
        c. causes toxic metals to become motile in the ecosystem.
        d. can be reduced in the local area by tall smokestacks.
    *   e. all of the above

M   12. Each substance contributes to wet acid deposition EXCEPT
    *   a. ozone.
        b. waste products from the burning of coal.
        c. nitrogen fertilizers.
        d. waste products from the burning of gasoline.

M   13. Acid rain is NOT a serious problem in some areas because of the presence of which substance in the soil?
        a. granite
    *   b. carbonate
        c. clay
        d. sand

M   14. The unequal distribution of acid rain over the United States is closely correlated with
        a. per capita energy use.
        b. fertilizer use.
    *   c. burning fossil fuels.
        d. average summer temperatures.

M   15. The region of the United States most affected by acid rain is the
        a. Northwest.
        b. Southwest.
    *   c. Northeast.
        d. Southeast.

E   16. Transportation-produced smog causes air to turn
        a. gray.
        b. black.
    *   c. brown.
        d. red.
        e. blue.

M   17.   A thermal inversion refers to
          a.   an abnormal occurrence not predicted by meteorologists.
          b.   an Indian summer.
          c.   an unusually quick change in weather patterns.
          d.   the process of cool air drainage at night.
    *   e.   a layer of cool air trapped underneath a warm air blanket.

E   18.   When fossil fuel burning gives off particulates and sulfur oxides, we have
          a.   photochemical smog.
    *   b.   industrial smog.
          c.   a thermal inversion.
          d.   both a and c
          e.   all of the above

E   19.   Industrial smog causes air to turn
    *   a.   gray.
          b.   black.
          c.   brown.
          d.   red.
          e.   blue.

M   20.   Which city has brown fog?
          a.   London
    *   b.   Los Angeles
          c.   Chicago
          d.   New York
          e.   Pittsburgh

M   21.   When fossil fuel burning gives off particulates and sulfur oxides, what results?
          a.   photochemical smog
    *   b.   industrial smog
          c.   a thermal inversion
          d.   both a and c, but not b
          e.   all of the above

M   22.   Which factor is NOT characteristic of a city primarily plagued by industrial smog?
          a.   high concentration of sulfur oxides
          b.   dependence on fossil fuel for manufacturing
          c.   cold, wet winters
    *   d.   high concentration of nitrogen oxides

M   23.   Which factor is NOT characteristic of a city primarily plagued by photochemical smog?
    *   a.   high concentration of sulfur oxides
          b.   high concentration of nitrogen oxides
          c.   significant amounts of PANs
          d.   large numbers of internal combustion engines

M   24.   In brown air fog, which substance combines with nitrogen dioxide in the sunlight to form photochemical smog?
          a.   carbon monoxide
          b.   water vapor
    *   c.   hydrocarbons
          d.   sulfuric acid
          e.   all of the above

D 25. What results when nitrogen dioxide and hydrocarbons react in the presence of sunlight?
* a. photochemical smog
  b. industrial smog
  c. a thermal inversion
  d. both a and c
  e. all of the above

CHANGES IN THE HYDROSPHERE

E 26. For every million liters of water in the world, only about _____ liters are in a form that can be used for human consumption or agriculture.
* a. 6
  b. 60
  c. 600
  d. 6,000

E 27. Primary treatment of sewage involves
* a. filtration and sedimentation, which physically treats water.
  b. the biological degradation of the organic material.
  c. the most expensive sewage treatment process.
  d. the chemical treatment of the water to neutralize its effects.
  e. chlorination or ultrasonic vibration, removal of nitrogen from ammonia, and precipitation of phosphate compounds.

M 28. After secondary sewage treatment, the water may contain all of the following EXCEPT
  a. viruses.
  b. oxygen-demanding wastes.
  c. nitrates and phosphates.
* d. large suspended solids.
  e. pesticides and industrial chemicals.

M 29. Which process is NOT generally considered a component of tertiary wastewater treatment?
* a. microbial action
  b. precipitation of suspended solids
  c. reverse osmosis
  d. absorption of dissolved organic compounds

M 30. Primary treatment of wastewater does NOT involve using which of the following?
  a. sedimentation tanks
* b. aeration with pure oxygen
  c. mechanical screens
  d. chemicals such as aluminum sulfate

M 31. Irrigated land accounts for approximately what percentage of human food production?
  a. 10
* b. 30
  c. 50
  d. 75

M 32. Which is NOT a result or effect of irrigation?
  a. increased food production
  b. waterlogging of soil
  c. raised water tables
* d. alteration of soil type

CHANGES IN THE LAND

E   33. About how many beverage containers sold in the United States each year are nonreturnable cans and bottles, many of which are discarded in public places?
   a. 25 million
   b. 25 billion
   c. 50 million
 * d. 50 billion
   e. 100 million

E   34. What percentage of urban wastes are paper products?
   a. 10
   b. 20
 * c. 50
   d. 75
   e. more than 90

E   35. Using recycled paper could reduce the air pollution that results from paper manufacturing by
   a. 50 percent.
 * b. 95 percent.
   c. 5 percent.
   d. 0 percent.
   e. 75 percent.

E   36. Landfills should contain
   a. all garbage.
   b. nonbiodegradable wastes.
 * c. nonrecycled solid wastes.
   d. glass and metallic debris.
   e. organic litter.

E   37. How many trees are required just to print all the Sunday newspapers in the United States?
   a. 1 million
   b. 100,000
 * c. 500,000
   d. 2 billion
   e. None because all the paper is recycled.

M   38. Approximately 50 percent of the billions of tons of solid wastes produced in the United States is
   a. glass.
 * b. paper.
   c. aluminum.
   d. plastic.

M   39. Of the earth's land, what is the maximum percentage now being used for agriculture?
   a. 10
 * b. 21
   c. 50
   d. 75

M   40. The new high-yield crops require which of the following that cannot be supplied by subsistence agriculture?
   a. irrigation
   b. pesticides
   c. fertilizers
   d. fossil fuel energy
 * e. all of the above

M   41. For a given crop yield, modern agricultural practices require how many times more energy and mineral resources than is required by subsistence agricultural practices?
        a. .01
        b. .25
        c. 4
        d. 25
    *   e. 100

M   42. Tropical plants or their products have provided humans with all of the following EXCEPT
        a. medicines.
    *   b. grain.
        c. spices.
        d. fuel.

M   43. Deforestation results in
        a. increased air temperatures.
        b. decreased soil fertility.
        c. decreased transpiration rates of individual plants.
    *   d. a and b
        e. a, b, and c

M   44. At current rates of clearing and degradation, the disappearance of the tropical rain forest biome will be complete by the year
    *   a. 2035.
        b. 2100.
        c. 2150.
        d. 2200.

M   45. The primary cause of desertification in the world today is
        a. increased salinity resulting from irrigation practices.
    *   b. overgrazing of marginal lands.
        c. clearing and degradation of tropical forests.
        d. herbicide and fertilizer runoff.

A QUESTION OF ENERGY INPUTS

E   46. Colorado, Utah, and Wyoming have large amounts of _____, which can be used to produce shale oil.
        a. pyrite
    *   b. kerogen
        c. coal
        d. tar or asphalt
        e. kerosene

E   47. The most harmful element in coal that causes serious pollution problems is
        a. nitrogen.
        b. silver.
        c. carbon.
    *   d. sulfur.
        e. chlorine.

M   48. If one kind of plutonium isotope is not removed, the wastes from a nuclear power reactor must be kept out of the environment for how many years before they are safe?
  a. 25
  b. 250
  * c. 250,000
  d. 1 million
  e. 250 million

M   49. Which statement about nuclear power plants is true?
  * a. Their net energy production is relatively low.
  b. Their waste products lead to the production of acid rain.
  c. Their waste products are not radioactive.
  d. a and b
  e. a, b, and c

M   50. Problems associated with the extraction or use of oil shale as a large-scale source of energy include all of the following EXCEPT
  a. high cost of extraction.
  * b. fragility of the continental shelf environment.
  c. water-intensive extraction processes.
  d. production of potential pollutants.

M   51. Problems associated with the extraction or use of coal as a large-scale source of energy include all of the following EXCEPT
  a. production of sulfur oxides.
  b. stripmining in fragile semiarid environments.
  * c. limited reserves.
  d. amplification of the general warming trend of the earth.

E   52. The intentional damaging of the environment as an instrument of war is termed
  a. photochemical warfare.
  * b. environmental terrorism.
  c. chemical warfare.
  d. biological weaponry.
  e. nuclear winter.

Matching Questions

D   53.   Choose the one most appropriate answer for each.

1 _____ breeder reactor

2 _____ dry acid depositions

3 _____ fossil fuels

4 _____ salination

5 _____ fusion power

6 _____ kerogen

7 _____ meltdown

8 _____ oil shale

9 _____ primary treatment

10 _____ PANS

11 _____ reverse osmosis

12 _____ thermal inversion

13 _____ secondary treatment

A. a process that is part of tertiary wastewater treatment

B. could happen in a conventional nuclear fission reactor

C. coal, oil, gas

D. photochemical smog component, like tear gas

E. dense air trapped beneath a layer of warm air

F. its reactions resemble those occurring in the sun

G. depends on microbial action

H. buried rock rich in a source of energy

I. forms sludge from coarse, suspended solids

J. generates plutonium, the most toxic substance known

K. a hydrocarbon compound found in oil shale

L. tiny particles that attack marble and cause crop damage

M. salt deposition that results from irrigating arid zone soils

Answers: 1. J   2. L   3. C   4. M   5. F   6. K

            7. B   8. H   9. I   10. D   11. A   12. E

            13. G

Selecting the Exception

E   54.   Four of the five answers listed below are particulate wastes. Select the exception.
- a. smoke
- b. soot
- c. asbestos
- d. dust
- * e. ozone

E   55.   Four of the five answers listed below are nonrenewable resources. Select the exception.
- * a. biomass
- b. coal
- c. natural gas
- d. oil
- e. nuclear

M   56.   Four of the five answers listed below are effects of acid rain. Select the exception.
- a. attacks marble, metals, mortar, nylons
- * b. causes air inversion and pollution events
- c. makes toxic heavy metals more mobile
- d. has different effects in different watersheds
- e. produces sterile lakes

M   57. Four of the five answers listed below are human efforts to improve the carrying capacity of
            the earth for humans. Select the exception.
    *   a. desertification
         b. recycling
         c. green revolution
         d. irrigation
         e. conservation

CHAPTER 38
ANIMAL BEHAVIOR

Multiple-Choice Questions

MECHANISMS UNDERLYING BEHAVIOR

M   1. Which statement is false?
- a. Behavior is controlled by the environmental stimuli an organism receives.
- b. Behavior is partially genetic so that it undergoes natural selection and evolution.
- * c. Behavior refers only to responses to external stimuli.
- d. Behavior sometimes is nonadaptive.
- e. Behavior patterns can be learned.

M   2. The pineal gland responds to
- a. light intensity.
- * b. light duration or photoperiod.
- c. flashes of light.
- d. red light.
- e. different colors of light.

M   3. Melatonin specifically controls or interacts to control
- a. the growth of the gonads of birds.
- b. migration.
- c. sexual behavior patterns.
- d. singing and territorial behavior.
- * e. all of the above

M   4. Which hormone activates the song system when a bird sings?
- a. melatonin
- * b. testosterone
- c. thyroxin
- d. calcitonin
- e. epinephrin

M   5. Each statement concerning behavior is true EXCEPT
- a. the knee-jerk reflex is a behavior.
- * b. a behavior such as a complex courtship ritual is encoded by a single gene.
- c. behaviors are products of natural selection.
- d. behaviors are adaptive.

M   6. Behavior is the result of
- a. neural networks.
- b. hormonal interactions.
- c. genetic predisposition.
- d. environmental cues.
- * e. all of the above

INSTINCTIVE AND LEARNED BEHAVIOR

M   7. Bird song
- a. has to be heard before a bird can sing it.
- b. is learned during early life.
- c. is specific for each bird species.
- d. has a genetic component.
- * e. all of the above

M 8. Instinctive behavior is
   a. stereotyped.
   b. unlearned.
   c. induced each and every time the stimulus is presented.
   d. triggered by limited sets of clues.
 * e. all of the above

E 9. To get a young baby to smile, simply present a
   a. parent's smiling face.
   b. parent's nonsmiling face.
   c. person's face or a mask.
   d. picture of a face.
 * e. representation of a face, so long as it has two recognizable eyes.

M 10. Associative learning is said to occur when
 * a. two different stimuli elicit the same response.
   b. two different stimuli elicit two different responses.
   c. one stimulus elicits one response.
   d. one stimulus elicits two different responses.

E 11. Konrad Lorenz is noted for his studies on
   a. prenatal marking.
   b. mating behavior.
 * c. imprinting.
   d. habituation.
   e. insight learning.

E 12. Newly hatched baby geese follow any large moving objects to which they are exposed
   shortly after hatching. This is an example of
   a. homing behavior.
 * b. imprinting.
   c. piloting.
   d. migration.
   e. none of the above

M 13. Recent studies in humans have shown there is a close relationship between poor nutrition
   and poor learning ability. These studies suggest that
   a. there is only a minor genetic component to learned behavior.
 * b. behavior is modified by the environment.
   c. learning is adaptive.
   d. learning is instinctive.

E 14. Learning by use of landmarks is
 * a. spatial.
   b. insight.
   c. operant.
   d. habituation.
   e. imprinting.

M 15. In classical conditioning,
 * a. two different stimuli elicit the same response.
   b. two different stimuli elicit two different responses.
   c. one stimulus elicits one response.
   d. one stimulus elicits two different responses.

M   16.   A child grabs a dog's ear, and the dog responds by biting the child. Both behaviors are repeated once again the next day, and again a day later. The child never grabs a dog's ear again. This sequence of events is an example of
        a.   insight learning.
        b.   latent learning.
     * c.   operant conditioning.
        d.   imprinting.

E   17.   The ability of a rat to solve a maze to obtain a reward is increased if it has the chance to explore the maze before the test begins. This is an example of
        a.   insight learning.
     * b.   latent learning.
        c.   associative learning.
        d.   conditioning.
        e.   extinction.

D   18.   Horticulturists use periodic discharges of loud sounds to scare birds away from their fruit trees. After several days birds can be seen ignoring the sounds due to
     * a.   habituation.
        b.   imprinting.
        c.   conditioning.
        d.   insight learning.
        e.   instinct.

D   19.   Humans, and other primates to some extent, differ from other animals in their ability to learn by
        a.   conditioning.
        b.   imprinting.
        c.   habituation.
     * d.   insight.
        e.   latent learning.

THE ADAPTIVE VALUE OF BEHAVIOR

M   20.   The example used to demonstrate that Darwinian natural selection explains some behavioral traits better than group selection does is
        a.   the dilution effect in wildebeest and zebra populations.
        b.   siblicide among egrets.
        c.   courtship behavior in albatrosses.
     * d.   the dispersal of Norwegian lemmings when population densities became extremely high.
        e.   all of the above

M   21.   In many bird and mammal species, males compete for females, but females do NOT compete for males because
        a.   males are larger than females.
        b.   females are larger than males.
     * c.   females produce fewer gametes than males do.
        d.   females compete for territory.

D   22.   During aggressive encounters between members of the same species,
        a.   the strong members are always victorious.
        b.   the invader into a territory is able to replace the current resident of the territory unless he has already mated.
     * c.   opponents usually settle the dispute without bloodshed.
        d.   a fight to the death occurs, with the one higher in the pecking order being successful more often.

MECHANISMS OF SOCIAL LIFE

E   23. In the termite colony described in the text, the soldier termites defend the colony by
       a. stinging the invaders.
       b. removing the legs of the invaders.
       c. blinding the invaders.
   * d. covering the invaders with a sticky substance.
       e. decapitating the invaders after an exhausting combat.

E   24. Pheromones are
   * a. used in nonverbal communication.
       b. found only in the invertebrates.
       c. signals to members of other species.
       d. types of internal hormones that control maturation.

E   25. Pheromones are advantageous because
       a. they work in the dark.
       b. they are often unique to individual species.
       c. only small amounts are needed.
       d. they do not trigger a response in other species.
   * e. all of the above

M   26. Communication by means of visual signals has a minimum requirement of
       a. daylight.
       b. short distance.
   * c. a clear line of sight.
       d. keen eyesight.
       e. sharp hearing.

E   27. The communication signal requiring the most minimal distance between the sender and receiver animals is
       a. visual.
       b. chemical.
       c. acoustical.
   * d. tactile.

E   28. Social behavior among insects depends on
       a. genetic similarity.
       b. bonding early in youth.
   * c. communication.
       d. diversity.
       e. polymorphism.

E   29. The initial alarm signal given by workers to indicate that the termite nest has been broken is
       a. odor.
       b. taste.
       c. sound.
   * d. a set of vibrations.
       e. contact between antennae.

E   30. Which scientist won the Nobel Prize for his research on the behavior of bees and the discovery of the way bees communicated the location of a food source?
   * a. Karl von Frisch
       b. Nicholas Tinbergen
       c. Konrad Lorenz
       d. Skinner
       e. Pavlov

E 31. Bees learn the direction to a distant source of food by
    a. following the foraging scout.
    b. following a trail pheromone.
  * c. observing the tail-wagging dance.
    d. observing the round dance.
    e. both c and d, but not a or b

M 32. Bees use which information for locating food and the hive?
    a. local topographic features
    b. wind direction
    c. magnetism
  * d. the angle of the sun
    e. distance between plants

COSTS AND BENEFITS OF SOCIAL LIFE

M 33. Which statement concerning subordinate behavior as exemplified by interactions among members of wolf packs is true?
    a. It is gradually being removed by natural selection.
  * b. It is adaptive.
    c. It is self-sacrificing.
    d. It is inexplicable in terms of reproductive success.

E 34. A submissive animal that exposes its throat or genitals to a dominant member of the same group is said to be engaging in what type of behavior?
  * a. appeasement
    b. avoidance
    c. ritualized
    d. dispersive
    e. all of the above

M 35. The example used to demonstrate that competitive interactions lead to the formation of dominance hierarchies involved
    a. albatrosses.
    b. a honeybee colony.
  * c. baboon troops.
    d. greylag geese.
    e. all of the above

M 36. Which behavior is exhibited when one animal meets or interacts with a superior member of its group?
    a. aggressive
    b. neutral
    c. sexual
  * d. appeasement
    e. all of the above, at certain times

M 37. When researchers attempt to answer the question of why various animals exist in such a diversity of social units from solitary to complex societies, they use
    a. genetic analysis.
    b. habitat data.
  * c. cost-benefit analysis.
    d. environmental studies.
    e. time-density data.

D 38. All but which of the following are disadvantages to sociality?
 * a. predator avoidance
  b. cannibalism
  c. food depletion
  d. contagious diseases
  e. parasite infestation

D 39. The presence of the strongest competitors in the center of a group of animals may qualify the group for status as a(n)
  a. altruistic society.
 * b. selfish herd.
  c. kin group.
  d. dominance hierarchy.

THE EVOLUTION OF ALTRUISM

E 40. Altruistic behavior is
  a. selfish.
  b. sexually directed behavior.
 * c. self-sacrificing behavior.
  d. aggressive behavior.
  e. nonreactive, such as freezing at the sign of danger.

M 41. In highly integrated insect societies
  a. natural selection favors individual behaviors that lead to greater diversity among members of the society.
  b. there is scarcely any division of labor.
 * c. cooperative behavior predominates.
  d. patterns of behavior are flexible, and learned behavior predominates.

E 42. A female insect can often be distinguished from the male by her
  a. wing patterns.
  b. mating calls.
 * c. larger size.
  d. bigger antennae.
  e. longer feet.

D 43. Altruism in animals other than humans is
 * a. probably a perception by human observers.
  b. gene-based.
  c. a conscious effort to preserve the species.
  d. just lucky behavior.

HUMAN SOCIAL BEHAVIOR

D 44. Only in judging human behaviors does the concept of "_____" supplant "adaptation."
  a. self-sacrifice.
  b. altruism
  c. judgment
 * d. morality

Matching Questions

D   45.   Choose the one most appropriate answer for each. Some letters may not be used.

1 _____ altruism

2 _____ insight

3 _____ instinctive behavior

4 _____ imprinting

5 _____ learning

6 _____ Lorenz

7 _____ lek

A. communal display ground

B. imprintings in baby geese

C. capacity of an animal to complete complex, stereotyped responses to first-time encounters to key stimuli

D. problem solving without trial and error

E. an adaptive change in behavior

F. occurs during a sensitive period in which a following response or social attachment becomes fixed on a particular moving object

G. self-sacrificing behavior

Answers: 1. G   2. D   3. C   4. F   5. E   6. B
                 7. A

Classification Questions

Answer questions 46–50 in reference to the five kinds of behavior listed below:

      a. imprinting
      b. sexual selection
      c. anti-predator behavior
      d. female-defense behavior
      e. altruism

M   46.   The extreme variation observed among the males of various species of ducks is thought to be due to which of the above kinds of behavior?

E   47.   Many organisms increase their apparent size when startled by another. This is an example of which behavior?

E   48.   If the young of newly hatched birds (for example, chickens or ducks) are continually shown a large moving object during the first few days of their lives, they will follow that object. This is an example of what?

M   49.   The adult male who jumps overboard to save a drowning niece is exhibiting what behavior?

M   50.   Two male bison butting one another during the breeding season are probably exhibiting which behavior?

Answers: 46. b   47. c   48. a   49. e   50. d

Answer questions 51–55 in reference to the four kinds of reception listed below that are used by social animals:

      a. tactile
      b. auditory
      c. visual
      d. chemical

M   51.   Which sensory modality is used by honey bees during the waggle dance?

E   52.   The sex pheromone emitted by a female gypsy moth relies on which of the male senses?

E 53. The elaborate posturing displays of male birds of paradise use which of the female senses?

D 54. What is the primary signal sent out by receptive female primates likely to be?

D 55. What is the alarm signal one snail sends to another most likely to be?

Answers: 51. a   52. d   53. c   54. d   55. d

Answer questions 56–60 in reference to the four kinds of social behavior listed below:
a. altruism
b. cooperation
c. self-sacrifice
d. kin selection

D 56. When the offspring of one brood of Florida scrubjays help their parents in taking care of their siblings in the next brood, this is an example of which behavior?

M 57. When a bluejay gives an alarm call at the intrusion of a crow into a woodlot, this is an example of which behavior?

E 58. When two or more female lions attack a wildebeest together, this is an example of which behavior?

M 59. When a female woodcock flutters off her nest exhibiting a cripple-wing display to distract a predator, this is an example of which behavior?

M 60. When a woman raises her brother's children, this is an example of which behavior?

Answers: 56. d   57. a   58. b   59. c   60. d

Selecting the Exception

E 61. Four of the five answers listed below are behaviors that are inborn. Select the exception.
  * a. modified by the environment
      b. stereotyped
      c. performed the first time stimulus is presented
      d. innate
      e. automatic

M 62. Four of the five answers listed below are characteristic of associative learning. Select the exception.
      a. reward
      b. punishment
      c. trial and error
      d. selection
  * e. ignoring stimulus

M 63. Four of the five answers listed below are castes of termites. Select the exception.
  * a. drone
      b. king
      c. queen
      d. soldier
      e. worker

M   64.   Four of the five answers listed below are activities of the same type of bee. Select the exception.
*   a.   lay eggs
   b.   feed larvae
   c.   guard hive
   d.   clean and maintain nest
   e.   forage for food

INTERACTIVE ELECTRONIC
STUDY GUIDE QUESTIONS

CHAPTER 1
METHODS AND CONCEPTS IN BIOLOGY

1. The instructions for each trait passed on from one generation to another are found in
   a. blood.
   b. semen.
   c. deoxyribonucleic acid.
   d. proteins.

   a. no; an old wives' tale, blood has no impact on heredity
   b. no; this is only the fluid that contains sperm
   *c. yes; the chemical name for a gene
   d. no; proteins are complex organic chemicals that have a large number of functions, but heredity is not one of them

2. Diversity found in living organisms is a result of
   a. natural selection.
   b. biogenesis.
   c. biosynthesis.
   d. life.

   *a. yes; the environment influences which forms will survive
   b. no; living organisms produce living organisms, but this is not a sufficient explanation by itself for the differences we see
   c. no; different biosynthetic pathways result in different end-products, but this does not explain all of the differences we see
   d. no; does not explain the source of diversity

3. Life is
   a. a way of capturing and using energy and materials.
   b. a commitment to programs of growth and development and a capacity for reproduction.
   c. adaptive both in the short term and through subsequent generations.
   d. all of the above

   a. yes; a partial answer
   b. yes; a partial answer
   c. yes; a partial answer
   *d. yes; all of the above (and more) are correct

4. The basic unit of life is a(n)
   a. population.
   b. organ.
   c. cell.
   d. ecosystem.

   a. no; a group of living and interbreeding members of the same species
   b. no; a group of living tissues united to perform common functions
   *c. yes; the fundamental unit of life whether considering unicellular or multicellular organisms
   d. no; consists of both living and nonliving components

5. Which of the following is the most inclusive?
   a. community
   b. population
   c. ecosystem
   d. biosphere

   a. no; part of an ecosystem
   b. no; part of a community
   c. no; part of the biosphere
   *d. yes; includes all of the ecosystems

6. A community is composed of
   a. individual organisms.
   b. different species.
   c. various populations.
   d. all of the above

   a. yes; a partial answer; composed of groups of interacting individuals (populations)
   b. yes; a partial answer; different species are found in communities
   c. yes; a partial answer; all of the populations of an area form a community
   *d. yes; all of the above are correct

7. Which of the following levels of organization include the chemical and physical environment as well as the living components?
   a. individual organisms
   b. ecosystems
   c. communities
   d. populations

   a. no; include only the single organism
   *b. yes; include both the physical features and the organisms
   c. no; include only living populations
   d. no; include only interacting individuals of same species

8. The great pattern of organization in nature is maintained by the
   a. flow of energy from the sun.
   b. annual climatic changes.
   c. action of animals in the control of nature.
   d. activity of microorganisms.

   *a. yes; essentially all energy comes from the sun
   b. no; may affect natural phenomena but are not responsible for its organization
   c. no; may contribute, but other factors are at work
   d. no; important controlling factor in some facets of nature

9. The compound most intimately associated with energy transfer in living organisms is
   a. oxygen.
   b. ATP.
   c. glucose.
   d. fat.

   a. no; anaerobic respiration involves the liberation of energy without free oxygen
   *b. yes; adenosine triphosphate has high-energy phosphate bonds that can be transferred from one compound to another
   c. no; glucose may function as a source of energy but is not a transfer agent
   d. no; fats represent an effective way to store but not to transfer energy

10. Homeostasis is the
    a. maintenance of a constant internal environment.
    b. application of a positive feedback system in living organisms.
    c. use of the buffer system of the body.
    d. recovery from stress.

    *a. yes; by definition homeostasis involves the maintenance of a dynamic equilibrium
    b. no; negative feedback systems are usually involved
    c. no; an example of only one facet of a homeostatic system
    d. no; homeostasis may be involved in recovery, but this concept is more appropriately termed resiliency

11. Which stage in the metamorphosis of a moth involves extensive remodeling and reorganization of moth tissue?
    a. egg
    b. adult
    c. larva
    d. pupa

    a. no; a stage of inactivity
    b. no; the organism is mature
    c. no; a period of active growth and development
    *d. yes; the insect undergoes complete structural change that may involve change in appearance, habitat, life style, etc.

12. Most mutations are
    a. harmful.
    b. neutral.
    c. beneficial.
    d. none of the above

    *a. yes; any change in a functional gene that has withstood natural selection over evolutionary time is most likely to be nonadaptive and therefore harmful
    b. no; a number of mutations might not have any harmful effect, but they would be hard to identify
    c. no; if most mutations were beneficial, then the organism's phenotypes (physical characteristics) would be highly volatile and organisms would be subjected to continual change
    d. no; one of the above is correct

13. Which of the following is the least inclusive of those taxonomic categories listed?
    a. class
    b. family
    c. phylum
    d. order

    a. no; all related orders belong to the same class
    *b. yes; all related genera (not listed) are placed in the same family
    c. no; all related classes belong to the same phylum
    d. no; all related families belong to the same order

14. The simplest forms of life belong to the Kingdom
    a. Plantae.
    b. Fungi.
    c. Protista.
    d. Monera.

    a. no; eukaryotic, multicellular
    b. no; eukaryotic, multicellular
    c. no; eukaryotic
    *d. yes; prokaryotic, lacks a nucleus and membrane-bound organelles

15. Charles Darwin cited breeding experiments with _____ to show how selection could occur in a population.
    a. pigeons
    b. cats
    c. fruit flies
    d. dogs

    *a. yes; a common pet used in competitive shows, similar to cat and dog shows
    b. no; available, but not used by Darwin
    c. no; used by Thomas H. Morgan and others in the twentieth century in genetic research
    d. no; a commonly used example, but not used by Darwin

16. Which of the following points apply (applies) to the process of evolution?
    a. More organisms are produced than can possibly survive.
    b. Differential reproduction is a form of natural selection.
    c. Over time the characteristics of a species might change.
    d. all of the above

    a. yes; a partial answer; a large number of organisms leads to a decline in necessary support systems
    b. yes; a partial answer; the environment (through natural selection) determines which members of a population will have the greatest and least genetic impact on the next generation
    c. yes; a partial answer; this statement could be used as a short definition for evolution
    *d. yes; all of the above are correct

17. A tentative explanation to account for an observation is a
    a. theory.
    b. hypothesis.
    c. principle.
    d. law.

    a. no; a generalization used to explain a series of observations
    *b. yes; a statement, often in the form of a question that can be tested
    c. no; a generalization used to explain a series of observations
    d. no; a generalization used to explain a series of observations

CHAPTER 2
CHEMICAL FOUNDATIONS FOR CELLS

1. All forms of matter are made up of one or more naturally occurring fundamental substances called
   a. atoms.
   b. molecules.
   c. compounds.
   d. none of the above

   a. no; the smallest unit of matter unique to an element
   b. no; a unit consisting of two or more atoms of the same element
   c. no; a unit consisting of two or more atoms of different elements
   *d. yes; none of the above is correct; the correct answer is element—the fundamental substance

2. The negatively charged subatomic particle is the
   a. nucleus.
   b. neutron.
   c. electron.
   d. proton.

   a. no; contains neutron and proton
   b. no; uncharged subatomic particle
   *c. yes; negatively charged subatomic particle
   d. no; positively charged subatomic particle

3. Isotopes of an element differ from other isotopes of the same element by the
   a. number of protons.
   b. number of neutrons.
   c. functions of the isotope in a biological organism.
   d. chemical properties of the isotope.

   a. no; atoms with the same number of protons are the same and fit in the same place (iso/tope = equal/place) in a periodic table
   *b. yes; isotopes have different atomic weights due to a difference in the number of neutrons
   c. no; isotopes behave the same biologically
   d. no; isotopes have the same number of protons so they behave the same chemically, but not physically,

4. If a person were injected with some radioactive iodine, it would appear in a radioisotope scan of the _____ gland.
   a. pancreas
   b. adrenal
   c. thyroid
   d. parotid

   a. no; not a site for iodine metabolism
   b. no; neither the adrenal medulla nor cortex concentrates iodine
   *c. yes; iodine is an element used in the manufacture of thyroid hormones
   d. no; the parotid gland is one of the salivary glands and does not use or concentrate iodine

5. In ionic bonding, the electrons of two or more atoms are
   a. shared.
   b. exchanged.
   c. lost or gained.
   d. attracted to positive charges of other atoms.

   a. no; typical of covalent bonding
   b. no; does not affect the characteristics of the atoms
   *c. yes; and the two atoms become ionized when the atoms separate
   d. no; this happens in the formation of polar bonds

6. Which of the following compounds could be used as an example of an ionic bond?
   a. hydrochloric acid
   b. glucose
   c. molecular nitrogen
   d. proteins

   *a. yes; the molecule will dissociate to form ions
   b. no; the carbon, hydrogen, and oxygen share electrons
   c. no; the nitrogen atoms share electrons
   d. no; the atoms are bound together by sharing electrons

7. Hydrophobic molecules tend to be
   a. inorganic minerals.
   b. nonpolar.
   c. ionic.
   d. water soluble.

   a. no; tend to form ionic compounds that would be water soluble
   *b. yes; do not mix with water
   c. no; readily dissociate in water, therefore hydrophilic
   d. no; water-soluble substances dissolve in water easily

8. Normal rainfall has a pH of
   a. 3.8.
   b. 5.6.
   c. 7.0.
   d. 8.1.

   a. no; but "acid precipitation" may be even more acidic
   *b. yes; the pH of rain is slightly acid
   c. no; a pH of 7 is neutral; dissolved material makes rain acidic
   d. no; slightly basic, too much so for normal rainfall

9. Buffers are chemical compounds that
   a. maintain a specific pH.
   b. make a solution neutral.
   c. prevent drastic changes in pH.
   d. absorb hydrogen ions to prevent a solution from becoming acidic.

   a. no; common misconception; would be accurate if there were an indication that buffers
      tended to maintain pH within a small range
   b. no; buffers can be prepared to control pH under acid or basic conditions·
   *c. yes; unless too many hydrogen or hydroxyl ions are added to the solution to exceed the
      buffer's capacity
   d. no; a buffer will absorb either hydrogen or hydroxyl ions

10. Organic compounds
    a. form long unbranched chains.
    b. may be branched.
    c. form rings.
    d. all of the above

    a. yes; a partial answer; such as hydrocarbons
    b. yes; a partial answer; such as tertiary butyl alcohol
    c. yes; a partial answer; such as benzene, purines, pyrimidines, steroids
    *d. yes; all of the above are correct

11. Which of the following compounds is a disaccharide?
    a. glucose
    b. ribose
    c. sucrose
    d. galactose

    a. no; a hexose monosaccharide
    b. no; a pentose monosaccharide
    *c. yes; composed of the two monosaccharides, glucose and fructose
    d. no; another hexose monosaccharide

12. A phospholipid is composed of a phosphate group, two fatty acids, and a(n)
    a. glycogen.
    b. glycerol.
    c. oil.
    d. polysaccharide.

    a. no; a polysaccharide
    *b. yes; glycerol forms the backbone of the molecule
    c. no; a type of fat characteristic of plants
    d. no; a form of carbohydrate, not a lipid

13. The building blocks of proteins are the
    a. nitrogenous bases.
    b. amino acids.
    c. nucleotides.
    d. fatty acids.

    a. no; components of nucleotides
    *b. yes; the sequence of amino acids controls the nature of proteins
    c. no; building blocks of nucleic acids
    d. no; components of fats

14. Nucleotides are composed of three parts: a five-carbon sugar, a phosphate group, and a(n)
    a. nitrogenous base.
    b. amino acid.
    c. carbohydrate residue.
    d. fatty acid.

    *a. yes
    b. no
    c. no
    d. no

CHAPTER 3
CELL STRUCTURE AND FUNCTION

1. All cells are characterized by all but which of the following?
   a. nucleus
   b. plasma membrane
   c. cytoplasm
   d. ribosomes

   *a. correct; prokaryotes have DNA molecules, but no definite nucleus
   b. incorrect; all cells have a plasma membrane to control internal composition
   c. incorrect; all cells have cytoplasm (even prokaryotes)
   d. incorrect; all cells have ribosomes (even prokaryotes)

2. Which of the following is NOT one of the premises of the cell theory?
   a. All living organisms are made of cells.
   b. Only plants and animals are composed of cells.
   c. Cells come from preexisting cells.
   d. Cells are the basic structural and functional units of life.

   a. incorrect; this is part of the cell theory
   *b. correct; fungi are multicellular and monera and some protista are unicellular
   c. incorrect; this is part of the cell theory
   d. incorrect; this is part of the cell theory

3. In 1665, Robert Hooke saw a _____ in a microscope and gave it the name of cell.
   a. red blood cell
   b. bacterium
   c. cork cell
   d. liver cell

   a. no
   b. no
   *c. yes
   d. no

4. Which of the following gives the greatest magnification?
   a. scanning electron microscope
   b. transmitting electron microscope
   c. compound light microscope
   d. interference contrast microscope

   a. no; very useful to study surface characteristics
   *b. yes; gives the greatest magnification
   c. no; maximum magnification is around 2,000×
   d. no; maximum magnification is around 2,000×

5. The most widely accepted current concept that best explains the functioning of a plasma membrane is a
   a. protein-lipid sandwich.
   b. lipid bilayer.
   c. fluid mosaic model.
   d. porous phospholipid lining.

   a. no; the membrane is made of both, but not accurately described as a sandwich
   b. no; not a complete explanation
   *c. yes; most recent explanation
   d. no; not a complete concept

6. Cellular gates or channels are
   a. openings through membrane proteins.
   b. spaces between cells.
   c. gaps in the nuclear envelope.
   d. none of the above

   *a. yes
   b. no; gap junctions may be involved
   c. no; pores may exist, but not usually referred to as gates or channels
   d. no; one of the above is correct

7. A red blood cell placed in a hypotonic solution will
   a. shrink.
   b. exhibit no change.
   c. swell or explode.
   d. form a sickle shape.

   a. no; this happens in a hypertonic solution
   b. no; there is no change in an isotonic solution
   *c. yes; as osmosis occurs, water moves from high to low concentration outside the cell to lower inside
   d. no; happens to some red blood cells under oxygen tension

8. Which of the following is a form of transport that does not involve the expenditure of energy?
   a. sodium-potassium pump
   b. osmosis
   c. endocytosis
   d. active transport

   a. no; involves movement against a concentration gradient
   *b. yes; controlled only by the water concentration and permeability of the membrane
   c. no; involves the construction of a vesicle that pinches off from the membrane
   d. no; requires the use of ATP and expenditure of energy

9. Which of the following organelles is involved in lipid synthesis?
   a. Golgi bodies
   b. lysosomes
   c. endoplasmic reticulum
   d. mitochondria

   a. no; involved in cellular secretion
   b. no; involved in cellular digestion
   *c. yes; involved in both lipid and protein synthesis
   d. no; involved in packaging energy

10. Which of the following cellular organelles is involved in cellular respiration?
    a. Golgi bodies
    b. lysosomes
    c. endoplasmic reticulum
    d. mitochondria

    a. no; involved in cellular secretion
    b. no; involved in cellular digestion
    c. no; involved in protein and lipid synthesis
    *d. yes; involved in cellular respiration

11. Which of the following structures would NOT be characteristic of most plant cells?
    a. a cellulose cell wall
    b. chloroplasts
    c. a centriole
    d. a central vacuole

    a. incorrect; characteristic of plants and some fungi and protista
    b. incorrect; used to produce food
    *c. correct; found in animal cells, but not common in plants (see diagram in text)
    d. incorrect; characteristic of many plant cells

12. Which of the following is one of the types of vesicles produced by the Golgi body?
    a. lysosomes
    b. ribosomes
    c. nucleolus
    d. chromatin

    *a. yes; contain digestive enzymes that destroy wastes and foreign particles
    b. no; associated with endoplasmic reticulum
    c. no; RNA-containing organelle in the nucleus
    d. no; nuclear material containing DNA

13. Which of the following is NOT associated with the internal transport system of a cell?
    a. vacuoles
    b. mitochondria
    c. microsomes
    d. endoplasmic reticulum

    a. incorrect; formed during endocytosis
    *b. correct; organelles associated with cellular respiration
    c. incorrect; formed as buds from endoplasmic reticulum and contain enzymes
    d. incorrect; the cytomembrane system through which many substances travel

14. Which organelle of a cell is shaped like a stack of pancakes?
    a. Golgi body
    b. mitochondrion
    c. chromatin
    d. nuclear envelope

    *a. yes; often molecules are packaged in secretory vesicles that break off from the Golgi body
    b. no; has an internal membrane but shaped more like a hot dog roll or a sphere
    c. no; a dispersed threadlike material filling the nucleus
    d. no; a double membrane surrounding the nucleus

15. The stacks of disks containing chlorophyll in a chloroplast are the
    a. grana.
    b. microfilaments.
    c. plastids.
    d. stroma.

    *a. yes; contain pigments and enzymes associated with photosynthesis
    b. no; part of the cytoskeleton
    c. no; pigmented organelles such as chloroplasts found in plant cells
    d. no; fluid surrounding the grana

16. _____ are found in flagella and cilia.
    a. Microtubules
    b. Intermediate filaments
    c. Microfilaments
    d. Spindle fibers

    *a. yes; a definite pattern of microtubules is found inside the flagella and cilia
    b. no
    c. no; found in muscle fibers
    d. no; involved in moving chromosomes during mitosis

17. Which of the following does NOT have a cell wall?
    a. plant cells
    b. fungal cells
    c. bacteria
    d. animal cells

    a. incorrect; have cell walls that give them shape
    b. incorrect; have cell walls that give them shape
    c. incorrect; cell walls give shape to bacteria
    *d. correct; do not have a cell wall

CHAPTER 4
GROUND RULES OF METABOLISM

1. The human body is estimated to have 65 _____ cells.
   a. thousand
   b. million
   c. billion
   d. trillion

   a. no; much more
   b. no; much more
   c. no; much more
   *d. yes

2. Which of the following is part of the first law of thermodynamics?
   a. Some energy is lost when it is transferred.
   b. The amount of energy in the universe is decreasing.
   c. The amount of energy in the universe is constant.
   d. The amount of energy in the universe is increasing.

   a. no; true but appropriate to the second law of thermodynamics
   b. no; energy may disperse and be less useful (entropy increases), but the amount is the same
   *c. yes; the law is often referred to as the law of conservation of matter and energy
   d. no; there is no source for additional energy input

3. The amount of high-quality energy in the universe
   a. is constantly increasing.
   b. is called entropy.
   c. is constant.
   d. continually declines.

   a. no; the direction is to reduce high-quality energy
   b. no; entropy refers to the decrease in high-quality energy
   c. no; high-quality energy is in high demand
   *d. yes; high-quality energy is continually used and converted to low-quality energy

4. Which of the following is an example of low-quality energy?
   a. atomic reactor
   b. starch in a potato
   c. heat in the atmosphere
   d. a barrel of crude oil

   a. no; represents high-quality energy that can be used to do work
   b. no; high-quality chemical energy that can be used as energy to contract muscles
   *c. yes; not concentrated and not a useful form of energy in a dispersed state
   d. no; a source of high-quality energy that can be used to power an internal combustion engine

5. Which of the following statements is false?
   a. The amount of entropy is increasing.
   b. The ultimate end of material things in the universe will be a state of maximum entropy.
   c. Billions of years from now the universe will consist of isolated hot spots with the remainder of the universe at a common low temperature.
   d. Living organisms do not represent a temporary exception to entropy.

   a. incorrect; statement is true; energy is being dispersed continually
   b. incorrect; statement is true; energy will be completely dispersed (maximum entropy)
   *c. incorrect; statement is true; all energy will be evenly dispersed
   d. correct; statement is false; they are able to concentrate energy, but it has to be continually supplied from elsewhere (the sun)

6. The flow of energy through an ecosystem is best described as a
   a. ladder.
   b. web.
   c. chain.
   d. cycle or circle.

   a. no; implies climbing rather than flowing down and through
   *b. yes; implies an intricate net of interconnected lines of energy flow
   c. no; too simple, although the web of life is made up of food chains
   d. no; nutrients cycle in the ecosystem; energy flow is one-way

7. In reversible biological reactions,
   a. the direction is dependent on the concentrations of the reactants and the products.
   b. the direction is dependent on the metabolic condition of the organism.
   c. the rates of forward and reverse reactions are the same in a dynamic equilibrium.
   d. all of the above

   a. yes; a partial answer
   b. yes; a partial answer
   c. yes; a partial answer
   *d. yes; all of the above are correct

8. Phenylketones in the genetic disorder phenylketonuria (PKU) lead to
   a. weight accumulation.
   b. accumulation of phenylalanine.
   c. mental retardation.
   d. none of the above

   a. no; not an obvious effect of phenylketones
   b. no; phenylalanine is a precursor to phenylketone
   *c. yes; the phenotypic expression of PKU includes mental retardation
   d. no; one of the above is correct

9. Enzymes are
   a. proteins.
   b. carbohydrates.
   c. nucleotides.
   d. steroids.

   *a. yes
   b. no
   c. no
   d. no

10. Which of the following is an energy carrier?
    a. enzymes
    b. adenosine triphosphate
    c. reactant
    d. cofactors

    a. no; organic catalysts that enable a reaction to occur
    *b. yes; the energy currency of a cell
    c. no; a possible source for the energy in high-energy bonds
    d. no; necessary components in enzyme systems

11. Metabolic pathways may be
    a. linear.
    b. cyclic.
    c. branched.
    d. all of the above

    a. yes; a partial answer
    b. yes; a partial answer
    c. yes; a partial answer
    *d. yes; all of the above are correct

12. Enzymes
    a. are the only way some biological reactions could occur.
    b. are nonspecific and can mediate a great many different reactions.
    c. are altered or used up by the reactions they control.
    d. act by lowering the activation energy required for a reaction to occur.

    a. no; enzymes only affect the speed of a reaction that would happen anyway
    b. no; enzymes are highly specific and limited in the type of reactions they can control
    c. no; enzymes can be used over and over again
    *d. yes; activation energy can be supplied by the enzyme or by other sources, such as heat

13. The activation site of an enzyme
    a. can be altered by excessive change in pH.
    b. may be distorted so that it will not bind with a substrate.
    c. can be destroyed by high temperatures such as found in high fevers.
    d. all of the above

    a. yes; a partial answer
    b. yes; a partial answer
    c. yes; a partial answer
    *d. yes; all of the above are correct

14. The characteristic dark color of the tail, ears, face, and paws of a Siamese cat is due to the fact that
    a. an enzyme inhibitor blocks the expression of the light color in these regions.
    b. the higher temperatures found in these regions tend to inactivate the enzyme controlling the production of melanin pigment.
    c. the lower temperatures found in these regions denature the enzyme necessary for the production of color.
    d. all of the above

    a. no; the color pattern is not due to an enzyme inhibitor in the dark areas
    *b. yes; a heat-sensitive enzyme controlling melanin pigment production would yield the typical color pattern
    c. no; the inactivation is produced by higher temperatures
    d. no; one of the above is correct

15. The sugar associated with ATP is
    a. glucose.
    b. ribose.
    c. deoxyribose.
    d. fructose.

    a. no
    *b. yes; a component of adenosine
    c. no
    d. no

16. Which statement about an energy transport system is true?
    a. Bioluminescence is a manifestation of electron transport.
    b. ATP is a precursor of ADP.
    c. Oxidized acceptors have more energy than reduced forms.
    d. A reduced cytochrome molecule may accept electrons from another molecule in the electron transport series.

    *a. correct; statement is true; energy is given off in the form of light
    b. incorrect; statement is false; ADP becomes ATP by adding a high-energy phosphate
    c. incorrect; statement is false; reduced acceptors release energy when they are oxidized or give up electrons
    d. incorrect; statement is false; oxidized acceptors become reduced when they accept an electron

CHAPTER 5
ENERGY-ACQUIRING PATHWAYS

1. In all living organisms, organic molecules have a backbone of _____ atoms.
   a. nitrogen
   b. oxygen
   c. carbon
   d. phosphorus

   a. no; important in some organic compounds such as proteins, but not found in others such as carbohydrates
   b. no; a common atom in most organic compounds, but does not form a backbone
   *c. yes; carbon chains form the center of all organic compounds
   d. no; found in a limited number of organic compounds

2. Organisms capable of extracting carbon and energy directly from the environment are called (select the *best* answer)
   a. plants.
   b. heterotrophs.
   c. autotrophs.
   d. photosynthesizers.

   a. no; generally acceptable, but many plants are parasitic
   b. no; heterotrophs obtain their energy and carbon from other organisms
   *c. yes; autotrophs include all organisms (plants, protists, and monerans) that synthesize their own food
   d. no; this choice leaves out those organisms that gain through chemosynthesis

3. Which of the following includes the chemosynthetic organisms?
   a. Plantae
   b. Fungi
   c. Protista
   d. Monera

   a. no; most are photosynthetic, few parasites and saprophytes
   b. no; mostly saprophytes (living on dead material)
   c. no; various forms of nutrition, but does not include chemosynthesis
   *d. yes; includes the chemosynthetic bacteria

4. Which pathway of degradation releases the most energy?
   a. aerobic respiration
   b. glycolysis
   c. fermentation
   d. putrefaction

   *a. yes; releases greatest amount of energy to be transferred to ATP
   b. no; only the first step in aerobic respiration
   c. no; anaerobic respiration releases only a small amount of energy locked in the glucose molecule through glycolysis
   d. no; anaerobic breakdown of proteins does not yield large amounts of energy

5. The hydrogen (electron) acceptor in the light-dependent reaction is
   a. FAD.
   b. oxygen.
   c. NADP.
   d. glucose.

   a. no; an acceptor in aerobic respiration
   b. no; an acceptor in aerobic respiration
   *c. yes; the hydrogen (electron) acceptor
   d. no; part of the light-independent reactions

6. Photosynthesis occurs in cytoplasmic organelles called
   a. Golgi bodies.
   b. chloroplasts.
   c. chromoplasts.
   d. mitochondria.

   a. no; specialized for secretion
   *b. yes; organelles with chlorophyll
   c. no; colored plastids lend colors to flowers and fruits
   d. no; cellular organelles associated with respiration

7. In plants, photosynthesis takes place in the
   a. stroma.
   b. cytoplasm.
   c. grana.
   d. both (a) and (c)

   a. yes; a partial answer; only the light-dependent reactions of photosynthesis occur here
   b. no; photosynthesis occurs only in association with chloroplasts
   c. yes; a partial answer; only the light-independent reactions of photosynthesis occur here
   *d. yes; both (a) and (c) are correct; photosynthesis includes both light-dependent and light-independent reactions

8. Which of the following colors is absorbed by carotenoid pigments?
   a. red
   b. blue
   c. yellow
   d. orange

   a. no; carotenoids reflect this color
   *b. yes; carotenoids absorb this color
   c. no; carotenoids reflect this color
   d. no; carotenoids reflect this color

9. Which color of light is reflected by chlorophyll?
   a. red
   b. blue
   c. orange
   d. green

   a. no; absorbed radiant energy converted to chemical energy
   b. no; absorbed radiant energy converted to chemical energy
   c. no; absorbed radiant energy converted to chemical energy
   *d. yes; this is why leaves appear green—we see the reflected light

10. The function of chlorophyll in the photosystems of chloroplasts is to
    a. harvest sunlight.
    b. release oxygen.
    c. reduce carbon dioxide.
    d. split water.

    *a. yes; they absorb the energy of the photons they receive
    b. no; an end result of noncyclic photophosphorylation
    c. no; occurs in the light-independent reactions
    d. no; end result of the absorption of energy

11. The oxygen liberated in photosynthesis comes from
    a. atmospheric oxygen.
    b. carbon dioxide.
    c. water.
    d. glucose.

    a. no; not used in photosynthesis
    b. no; is fixed by ribulose bisphosphate
    *c. yes; during photolysis of water
    d. no; the other product of photosynthesis (in addition to oxygen)

12. The portion of the electromagnetic spectrum absorbed by chlorophyll is
    a. x-ray.
    b. ultraviolet.
    c. visible.
    d. infrared.

    a. no; enough energy to produce ionization and destroy cells
    b. no; enough energy to excite some molecules, but not involved in photosynthesis
    *c. yes; this electromagnetic energy is converted into chemical energy
    d. no; heat energy that does not contribute directly to photosynthesis

13. Which of the following was NOT part of Englemann's classic experiment to elucidate the nature of photosynthesis?
    a. a prism
    b. carbon dioxide labeled with carbon 14
    c. elodea, a water plant
    d. aerobic bacteria

    a. incorrect; a prism was used to separate light into different colors (wavelengths) in the experiment
    *b. correct; radioactive carbon not available in 1882; part of later research on the nature of photosynthesis
    c. incorrect; this water plant liberated oxygen bubbles during photosynthesis in the experiment
    d. incorrect; the aerobic bacteria clustered around areas of active photosynthesis (dependent on the wavelength of the light hitting the cells) in the experiment

14. Which of the following is NOT one of the pigments commonly found in the leaves of plants that turn yellow or golden in the autumn?
    a. anthocyanin
    b. carotene
    c. chlorophyll
    d. xanthophyll

    *a. correct; pigment responsible for red or purple colors, not found in the yellow or golden leaves
    b. incorrect; the orange pigment found in these leaves
    c. incorrect; this green pigment masks the presence of the other pigments while the leaf is green in the summer
    d. incorrect; this is the yellow pigment that becomes visible in the fall

15. Which of the following is associated with cyclic photophosphorylation?
    a. photosystem I
    b. photosystem II
    c. light of 680 nanometers
    d. both (b) and (c)

    *a. yes; the system that captures and passes on the energy used in cyclic photophosphorylation
    b. no; the system involved in noncyclic photophosphorylation
    c. no; 680 nanometers used in noncyclic photophosphorylation; 700 nanometers used in cyclic photophosphorylation
    d. no; only (a) is correct for cyclic photophosphorylation

16. The oldest means of ATP production is thought to be
    a. glycolysis.
    b. noncyclic photophosphorylation.
    c. cyclic photophosphorylation.
    d. aerobic respiration.

    a. no; characteristic of anaerobic organisms, both uses and produces ATP
    b. no; a more complex process associated with photosynthesis and thought to arise later
    *c. yes; the simple way for primitive organisms to tap the continual influx of energy from the sun
    d. no; dependent on the availability of free oxygen, which is dependent on the prior existence of noncyclic photophosphorylation

17. ATP is formed in the chemiosmotic process by (choose the *best* answer)
    a. enzymes in the stroma surrounding the chlorophyll.
    b. photosystem I.
    c. enzymes in a protein channel in the thylakoid membrane.
    d. enzymes in the thylakoid compartment where the hydrogen ions accumulate.

    a. no; enzymes are associated with protein channels between the thylakoid compartment and the stroma
    b. yes; but not as good an answer as one of the more detailed choices
    *c. yes; ATP formation occurs as the protons flow through the channel in response to an electrical and concentration gradient
    d. no; hydrogen ions accumulate in the compartment, but ATP syntheses are associated with the protein channel

18. In noncyclic photophosphorylation, which of the following compounds are produced?
    a. oxygen
    b. ATP
    c. NADPH
    d. all of the above

    a. yes; a partial answer; during photolysis
    b. yes; a partial answer; during chemiosmosis
    c. yes; a partial answer; as an electron acceptor
    *d. yes; all of the above are correct

19. Which of the following people discovered the pathway of carbon in photosynthesis?
    a. Calvin
    b. Hill
    c. Benson
    d. both (a) and (c)

    a. yes; a partial answer
    b. no
    c. yes; a partial answer
    *d. yes; both (a) and (c) are correct

20. The carbon dioxide in the light-independent reactions becomes fixed to
    a. phosphoglycerate (PGA).
    b. phosphoglyceraldehyde (PGAL).
    c. ribulose bisphosphate (RuBP).
    d. oxaloacetate.

    a. no; formed by this reaction
    b. no; a compound formed after carbon dioxide fixation occurs
    *c. yes; combines with carbon dioxide to form an unstable intermediate compound that eventually forms PGA
    d. no; found in C4 photosynthesis

21. In photorespiration, oxygen becomes attached to
    a. PGA.
    b. PGAL.
    c. RuBP.
    d. oxaloacetate.

    a. no; formed by photorespiration
    b. no; found in both photorespiration and the Calvin-Benson cycle
    *c. yes; to form one PGA and one phosphoglycolate
    d. no; part of the C4 cycle

22. Which of the following compounds is found exclusively in C4 plants?
    a. phosphoglyceraldehyde
    b. phosphoglycerate
    c. oxaloacetate
    d. ribulose bisphosphate

    a. no; found in C3 and C4 plants
    b. no; found in C3 and C4 plants
    *c. yes; characteristic intermediate found in C4 plants
    d. no; found in C3 and C4 plants

CHAPTER 6
ENERGY-RELEASING PATHWAYS

1. The number of molecules of ATP produced by the complete aerobic breakdown of a molecule of glucose is
   a. 2.
   b. 32.
   c. 36.
   d. 52.

   a. no; the number produced by glycolysis or by the Krebs cycle
   b. no; too few, the number produced in electron transport phosphorylation
   *c. yes; 36 is the usual amount, but could be more
   d. no; too many

2. The aerobic breakdown of glucose known as respiration involves
   a. the Krebs cycle.
   b. glycolysis.
   c. electron transport phosphorylation.
   d. all of the above

   a. yes; a partial answer; intermediate reactions
   b. yes; a partial answer; the initial stage
   c. yes; a partial answer; the final process in aerobic respiration
   *d. yes; all three reaction series are involved

3. The last molecule formed in glycolysis is
   a. phosphoglyceraldehyde.
   b. fructose bisphosphate.
   c. pyruvate.
   d. citric acid.

   a. no; an intermediate formed by the splitting of fructose bisphosphate
   b. no; an intermediate formed by the phosphorylation of glucose
   *c. yes; the end-product of glycolysis
   d. no; the first compound in the Krebs cycle

4. Glycolysis takes place in the
   a. ribosomes.
   b. cytoplasm.
   c. mitochondria.
   d. all of the above

   a. no; site for protein synthesis
   *b. yes; the enzymes and intermediate products are found in the cytoplasm
   c. no; site for aerobic respiration
   d. no; one of the above is correct

5. Fermentation is part of
   a. glycolysis.
   b. electron transport phosphorylation.
   c. the Krebs cycle.
   d. none of the above

   *a. yes; fermentation is an anaerobic continuation of pyruvate metabolism
   b. no; requires oxygen
   c. no; requires oxygen
   d. no; one of the above is correct

6. Which of the following statements is false?
   a. Six molecules of carbon dioxide are produced for each molecule of glucose entering aerobic respiration.
   b. Glycolysis forms NADH, a reusable coenzyme.
   c. The glucose molecule is broken down to form three molecules of acetyl CoA.
   d. Some ATP is used to initiate the glycolysis reactions.

   a. incorrect; statement is true; the six-carbon compound combines with six molecules of oxygen
   b. incorrect; statement is true; NADH functions as a proton/electron carrier
   *c. correct; statement is false; only two acetyl CoAs are formed from the two pyruvates produced at the end of the glycolysis of a single glucose molecule
   d. incorrect; statement is true; the deficit of 2 ATP involved in the phosphorylation of glucose to fructose bisphosphate is compensated by the production of 4 ATP in glycolysis to give a net yield of 2 ATP

7. The compound that enters mitochondria to undergo aerobic respiration is
   a. phosphoglyceraldehyde.
   b. acetyl CoA.
   c. oxaloacetate.
   d. pyruvate.

   a. no; part of glycolysis found in the cytoplasm
   b. no; transitional compound formed in mitochondria
   c. no; compound already found in mitochondria
   *d. yes; pyruvate enters mitochondria

8. Oxaloacetate is
   a. regenerated by passage through the Krebs cycle.
   b. the first compound in electron transport phosphorylation.
   c. the compound produced immediately in the first step in the degradation of citric acid.
   d. a compound limited to anaerobic organisms.

   *a. yes; at the end of the Krebs cycle, oxaloacetate may combine with acetyl CoA to form citric acid to start the Krebs cycle again
   b. no; not an electron acceptor
   c. no; produced at the end of the Krebs cycle
   d. no; found in the Krebs cycle, which is part of aerobic respiration

9. The second stage of aerobic respiration
   a. loads many coenzymes with hydrogen ions and electrons.
   b. produces ATP by substrate-level phosphorylation.
   c. produces the same number of ATP as does the first stage of aerobic respiration.
   d. all of the above

   a. yes; a partial answer; the hydrogen is produced in the breakdown of compounds in the Krebs cycle
   b. yes; a partial answer; involves GDP and GTP
   c. yes; a partial answer; a total of two, one for each turn of the cycle
   *d. yes; all of the above are correct

10. The final hydrogen acceptor in electron transport phosphorylation is
    a. NAD.
    b. cytochrome.
    c. FAD.
    d. free oxygen.

    a. no; a primary hydrogen acceptor from the Krebs cycle
    b. no; an intermediate hydrogen acceptor in the electron transport system
    c. no; a primary hydrogen acceptor from the Krebs cycle
    *d. yes; combines with the electrons and protons to form metabolic water

11. The electron acceptors in the electron transport system are found
    a. in the cytoplasm.
    b. on the external membrane of mitochondria.
    c. on the internal membrane of mitochondria.
    d. in the matrix of mitochondria.

    a. no; electron transport is associated with mitochondria
    b. no; located elsewhere
    *c. yes; embedded in the internal membrane of mitochondria
    d. no; located elsewhere

12. The production of ATP in mitochondria
    a. is referred to as chemiosmotic theory.
    b. occurs when free hydrogen ions outside the mitochondrion leak inside through protein channels.
    c. is dependent on ATP syntheses, an enzyme found dissolved in the inner compartment of mitochondria.
    d. both (a) and (c)

    *a. yes; the chemiosmotic theory is the current explanation for ATP production in mitochondria
    b. no; the free hydrogen ions are found inside the mitochondrial membrane
    c. no; ATP syntheses is found in the protein channel between the inner and outer compartments of mitochondria
    d. no; only one of the above is correct

13. The main storage form for glucose in animals is
    a. fat.
    b. glycogen.
    c. complex carbohydrates.
    d. none of the above

    a. no; fat is a different compound used
    *b. yes; the body contains about a 24-hour supply
    c. yes; but the *specific* carbohydrate is glycogen
    d. no; one of the above is correct

14. In alcoholic fermentation, the final hydrogen acceptor is
    a. oxygen.
    b. acetaldehyde.
    c. lactic acid or lactate.
    d. pyruvate.

    a. no; characteristic of aerobic respiration
    *b. yes; the hydrogen reacts with acetaldehyde to form ethyl alcohol
    c. no; the hydrogen acceptor in lactate fermentation
    d. no; not a hydrogen acceptor

15. In alcoholic fermentation, the end-products are ethyl alcohol and
    a. hydrogen.
    b. water.
    c. acetyl CoA.
    d. carbon dioxide.

    a. no; hydrogen is not released
    b. no; no oxygen available to form water
    c. no; formed from pyruvate in aerobic respiration
    *d. yes; as bubbles in beer or sparkling wine (champagne)

16. Adipose tissue is
    a. a tissue that is found evenly dispersed throughout the body.
    b. the tissue where fat is stored.
    c. a type of glandular tissue.
    d. a tissue limited to humans.

    a. no; the amount of fat varies in different parts of the body
    *b. yes
    c. no; simply a place to store excess energy in the form of fat
    d. no; many animals have fat

17. In the complete aerobic breakdown of proteins to carbon dioxide and water, the chemical fragments enter the aerobic pathway for metabolism of complex carbohydrates
    a. in glycolysis.
    b. in the Krebs cycle.
    c. in electron transport phosphorylation.
    d. as simple carbohydrates.

    a. no; restricted to simple compounds
    *b. yes; enters as an intermediate in the Krebs cycle
    c. no; only hydrogen enters the electron transport system
    d. no; as amino acids converted into elements of the Krebs cycle

CHAPTER 7
CELL DIVISION AND MITOSIS

1. Which of the following cells is produced by a type of division different from the other cells listed?
   a. nerve cells
   b. egg cells
   c. muscle cells
   d. pancreatic cells

   a. no; produced by mitosis
   *b. yes; produced by meiosis, others by mitosis
   c. no; produced by mitosis
   d. no; produced by mitosis

2. Division of cytoplasm is described by the word
   a. mitosis.
   b. meiosis.
   c. cytokinesis.
   d. all of the above

   a. no; a nuclear division
   b. no; a nuclear division
   *c. yes
   d. no; one of the above is correct

3. Mitosis and meiosis do NOT occur in
   a. insects.
   b. bacteria.
   c. fungi.
   d. red and brown algae.

   a. incorrect; insects undergo mitosis and meiosis as do all eukaryotes
   *b. correct; prokaryotes do not undergo mitosis or meiosis
   c. incorrect; fungi and all eukaryotes undergo mitosis and meiosis
   d. incorrect; both types of algae are eukaryotes and undergo mitosis and meiosis

4. _____ attaches to chromosomes at the centromere.
   a. A sister chromatid
   b. A spindle apparatus
   c. A microfilament
   d. The nuclear membrane

   a. no; two chromatids may be connected at the centromere
   *b. yes; the site where the spindle fibers attach
   c. no; microtubules, not microfilaments, are involved with chromosomes in cell division
   d. no; no relationship; the chromosomes may appear anywhere inside the nucleus

5. A single pair of chromosomes consisting of one maternal and one paternal chromosome and possessing genes for the same traits are called
   a. autosomes.
   b. homologous chromosomes.
   c. chromatids.
   d. somatic chromatids.

   a. no; name given to nonsex chromosomes
   *b. yes; same except for different alleles and they come from different parents
   c. no; name given to replicated chromosomes
   d. no; somatic refers to body tissues

6. The ultimate reason that two chromosomes are called homologous is that they
   a. possess genes for the same traits.
   b. possess the same alleles.
   c. are the same length and have their centromeres in the same place.
   d. pair or synapse during meiosis.

   a. no; essentially correct but does not address X and Y chromosomes that are said to be homologous (better answer given)
   b. no; not necessarily true, as one homologous chromosome could have a dominant allele while the other carries a recessive one
   c. no; true of all homologous chromosomes except the X and Y chromosomes (better answer given)
   *d. yes; homologous chromosomes by definition pair during synapsis. The other statements may be partially true, but they do not apply to the sex chromosomes, which are homologous but quite different in appearance and the genes they carry.

7. In most sexually reproducing organisms, the cells of the adult organisms are
   a. triploid.
   b. haploid.
   c. diploid.
   d. tetraploid.

   a. no; three sets of chromosomes, organism usually sterile
   b. no; one set of chromosomes, characteristic of gametes or haploid life cycle
   *c. yes; two sets of chromosomes per cell—one paternal, one maternal
   d. no; four sets of chromosomes; a few domesticated varieties of plants are tetraploid, most are diploid

8. A cell spends 90 percent of the cell cycle in
   a. interphase.
   b. metaphase.
   c. telophase.
   d. prophase.

   *a. yes; the majority of the time in the cell cycle is spent in interphase, only a small portion is spent in mitosis
   b. no; only a small part of the cell cycle is spent in mitosis
   c. no; only a small part of the cell cycle is spent in mitosis
   d. no; only a small part of the cell cycle is spent in mitosis

9. Which of the following phases of the cell cycle occurs after the genetic material has been replicated and prepares the cells for division?
    a. M
    b. G_1
    c. G_2
    d. S

    a. no; the actual division process
    b. no; period of growth before DNA duplication
    *c. yes; occurs immediately after DNA duplication
    d. no; the actual replication stage

10. Which of the following events does NOT occur in prophase?
    a. The spindle apparatus forms.
    b. The centromeres divide.
    c. The centrioles separate and move to poles of the cell.
    d. The chromosomes become visible as separate entities.

    a. incorrect; the spindle fibers appear in prophase
    *b. correct; the division of the centromeres marks the beginning of anaphase
    c. incorrect; this is the first step of mitosis and occurs in prophase
    d. incorrect; the chromosomes first appear during prophase

11. The chromosomes are first aligned along the spindle equator during
    a. telophase.
    b. anaphase.
    c. prophase.
    d. metaphase.

    a. no; the chromosomes have already separated into two groups, one at each pole
    b. no; the chromosomes have begun to separate although at early anaphase they may still be at the spindle equator
    c. no; the chromosomes and spindle fibers first appear; there has not been enough time to arrange the chromosomes in the center
    *d. yes; the chromosomes move to the center of the cell before the centromeres divide

12. Which of the following processes occurs during telophase?
    a. The chromosomes decondense to become threadlike forms.
    b. The nuclear envelope disappears.
    c. The spindle fibers move the chromosomes to the center of the spindle.
    d. The two chromatids divide and separate.

    *a. yes; occurs in preparation for their functioning in interphase
    b. no; occurs during prophase
    c. no; occurs during metaphase
    d. no; the chromosome is made up of two chromatids until the centromere divides during anaphase

13. Which of the phases of mitosis is the least complex?
    a. anaphase
    b. prophase
    c. telophase
    d. metaphase

    a. no; during this phase the centromeres divide and the chromosomes separate and move toward the poles
    b. no; probably the most complex phase, involving construction of the spindle, condensation of the chromosomes, and disappearance of the nucleolus and nuclear membrane
    c. no; the reverse of the events of prophase
    *d. yes; all that has to happen is to move the chromosomes to the center of the spindle

14. The hereditary material becomes separated from the cytoplasm during
    a. metaphase.
    b. prophase.
    c. telophase.
    d. anaphase.

    a. no; the chromosomes are in the center of the cell surrounded by the cytoplasm and the spindle
    b. no; at the beginning, the hereditary material is isolated by the nuclear membrane, but it quickly disappears
    *c. yes; toward the end of telophase the nuclear membrane reforms, thus isolating the genetic material
    d. no; the chromosomes are pulled through the cytoplasm by the spindle fibers but remain in contact with the cytoplasm

15. A cell spindle furrow is characteristic of cytokinesis in
    a. animals.
    b. bacteria.
    c. plants.
    d. fungi.

    *a. yes; no cell wall is involved with cytokinesis
    b. no; no mitosis but fission
    c. no; a cell plate forms
    d. no; sometimes cytokinesis does not occur, and when it does, a cell wall is involved

CHAPTER 8
MEIOSIS

1. Asexual reproduction
   a. is the common form of reproduction in higher organisms.
   b. requires only one parent.
   c. produces wide variety of offspring.
   d. both (b) and (c)

   a. no; natural selection favors sexual reproduction in higher organisms
   *b. yes; and the offspring resemble the parent
   c. no; offspring are alike
   d. no; one of the above is correct

2. Sexual reproduction, when compared to asexual reproduction,
   a. is more efficient.
   b. produces more variety in the offspring.
   c. requires only one parent.
   d. produces more offspring.

   a. no; asexual reproduction is more simple in that it does not require that gametes meet and a single cell can reproduce
   *b. yes; clearly the correct answer; variety is the chief advantage of sexual reproduction and the reason why it is favored by natural selection
   c. no; although a very few hermaphroditic sexually reproducing forms might be able to reproduce alone
   d. no; the number of offspring is not controlled by the type of reproduction; some sexually reproducing parasites and spore-producing fungi may exceed 1 million offspring

3. In animals, meiosis occurs to produce
   a. somatic cells.
   b. gametes.
   c. cells of the sex organs.
   d. diploid cells.

   a. no; body cells are produced by mitosis
   *b. yes; gametes are formed by meiosis in gametogenesis
   c. no; a possible answer because germ cells are in the sex organs, but most cells are produced by mitosis; another answer is a much better choice
   d. no; majority of animals are diploid so that meiosis would produce haploid cells

4. A set of chromosomes (a genome) is indicated by the letter
   a. a.
   b. f.
   c. g.
   d. n.

   a. no
   b. no
   c. no
   *d. yes; as in 1n, 2n, etc.

5. The two parts of a duplicated chromosome are called _____ chromatids.
   a. mother and daughter
   b. sister
   c. maternal and paternal
   d. brother

     a. no; used to describe mother cell and the daughter cell produced by mitosis
   *b. yes
     c. no; applies to the pair of homologous chromosomes
     d. no

6. In meiosis, DNA replication occurs
   a. during interphase.
   b. between meiosis I and meiosis II.
   c. during prophase I.
   d. after meiosis II.

   *a. yes; as it does in mitosis
     b. no; usually meiosis II follows meiosis I so rapidly there is not enough time for replication
     c. no; this is the time for synapsis
     d. no; this would restore the diploid condition and negate the reduction in chromosomes that occurred in meiosis

7. Synapsis occurs
   a. during interphase.
   b. between meiosis I and meiosis II.
   c. during prophase I.
   d. during prophase II.

     a. no; replication takes place in interphase before chromosomes condense and move around
     b. no; synapsis has already occurred
   *c. yes; at the beginning of meiosis
     d. no; synapsis has already occurred

8. Sister chromatids of each chromosome are separated from each other during
   a. interphase.
   b. prophase I.
   c. anaphase I.
   d. anaphase II.

     a. no; the phase when the chromosomes are replicated
     b. no; the phase when pairing occurs
     c. no; the homologues separate during anaphase I
   *d. yes; the sister chromatids separate during anaphase II

9. During crossing over, _____ undergo breakage and exchange segments.
   a. sister chromatids
   b. nonsister chromatids of a homologous pair
   c. nonhomologous chromatids
   d. X and Y chromosomes

     a. no; there would be no change because they are replicates
   *b. yes; this allows new combinations of paternal and maternal alleles
     c. no; different genes on different chromosomes do not pair
     d. no; although these chromosomes pair, they pair only at one end and do not exchange

10. _____ results in recombination of genes.
    a. Crossing over
    b. Pairing
    c. Duplication
    d. none of the above

    *a. yes; breakage and exchange take place
    b. no; pairing only produces conditions that allow recombination
    c. no; just duplicates the existing genes, does nothing to reshuffle them
    d. no; one of the above is correct

11. The centromeres divide during
    a. prophase I.
    b. anaphase I.
    c. prophase II.
    d. anaphase II.

    a. no; synapsis occurs
    b. no; homologues separate but chromatids remain attached by centromeres
    c. no
    *d. yes; centromeres divide and chromatids become chromosomes and move toward
        the poles

12. If a diploid organism has a genome consisting of four chromosomes, it can produce
    _____ different combinations of maternal and paternal chromosomes disregarding
    crossing over.
    a. 4
    b. 8
    c. 16
    d. 32

    a. no
    b. no
    *c. yes; 2 to the 4th power is 16
    d. no

13. The paired homologous chromosomes are found at the spindle equator during
    a. metaphase I.
    b. telophase I.
    c. prophase II.
    d. anaphase II.

    *a. yes; the homologues separate during anaphase I
    b. no; the homologues have already separated
    c. no; the homologues have already separated
    d. no; the homologues have already separated

14. When oocytes undergo meiosis, they produce a total of _____ polar body (bodies).
    a. one
    b. two
    c. three
    d. four

    a. no; only one polar body is produced after meiosis I
    b. no; would be the correct answer if only the primary and secondary oocytes produced
       polar bodies, but the first polar body also divides
    *c. yes
    d. no; one of the four cells produced is the egg; not all can be polar bodies

15. Which of the following statements about meiosis is NOT true?
    a. Meiosis produces clones.
    b. Meiosis reduces the number of chromosomes.
    c. Meiosis promotes variation.
    d. Meiosis produces gametes.

    *a. correct; statement is not true; meiosis produces differences, not similarity
    b. incorrect; statement is true
    c. incorrect; statement is true
    d. incorrect; statement is true

16. The reason that sexually reproducing organisms produce offspring different from themselves is
    a. crossing over.
    b. random arrangement of chromosomes from the spindle equator.
    c. fertilization is a chance mix of genetically different gametes.
    d. all of the above

    a. yes; a partial answer
    b. yes; a partial answer
    c. yes; a partial answer
    *d. yes; all of the above are correct

CHAPTER 9
OBSERVABLE PATTERNS OF INHERITANCE

1. The discoverer of the laws of genetics was
   a. Alfred Wallace.
   b. Jean-Baptiste Lemarck.
   c. Gregor Mendel.
   d. Charles Darwin.

   a. no; coauthor of evolution theory, did not know of genetics
   b. no; proposed the inheritance of acquired characteristics
   *c. yes; proposed the laws of genetics
   d. no; coauthor of evolution theory, did not know of genetics

2. Which of the following is NOT one of the principles of heredity proposed by the father of genetics?
   a. law of dominance
   b. law of incomplete dominance
   c. law of independent assortment
   d. law of segregation

   a. incorrect
   *b. correct; he did not propose a *law* for incomplete dominance
   c. incorrect
   d. incorrect

3. Which of the following was discovered by Mendel?
   a. linkage
   b. relationship of genetic behavior to laws of probability
   c. location of genes on chromosomes
   d. role of chromosomes in sex determination

   a. no; no evidence to show that he understood this phenomenon
   *b. yes; his detailed statistical evidence supports this observation
   c. no; the role of chromosomes was not discovered until much later
   d. no; the relationship of chromosomes to genetics was not known in Mendel's time

4. In his research, Gregor Mendel used
   a. snapdragons.
   b. fruit flies.
   c. chickens.
   d. none of the above

   a. no
   b. no; used later by T. H. Morgan
   c. no
   *d. yes; Mendel restricted his genetics work to garden peas

5. At Mendel's time, the conventional wisdom stated that
    a. the sperm controlled the development of an individual.
    b. the egg controlled the development of an individual.
    c. blood was the factor that controlled genetics.
    d. characteristics of the parents blended together in the offspring.

    a. no; an earlier theory of preformation that stated the sperm had miniature adults preformed in them
    b. no; an earlier theory of preformation that held the egg had miniature adults preformed in them
    c. no; "bad blood" and "blue blood" were often used, but this was not the dominant theory (they are still referred to today)
    *d. yes; people believed in blended inheritance

6. An individual homozygous at a particular locus
    a. has the same alleles located at the homologous locus.
    b. has the same genotype as its parents.
    c. can be identified by examining its phenotype.
    d. will contribute different alleles to its offspring.

    *a. yes; they have the same alleles
    b. no; not necessarily—two heterozygotes could produce a homozygote
    c. no; this would be possible for a recessive, but not a dominant, individual
    d. no; all gametes will receive the same allele

7. If Mendel crossed two purple pea plants chosen at random (purple is dominant to white),
    a. the offspring would be hybrids.
    b. the offspring could have some white flowers among the offspring.
    c. they could breed true.
    d. both (b) and (c)

    a. no; hybrids are the offspring of two pure-breeding organisms with different phenotypes
    b. yes; a partial answer; if the two purples were heterozygous
    c. yes; a partial answer; the only way that could happen would be if the two purple plants were homozygous
    *d. yes; both (b) and (c) are correct

8. Rose comb is dominant to single comb in chickens. If the F_1 (of the cross of pure-breeding rose and pure-breeding single chickens) were crossed, the next generation would have
    a. all rose-combed chickens.
    b. one-fourth rose, three-fourths single.
    c. one-half rose, one-half single.
    d. one-fourth single, three-fourths rose.

    a. no; the F_2 would contain some homozygous recessives
    b. no; there should be more rose and less single
    c. no; the ratio obtained from a testcross
    *d. yes; the typical 3:1 ratio with the large number attributed to the dominant trait

9. In garden peas, Mendel found that green pods are dominant to yellow pods and yellow seeds are dominant to green seeds. Which of the phenotypes would be more common in the second generation of a cross of a plant with yellow seeds and pods with a plant with green seeds and pods?
    a. yellow seeds, yellow pods
    b. yellow seeds, green pods
    c. green seeds, green pods
    d. green seeds, yellow pods

    a. no; 3/16 of the offspring
    *b. yes; 9/16 of the offspring
    c. no; 3/16 of the offspring
    d. no; 1/16 of the offspring

10. In garden peas, round and yellow seeds are controlled by dominant alleles while wrinkled and green are controlled by recessive alleles. If you found a plant with round and yellow seeds and wanted to determine its genotype, you would cross this plant with a plant that is pure-breeding for
    a. round and yellow seeds.
    b. round and green seeds.
    c. wrinkled and green seeds.
    d. wrinkled and yellow seeds.

    a. no; unable to determine the genotype of either trait
    b. no; unable to determine the genotype of the round seeds
    *c. yes; a cross called a testcross; if a recessive trait appears, the unknown is heterozygous for it; otherwise, it would be homozygous for the dominant trait
    d. no; unable to determine the genotypes of the yellow seeds

11. If a cross produces a 1:1 phenotypic ratio, the genotypes of the parents were
    a. both homozygous.
    b. both heterozygous.
    c. one homozygous dominant, the other heterozygous.
    d. one homozygous recessive, the other heterozygous.

    a. no; if both parents were homozygous dominant all offspring would have dominant phenotypes, and if both parents were homozygous recessive all offspring would have recessive phenotypes
    b. no; the ratio would be 3 dominant to 1 recessive
    c. no; two possible genotypes, but the phenotypes would all be dominant
    *d. yes; one-half would be heterozygous expressing the dominant trait, whereas the others would be homozygous recessive

12. Which of the following can be determined with monohybrid crosses?
    a. the law of dominance
    b. the law of independent assortment
    c. the law of segregation
    d. both (a) and (c)

    a. yes; a partial answer
    b. no; need a pair of genes to test
    c. yes; a partial answer
    *d. yes; both (a) and (c) are correct

13. If an organism had a genotype of *AaBbCc*, how many different gametes could it form according to the law of independent assortment?
    a. 4
    b. 8
    c. 12
    d. 16

    a. no
    *b. yes; *ABC, ABc, AbC, Abc, aBC, aBc, abC, abc*
    c. no
    d. no

14. Which of the following is the F$_2$ phenotypic ratio that would support the law of independent assortment?
    a. 3:1
    b. 9:3:3:1
    c. 1:2:1
    d. 7:1:1:7

    a. no; law of dominance
    *b. yes; derived from Punnett square
    c. no; a genotypic ratio or a monohybrid ratio showing incomplete dominance
    d. no; results produced by linkage, not independent assortment

15. A 1:2:1 phenotypic ratio in which the two individuals represent a blend of the other two phenotypes is *best* explained by
    a. codominance.
    b. incomplete dominance.
    c. multiple alleles.
    d. dominance.

    a. no; the ratio could be obtained, but the phenotype would not be a blend
    *b. yes; not enough product to give full phenotype expressed by the extreme
    c. no; other ratios could be obtained and blending is not necessarily a result
    d. no; the phenotypic ratio would be 3:1

16. If a person with blood type AB were crossed to a person with blood type O, the offspring would be
    a. AB or O.
    b. AB only.
    c. A or B, but not AB or O.
    d. none of the above

    a. no; impossible for individual to inherit both traits from one parent
    b. no; offspring has to inherit an O, therefore cannot be type AB
    *c. yes; would inherit an A or a B from one parent and an O from the other
    d. no; one of the above is correct

17. Pleiotropy refers to
    a. the extent to which a gene is expressed in an individual.
    b. a gene that has multiple effects.
    c. a condition in which one gene masks the expression of another gene.
    d. a gene that has a lethal effect.

    a. no; refers to expressivity
    *b. yes; such as sickle-cell anemia
    c. no; refers to epistasis
    d. no; refers to lethal genes

CHAPTER 10

CHROMOSOMES AND HUMAN GENETICS

1. In 1882 Walther Flemming discovered
    a. penicillin.
    b. sex linkage.
    c. chromosomes.
    d. the first human genetic disorder.

    a. no; Alexander Fleming made this discovery almost 50 years later
    b. no; coworkers of T. H. Morgan discovered this
    *c. yes
    d. no; many genetic traits were known to be passed on from parents even though the mechanism was unknown

2. In the 1880s, efforts to uncover the mysteries of heredity were triggered by
    a. the discovery of Mendel's research paper.
    b. Weismann's proposal that meiosis occurred and each sex contributed one-half of the hereditary information to the offspring.
    c. the frequency of hemophilia in the royal families descending from Queen Victoria.
    d. the development of many research prizes such as the Nobel Prize, the Award of the Royal Society of London, and the French Pasteur Prize.

    a. no; did not occur until 1900
    *b. yes; Weismann's theory and the newly discovered chromosomes provided a physical mechanism to explain some of the biological mysteries of heredity
    c. no; not a major research stimulus
    d. no; some of these are fictitious

3. The characteristics of autosomes and sex chromosomes can best be studied during _____ when they are in their most condensed state.
    a. interphase
    b. telophase
    c. anaphase
    d. metaphase

    a. no; chromosomes are dispersed
    b. no; chromosomes begin to decondense and are gathered together at the pole
    c. no; the division of the centromere makes it hard to separate twice as many chromosomes as they move toward the poles
    *d. yes

4. A karyotype is
    a. a visual representation of the chromosomes from the largest to the smallest.
    b. a visual representation of how genes combine to form the genotypes of the next generation.
    c. a visual presentation of how a human trait is inherited in a family.
    d. none of the above

    *a. yes; used in diagnosis of chromosomal diseases
    b. no; a Punnett square is used to show genetic combinations
    c. no; a pedigree chart is used to study human genetic patterns
    d. no; one of the above is correct

5. A chromosome can be distinguished from other chromosomes based on its
    a. length.
    b. centromere position.
    c. banding patterns.
    d. all of the above

    a. yes; a partial answer; not definitive by itself
    b. yes; a partial answer; not definitive by itself
    c. yes; a partial answer; a most discriminating feature
   *d. yes; all of the above are correct

6. Human males inherit their sex-linked traits
    a. from their mother.
    b. from their father.
    c. from both parents.
    d. It depends on the laws of chance.

   *a. yes; from the alleles on her X chromosome
    b. no; the alleles on the Y chromosome are called holandric and are found only in males
    c. no
    d. no

7. The genes responsible for the secondary sex characteristics are carried on
    a. the X chromosome.
    b. the Y chromosome.
    c. the autosomes.
    d. all of the chromosomes.

    a. yes; a partial answer; carries some secondary sex characteristics and all
       sex-linked alleles
    b. yes; a partial answer; carries male fertility genes and genes associated with the
       secondary sex characteristics of the male
    c. yes; a partial answer; carry many of the secondary sex traits
   *d. yes; all of the chromosomes have genes that influence the expression of secondary
       sex characteristics

8. Linkage
    a. increases variability.
    b. refers to the tendency of genes found on the same chromosome to be inherited together.
    c. is an exception to the law of segregation.
    d. is unaffected by crossing over.

    a. no; tends to reduce variability because certain traits would be inherited together
   *b. yes
    c. no; is an exception to the law of independent assortment
    d. no; crossing over breaks up linkage relationships

9. Red eye is dominant to white eye in *Drosophila.* It is an X-linked gene (located on the X chromosome). A mutation to white eye in a population of pure-breeding red-eyed fruit flies would be phenotypically expressed first in
   a. a male.
   b. a female.
   c. either sex—it would be impossible to predict.
   d. whichever sex the mutation occurred—the fly's eye color would turn white.

   *a. yes; since it has only one X chromosome, whenever a male inherits the X chromosome with the white-eye gene it will be expressed
   b. no; the presence of a wild-type allele on the other sex chromosome would mask the expression of white eye
   c. no; it can be predicted on the basis that the male has only one sex chromosome
   d. no; white eye is a recessive trait and would not affect the red eye color

10. Red eye is a sex-linked dominant gene; white eye is its recessive allele. If a red-eyed male fly were crossed to a white-eyed female, the F_1 generation would consist of
    a. all females red-eyed and all males white-eyed.
    b. all females white-eyed and all males red-eyed.
    c. all females red-eyed and 1/2 males red-eyed, 1/2 white-eyed.
    d. 1/2 females red-eyed, 1/2 white-eyed and 1/2 males red-eyed, 1/2 white-eyed.

    *a. yes
    b. no
    c. no
    d. no

11. Red eye is a sex-linked dominant gene; white eye is its recessive allele. If a red-eyed male fly were crossed to a white-eyed female, the F_2 generation would consist of
    a. all females red-eyed and all males white-eyed.
    b. all females white-eyed and all males red-eyed.
    c. all females red-eyed and 1/2 males red-eyed, 1/2 white-eyed.
    d. 1/2 females red-eyed, 1/2 white-eyed and 1/2 males red-eyed, 1/2 white-eyed.

    a. no
    b. no
    c. no
    *d. yes

12. Which of the following statements about linkage is false?
    a. The closer two genes are located on a chromosome the more likely they are to be inherited together.
    b. The farther apart two genes are on a chromosome the less likely they will be involved in recombination.
    c. The number of linkage groups is equal to the number of chromosomes found in a gamete.
    d. Two genes located far apart appear to assort independently.

    a. incorrect; this statement is true because the closer two genes are, the less likely crossing over will occur between them
    *b. correct; this statement is false; if the two genes are located 50 units or more a part they behave as if they were on separate chromosomes
    c. incorrect; this statement is true; all of the genes on one chromosome are linked together and represent the maternal or paternal contribution for that chromosome
    d. incorrect; this statement is true; the genes appear not to be linked

13. Which of the following is NOT one of the traits that would be desirable in an organism used for genetic experimentation?
    a. high fertility with large number of offspring
    b. long life cycle
    c. inexpensive and easy to raise
    d. many easily recognizable phenotypic variations

    a. incorrect; large number of offspring is desirable
    *b. correct; would be a disadvantage—need short generation time
    c. incorrect; would be a definite advantage to reduce the cost of research
    d. incorrect; an important feature needed by organisms used for genetic research

14. The carriers of a sex-linked recessive trait are _____ that do not express the recessive trait they carry.
    a. homozygous individuals of either sex
    b. heterozygous individuals of either sex
    c. heterozygous males
    d. heterozygous females

    a. no; homozygous individuals would express the recessive alleles they possess
    b. no; males cannot be heterozygous for a sex-linked trait
    c. no; males cannot be heterozygous for a sex-linked trait
    *d. yes; heterozygous females can carry a recessive sex-linked allele that is masked by the dominant allele found on the other X chromosome

15. Which of the following is (are) true of Huntington's disorder, an example of an autosomal dominant inheritance?
    a. An individual with this trait will pass it on to all of his/her offspring.
    b. Defective genes are able to persist in high frequencies in a population because heterozygotes are able to survive to reproduction.
    c. An individual with the disorder will often have completed reproduction before any symptoms of the disease appear.
    d. both (b) and (c)

    a. incorrect; this statement is false; only a 50-50 chance of passing on the trait
    b. correct; this statement is true but only a partial answer; organisms with this defect reproduce normally
    c. correct; this statement is true but only a partial answer; the onset of the disease is usually after age forty
    *d. correct; both (b) and (c) are true statements

16. If a male carries an X-linked recessive trait and his mate is homozygous normal,
    a. all sons will be affected.
    b. all daughters will be carriers.
    c. all daughters will be affected.
    d. the recessive gene will be expressed in all of the offspring.

    a. no; the sons will inherit the normal gene from their mother
    *b. yes; the daughters will inherit the normal gene from their mother and the recessive gene from their father
    c. no; the mother will pass on a normal dominant gene so that all daughters will be unaffected
    d. no; the recessive gene will not be expressed in any offspring

17. The European monarch associated most with hemophilia was
    a. Queen Victoria.
    b. Queen Elizabeth.
    c. King Louis XIV.
    d. King Henry VIII.

    *a. yes; a carrier who transmitted the gene to subsequent generations
    b. no
    c. no
    d. no

18. The transfer of a fragment of one chromosome to a nonhomologous chromosome is called
    a. translocation.
    b. inversion.
    c. deletion.
    d. duplication.

    *a. yes; part of one chromosome becomes attached to a nonhomologous chromosome
    b. no; the sequence of genes on the same chromosome is reversed
    c. no; some genes are simply lost from a chromosome
    d. no; involves duplicating a segment on the same chromosome so that there are two such sequences on the chromosome

19. The failure of chromosomes to separate during meiosis I or II is a
    a. deletion.
    b. duplication.
    c. nondisjunction.
    d. mutation.

    a. no; involves the loss of a segment of a chromosome
    b. no; involves a duplication of a segment of a chromosome
    *c. yes; the homologous chromosomes fail to separate and are inherited together
    d. no; an inheritable change in a gene

20. Down syndrome
    a. is known as trisomy 21.
    b. individuals live longer than normal unaffected individuals.
    c. increases in frequency among children born to older fathers.
    d. is not a genetic but an embryonic defect.

    *a. yes; a Down syndrome individual has three copies of chromosome 21
    b. no; usually a Down syndrome child has a shorter lifespan
    c. no; the frequency increases with the age of the mother
    d. no; although some manifestations of the syndrome may have an embryonic basis, the majority are the result of an extra chromosome

21. Which of the following chromosomal modifications has evolutionary consequences?
    a. duplication
    b. translocation
    c. deletion
    d. inversion

    *a. yes; allows the development of mutations in the duplicated segment that could survive because of the availability of a normal allele
    b. no; might result in trisomy that could reduce survival and adaptability
    c. no; the loss of genes is often fatal and you may lose the buffering effect of a normal gene if the one left on the remaining chromosome is a lethal gene
    d. no; may reduce fertility because of problems involved in synapsis

22. Turner syndrome is
    a. produced by mutation.
    b. produced by nondisjunction of an autosome.
    c. produced by nondisjunction of an X chromosome.
    d. trisomy X.

    a. no; mutations generally produce one effect rather than a large group of effects characteristic of a syndrome
    b. no; does not involve an autosome
    *c. yes; and it produces an XO individual, a female with only one sex chromosome
    d. no; this condition is possible but is not called Turner syndrome

23. The sex chromosomes in humans are referred to as
    a. A and B.
    b. M and F.
    c. X and O.
    d. X and Y.

    a. no
    b. no
    c. no
    *d. yes; female by X and male by Y

CHAPTER 11
DNA STRUCTURE AND FUNCTION

1. When Fred Griffith discovered bacterial transformation, he was
   a. attempting to develop a vaccine against a bacterium that produced pneumonia in humans.
   b. conducting experiments on bacteriophages.
   c. attempting to understand how antibiotics prevented the growth of bacteria.
   d. using *in vitro* (glassware) methods to elucidate the chemical nature of the gene.

   *a. yes; transformation was an unexpected bonus
   b. no; was not involved in viral-bacterial research
   c. no; even though penicillin was discovered at approximately the same time
   d. no; this was the experiment conducted by Avery and his coworkers that followed Griffith's experiment

2. Which of the following would NOT kill a mouse under test conditions?
   a. injection of rough bacteria
   b. injection of smooth bacteria
   c. injection of rough bacteria and heat-killed smooth bacteria
   d. both (a) and (c)

   *a. correct; rough bacteria were nonvirulent
   b. incorrect; smooth bacteria were pathogenic
   c. incorrect; this combination would kill a mouse because of genetic transformation
   d. incorrect; only one of the above is correct

3. The conversion of rough bacteria to smooth bacteria is known as
   a. transcription.
   b. translocation.
   c. translation.
   d. transformation.

   a. no; the production of RNA from instructions in DNA
   b. no; the exchange of genetic material between nonhomologous chromosomes
   c. no; the manufacture of a protein from instructions in RNA
   *d. yes; a permanent change from a rough to a smooth form because of the incorporation of the gene for S bacteria

4. The first person(s) to isolate from the nucleus a previously unknown substance that came to be known as DNA was (were)
   a. Miescher.
   b. Avery.
   c. Watson and Crick.
   d. Hershey and Chase.

   *a. yes; isolated and identified nucleic acids
   b. no; did *in vitro* analysis of genetic transformation
   c. no; proposed the double helix theory of DNA structure
   d. no; studied bacteriophages

5. In the Hershey and Chase experiment with bacteriophages, the most important clue to the chemical nature of the gene was the
    a. entrance of radioactive sulfur into bacteria.
    b. entrance of radioactive phosphorus into bacteria.
    c. accumulation of phosphorus on the surface of bacteria.
    d. accumulation of sulfur on the surface of bacteria.

    a. no; sulfur does not enter bacteria, it remains outside with the protein coat
    *b. yes; phosphorus is an element found in DNA, and its entrance indicated that nucleic acid was the active portion
    c. no; phosphorus does not accumulate outside bacteria, but enters with nucleic acids to participate in bacterial metabolic activities
    d. no; the fact that it accumulates outside bacteria indicates that protein does not participate in cellular activities

6. The sequence of activity in bacteriophage multiplication ends with
    a. attachment of the virus to the surface of a bacterium.
    b. rupture of the bacterial wall and release of viruses.
    c. injection of DNA into a bacterium.
    d. the virus controlling the metabolic machinery of a bacterium to produce more viruses.

    a. no; the first step
    *b. yes; the fourth or last step
    c. no; the second step
    d. no; the third step

7. Which of the following is NOT a component of a nucleotide?
    a. amino acid
    b. phosphate group
    c. pentose sugar
    d. nitrogenous base

    *a. correct; not part of a nucleotide, but part of proteins
    b. incorrect; found in all nucleic acids
    c. incorrect; either ribose or deoxyribose is present depending on whether considering RNA or DNA nucleotides
    d. incorrect; five possibilities are found in nucleotides: adenine, cytosine, guanine, thymine, and uracil

8. The presence of which of the following nitrogenous bases would indicate that the nucleic acid being analyzed was a molecule of DNA and not RNA?
    a. adenine
    b. uracil
    c. cytosine
    d. thymine

    a. no; adenine is found in both DNA and RNA
    b. no; uracil is found only in RNA
    c. no; cytosine is found in both DNA and RNA
    *d. yes; thymine is found only in DNA

9. The amount of uracil in a molecule of RNA is balanced by an equal amount of
   a. adenine.
   b. guanine.
   c. cytosine.
   d. thymine.

   *a. yes; uracil pairs with adenine
   b. no; cytosine pairs with guanine
   c. no; guanine pairs with cytosine
   d. no; thymine appears only in DNA and does not pair with uracil

10. Who among the following was NOT involved in the identification of the structure of DNA?
   a. James Watson
   b. Rosalind Franklin
   c. Francis Crick
   d. Oswald Avery

   a. incorrect; proposed the double helix
   b. incorrect; developed x-ray diffraction images of DNA
   c. incorrect; proposed the double helix
   *d. correct; reported the probable chemical nature of the gene

11. Which of the following techniques was used in the early 1950s to determine the structure of DNA?
   a. use of radioactive isotopes in autoradiography (using radiation from isotopes to take pictures)
   b. electron microscopy
   c. x-ray diffraction
   d. all of the above

   a. no; not important in determining structure of DNA
   b. no; not powerful enough to be useful
   *c. yes; indicated DNA was a long, thin molecule of uniform diameter
   d. no; only one of the above is correct

12. Which factor is most critical to the role of DNA in protein synthesis?
   a. the number of chains involved in the molecule
   b. the number of nucleotides in the molecule
   c. the sequence of the nucleotides in the molecule
   d. the pattern of nitrogenous base pairing

   a. no; only two chains are found in the double helix
   b. no; the number is essentially immaterial as long as it is possible to produce a functional protein
   *c. yes; the sequence controls the coding for the amino acid sequences found in the protein
   d. no; the pattern of pairing of nucleotides is standard and does not change

13. In replication,
    a. a stockpile of free nucleotides must be available to be used in the assembling.
    b. a separation of the two strands of DNA must occur.
    c. the process produces a double-stranded molecule, one strand of which is new and the other old.
    d. all of the above

    a. yes; a partial answer; must be a supply of new nucleotides available for the new strand of DNA
    b. yes; a partial answer; must be separated so that pairing of new nucleotides can be processed
    c. yes; a partial answer; makes for uniformity in DNA throughout time
    *d. yes; all of the above are correct

14. DNA polymerases
    a. are enzymes that are involved in replication.
    b. are available for proofreading assembled genes.
    c. govern the assembly of nucleotides on the parent strand.
    d. all of the above

    a. yes; a partial answer; an enzyme is needed to be able to assemble the new DNA molecules fast enough to be effective
    b. yes; a partial answer; on the average, only one mistake out of 100 million nucleotide pairs represents an error in the base pairing
    c. yes; a partial answer; the enzyme controls complementary pairing and therefore the sequence of complementary nucleotides as specified by the existing DNA strand
    *d. yes; all of the above are correct

15. The proteins most characteristically associated with DNA in the nucleosomes are
    a. globulins.
    b. enzymes.
    c. cytochromes.
    d. histones.

    a. no; these proteins are associated with blood proteins (immunoglobulins, hemoglobins, etc.)
    b. no; DNA has the blueprint of the nucleotide sequence for the enzymes, but, otherwise, enzymes have little connection with DNA
    c. no; these proteins are associated with the electron transport system
    *d. yes; histones are closely associated with nucleic acids, often serving as a spool to wind up segments of DNA (nucleosomes)

16. The folding of DNA in a chromosome results in the production of
    a. spindles.
    b. segments.
    c. coils or loops.
    d. all of the above

    a. no
    b. no
    *c. yes; the packing unit may allow the clustering of common genes
    d. no; only one of the above is correct

CHAPTER 12
FROM DNA TO PROTEINS

1. The DNA strand that is used as the instruction to generate an RNA strand is known as a(n)
   a. exon.
   b. codon.
   c. template.
   d. replicate.

   a. no; the expressed portion of a gene
   b. no; a sequence of three nucleotides that specify an amino acid
   *c. yes; provides information to form the complementary strand
   d. no; a replicate is a copy, not a complementary strand

2. The manufacture of RNA from DNA is called
   a. polymerization.
   b. translation.
   c. transcription.
   d. replication.

   a. no; a general term for the production of large molecules from small repeating units
   b. no; the manufacture of proteins from RNA codes
   *c. yes
   d. no; the duplication of DNA

3. During transcription, DNA's cytosine pairs with RNA's
   a. adenine.
   b. cytosine.
   c. uracil.
   d. guanine.

   a. no; thymine pairs with adenine
   b. no; does not pair with itself
   c. no; adenine pairs with uracil
   *d. yes; cytosine pairs with guanine

4. A promoter is
   a. the site where RNA polymerase binds.
   b. an active part of an RNA molecule.
   c. an enzyme that turns on a gene to transcribe an RNA molecule.
   d. all of the above

   *a. yes; the place where transcription begins
   b. no; part of the DNA molecule, not the RNA molecule
   c. no; not an enzyme, but part of a DNA molecule
   d. no; only one of the above is correct

5. The type of RNA that provides the site for protein synthesis is
   a. messenger RNA.
   b. ribosomal RNA.
   c. promoter RNA.
   d. transfer RNA.

   a. no; the RNA that carries the message from the DNA code
   *b. yes; in the ribosome
   c. no; not a type of RNA
   d. no; the RNA that brings the amino acid to the site of protein synthesis

6. RNA differs from DNA
   a. in the specific sugar found in the nucleotides.
   b. in that it is composed of two instead of just one strand.
   c. in that it has thymine rather than uracil.
   d. all of the above

   *a. yes; RNA contains ribose, DNA has deoxyribose
   b. no; RNA has one strand, DNA has two strands
   c. no; RNA has uracil, DNA has thymine
   d. no; only one of the above is correct

7. A mature messenger RNA
   a. contains a sequence of triplet codons that specify amino acids.
   b. has eliminated noncoding introns.
   c. leaves the nucleus and carries out its function in the cytoplasm.
   d. all of the above

   a. yes; a partial answer
   b. yes; a partial answer
   c. yes; a partial answer
   *d. yes; all of the above are correct

8. Which of the following is false?
   a. There are 64 different codons.
   b. All codons specify a specific amino acid.
   c. Some codons are used for initiation or termination of a gene.
   d. There are more codons than amino acids so that the code is redundant.

   a. incorrect; this statement is true
   *b. correct; this statement is false, as some are initiators or terminators
   c. incorrect; this statement is true
   d. incorrect; this statement is true

9. Which statement is true?
   a. Changing the first nucleotide in a codon is most likely to result in a change in the amino acid specified.
   b. Changing the second nucleotide in a codon is most likely to result in a change in the amino acid specified.
   c. Changing the third nucleotide in a codon is most likely to result in a change in the amino acid specified.
   d. All changes have the same chance of producing another amino acid.

   a. incorrect; this statement is false; a change in the first codon produces 5 to 6 different amino acids
   b. incorrect; this statement is false; a change in the second codon produces 4 to 7 different amino acids
   *c. correct; this statement is true; a change in the third codon produces 12 to 15 different amino acids
   d. incorrect; this statement is false; the number of amino acids varies

10. Anticodons are found in
    a. template DNA.
    b. messenger RNA.
    c. transfer RNA.
    d. ribosomal RNA.

    a. no; composed of codons
    b. no; composed of codons
    *c. yes; composed of anticodons
    d. no; composed of codons

11. Which of the following is NOT part of translation?
    a. elongation
    b. replication
    c. initiation
    d. termination

    a. incorrect; the second stage of translation
    *b. correct; refers to exact duplication of DNA
    c. incorrect; the first stage of translation
    d. incorrect; the third stage of translation

12. The greatest effect on gene translation would be caused by the
    a. insertion of three nucleotides into a gene sequence.
    b. addition or deletion of one nucleotide in a codon.
    c. substitution of one nucleotide in a codon.
    d. substitution of two nucleotides in a codon.

    a. no; leads to a protein with one additional amino acid
    *b. yes; results in a mutation that changes the way the whole DNA molecule is read after
        the addition or deletion
    c. no; may change one of the amino acids
    d. no; may change one of the amino acids

13. Barbara McClintock's "jumping" genes or transposable elements functioned by
    a. enabling genes to skip a generation.
    b. inactivating genes that are found next to them when they are inserted into a
       new location.
    c. producing changes in phenotypes.
    d. both (b) and (c)

    a. no; does not happen (may happen to recessive genes in some mating conditions)
    b. yes; a partial answer
    c. yes; a partial answer
    *d. yes; both (b) and (c) are correct

14. Mutations are
    a. rare.
    b. random.
    c. inherited.
    d. all of the above

    a. yes; a partial answer
    b. yes; a partial answer
    c. yes; a partial answer
    *d. yes; all of the above are correct

15. Mutations may be produced by
    a. ultraviolet radiation.
    b. mutagenic chemicals.
    c. viruses.
    d. all of the above

    a. yes; a partial answer
    b. yes; a partial answer
    c. yes; a partial answer
    *d. yes; all of the above are correct

16. Cells in a single organism differ from one another based on
    a. the repressors and operators that are active in each cell.
    b. the kinds of genes that they possess.
    c. the rates but not the types of transcription that occur in the cells.
    d. none of the above

    *a. yes; this is one of the factors that serve to make cells different
    b. no; cells possess the same kinds of genes
    c. no; *both* the rates and the types of transcriptions control the type of cells
    d. no; one of the above is correct

17. An operator is found
    a. on a different chromosome than the one that contains the gene loci it controls.
    b. between a promoter and the gene it activates.
    c. in the ribosome responsible for the protein being synthesized by the gene.
    d. covering the repressor protein that turns off the gene.

    a. no; this would produce wide variation in response and not give satisfactory control
    *b. yes; here the operator can control initiation
    c. no; no particular ribosomes are involved in producing specific proteins
    d. no; perhaps this could be a way to prevent repression but not a way to stimulate induction

18. An operon consists of
    a. an operator gene and a repressor protein.
    b. an operator gene and a promoter.
    c. an operator gene, a promoter, and a gene or functioning set of genes.
    d. any set of genetic material or protein associated with an operator gene.

    a. no; the repressor is antagonistic to the operator gene
    b. no; are only two of the three parts of an operon
    *c. yes; the three interact to form an operon
    d. no; too general and incomplete a choice

19. In the "lac operon" of *E. coli,*
    a. lactose functions as a repressor.
    b. galactose and glucose react to form lactose.
    c. the three genes associated in the operon are enzymes that digest lactose and its products.
    d. RNA polymerase is blocked by the presence of lactose.

    a. no; repressors are proteins; lactose is a disaccharide
    b. no; this reaction may happen, but the "lac operon" controls the reverse of this reaction
    *c. yes
    d. no; lactose bends (distorts) the repressor to allow RNA polymerase to initiate transcription

20. In the "lac operon," when the repressor is altered the
    a. concentration of lactose is low.
    b. genes for three digestive enzymes cannot be transcribed.
    c. repressor cannot bind to the promoter or operator.
    d. all of the above

    a. no; the repressor is altered when lactose concentrations are high
    b. no; they are actively transcribed while the repressor is altered and cannot work
    *c. yes; therefore the process of transcription can proceed
    d. no; only one of the above is correct

21. Differentiation
    a. arises through selective gene expression in different cells.
    b. results from differences in genes in different tissues of an organism.
    c. occurs only during embryonic development.
    d. both (a) and (c)

    *a. yes; the induction of specific genes in different cells could cause these cells to become different
    b. no; the genes are the same in all tissues of the same organism
    c. no; induction may occur at various times throughout an organism's life cycle
    d. no; only one of the above is correct

22. Anhidrotic ectodermal dysplasia
    a. occurs only in heterozygous females.
    b. is the result of inactivation of one of the female's sex chromosomes.
    c. results in patches of skin that are unable to perspire.
    d. all of the above

    a. yes; a partial answer
    b. yes; a partial answer
    c. yes; a partial answer
    *d. yes; all of the above are correct

23. Which of the following statements is true?
    a. Metastasis is the conversion of a benign tumor into a malignant one.
    b. Oncogenes are responsible for the repression and remission of cancers.
    c. Cancer is a fatal disease only in humans.
    d. Cancer may be caused by chemicals called carcinogens.

    a. incorrect; this statement is false; metastasis refers to the migration of cancer cells
    b. incorrect; this statement is false; oncogenes are responsible for the production of cancer
    c. incorrect; this statement is false; many animals, including laboratory mice, may be killed by cancer
    *d. correct; this statement is true; carcinogens are chemicals in the environment that may induce cancer

CHAPTER 13

RECOMBINANT DNA AND GENETIC ENGINEERING

1. In recombinant DNA experiments, which of the following events occurs last?
   a. Genes are inserted into an organism.
   b. Genes are isolated.
   c. Genes produce functional proteins.
   d. Genes are modified.

   a. no; occurs third
   b. no; occurs first
   *c. yes; occurs last
   d. no; occurs second

2. The enzyme responsible for fusing fragments of DNA together is
   a. DNA polymerase.
   b. reverse transcriptase.
   c. ligase.
   d. restriction endonuclease.

   a. no; used in DNA replication
   b. no; used in production of DNA from RNA
   *c. yes; enzyme that seals two DNA fragments together
   d. no; enzyme that cuts DNA into fragments

3. Plasmids
   a. are small circular DNA molecules.
   b. enable bacterial conjugation to occur.
   c. may become incorporated in the main chromosome.
   d. all of the above

   a. yes; a partial answer
   b. yes; a partial answer
   c. yes; a partial answer
   *d. yes; all of the above are correct

4. All of the DNA found in a haploid set of chromosomes is a
   a. plasmid.
   b. DNA library.
   c. genome.
   d. none of the above

   a. no; a small circular DNA molecule
   b. no; a collection of DNA fragments
   *c. yes; a complete set of chromosomes
   d. no; one of the above is correct

5. Which of the following enzymes cuts a chromosome into fragments with sticky ends?
   a. restriction endonuclease
   b. DNA ligase
   c. reverse transcriptase
   d. DNA polymerase

   *a. yes; cuts DNA at particular sites
   b. no; seals two fragments together
   c. no; enzymes that produce DNA from RNA
   d. no; enzyme involved in replication of DNA

6. Which of the following enzymes is used to manufacture DNA from RNA?
   a. restriction endonuclease
   b. DNA ligase
   c. reverse transcriptase
   d. DNA polymerase

   a. no; cuts DNA at particular sites
   b. no; seals two fragments together
   *c. yes; produces DNA from RNA
   d. no; involved in replication of DNA

7. cDNA refers to
   a. chromosomal DNA.
   b. copied DNA from mRNA.
   c. cytoplasmic DNA.
   d. none of the above

   a. no; no such term, simply described as DNA
   *b. yes; any DNA molecule copied from mRNA
   c. no; usually referred to by the organelle it is associated with (e.g., mitochondrial DNA)
   d. no; one of the above is correct

8. Amplification refers to the
   a. introduction of DNA into a plasmid.
   b. multiple replications of a gene.
   c. manufacture of many protein products.
   d. production of many molecules of any type.

   a. no; called insertion or splicing
   *b. yes; the most common method employs the polymerase chain reaction
   c. no; production of product is dependent on demand
   d. no; control over transcription is one mechanism of control

9. Which of the following statements is true?
   a. No two humans have the same genetic fingerprint.
   b. Pattern variations in genetic fingerprints can be detected with a radioactive probe.
   c. Biopsies provide a tissue sample of an individual, which is needed to run a genetic fingerprint.
   d. Semen or blood samples are insufficient to make a genetic fingerprint.

   a. incorrect; this statement is false; identical twins have the same genetic fingerprint
   *b. correct; this statement is true; the standard method used
   c. incorrect; this statement is false; other kinds of samples can be used
   d. incorrect; this statement is false; either could be used for genetic fingerprinting

10. The introns are separated from the exons during
    a. transcription.
    b. replication.
    c. translation.
    d. cloning.

    *a. yes; this way the mRNA is changed into useful genetic code
    b. no; both exons and introns are replicated
    c. no; they have already been separated and introns removed
    d. no; they are both duplicated during cloning

11. Restriction fragment length polymorphisms
    a. are used in genetic fingerprinting.
    b. are used in reassembling exons into a functional gene.
    c. are a method used to compare closely related species.
    d. refers to similarity in the primary structure of proteins.

    *a. yes; the common technique to compare a person's genes to a tissue, blood, or semen sample
    b. no; restriction enzymes and ligases are used to assemble a functional mRNA
    c. no; called melting of DNA in which single-stranded DNA is tested to see if it is complementary to test strands of DNA from other organisms
    d. no; primary structure of proteins refers to the sequence of amino acids

12. By using radioactive probes in association with restriction fragment length polymorphism, it is possible to
    a. distinguish between identical twins.
    b. detect certain mutant or defective alleles.
    c. clone certain human genes.
    d. all of the above

    a. no; identical twins are genetically identical and cannot be separated
    *b. yes; a technique that is useful in diagnosing certain genetic defects
    c. no; a different technique is involved
    d. no; only one of the above is correct

13. Which of the following products has NOT been produced by cloned human genes?
    a. insulin
    b. somatotropin
    c. interferons
    d. hemoglobin

    a. incorrect; has been produced and used to treat diabetes
    b. incorrect; has been produced and used to treat pituitary dwarfism
    c. incorrect; has been produced and used to treat cancer and some viral infections
    *d. correct; this product has not been developed yet

14. The first to insert foreign DNA into a bacterial plasmid was (were)
    a. Oswald Avery.
    b. Alfred Hershey and Martha Chase.
    c. Rosalind Franklin.
    d. Paul Berg.

    a. no; discovered the chemical identity of the gene
    b. no; worked with bacteriophages to demonstrate DNA's role in heredity
    c. no; used x-ray diffraction to characterize DNA
    *d. yes; he and coworkers are credited with the first insertion

15. Many researchers feel that there is no danger in recombinant DNA research because
    a. the genes involved are relatively harmless.
    b. the organisms used have been altered to prevent their survival outside the laboratory environment.
    c. the researchers generally use techniques that prevent dangerous forms from escaping.
    d. all of the above

    a. yes; a partial answer; special safeguards would be established if they were likely to become harmful
    b. yes; a partial answer; mutations restrict the organism to survival only under tightly prescribed conditions
    c. yes; a partial answer; otherwise, the pathogens scientists work with would escape
    *d. yes; all of the above are correct

16. Lindow's ice-minus bacteria
    a. infect a plant and prevent ice crystals from forming within leaf tissues.
    b. add electrolytes to cells to raise the freezing point of cell solutions.
    c. compete with bacteria that naturally occur on the surface of a leaf or stem.
    d. have had a dangerous gene removed from their genome.

    a. no; remain on the surface of the plant
    b. no; not the method of reaction
    c. no; may actually occur, but this is not the important characteristic
    *d. yes; that is why they are called ice-*minus*—they lack the genetic information to form the proteins involved in ice formation

17. Gene therapy refers to
    a. removing a defective gene.
    b. inserting potentially desirable genes.
    c. substituting a normal gene for a defective one.
    d. developing new genes through a gene machine.

    a. no; usually a functional gene would have to be available to provide a needed protein or enzyme
    b. no; called eugenic engineering and generally not considered ethical
    *c. yes; a desirable way to eliminate a genetic defect
    d. no; not yet possible and not the thrust of genetic research

CHAPTER 14
MICROEVOLUTION

1. By the mid-eighteenth century, fossils were used as evidence to support all but which of the following?
   a. All organisms were created in one place at the same time.
   b. Imperfections meant that species were not unalterably perfect and perhaps became modified over time.
   c. Simple forms were restricted to lower layers whereas those in upper strata were complex.
   d. Different layers held different kinds of fossils.

   *a. yes; not supported by the widespread occurrence of fossils; if they were created at the same time and place, the barriers would have stopped their spread
   b. no; supported by fossil evidence showing changes
   c. no; supported by the stratification of fossils
   d. no; supported by fossil variation through sediments

2. The mission of the ship H.M.S *Beagle* was to
   a. collect biological specimens from all over the world.
   b. supply British naval forts.
   c. map the coastline of South America.
   d. study geologic processes such as vulcanism (volcanic activities).

   a. no; although Darwin did make some collections
   b. no; not that type of ship
   *c. yes; a scientific expedition to complete mapping that had already started
   d. no; although some observations were made, this was not a major objective of the trip

3. Darwin's finches had distinctive _____ unlike those of other finches.
   a. color patterns
   b. feet
   c. feathers
   d. beaks

   a. no; these finches were relatively nondescript
   b. no; they had rather common generic type feet
   c. no; nothing distinctive about feathers
   *d. yes; variations in beaks allow finches to feed on different seeds, thereby reducing competition

4. Observations of which of these animals supplied Darwin with the most convincing evidence for his theory of natural selection?
   a. rabbits
   b. armadillos
   c. fishes
   d. finches

   a. no
   b. no; although he did observe these unusual creatures
   c. no
   *d. yes; from the Galápagos Islands

5. The person who suggested that a population tends to outgrow its resource base was
    a. Malthus.
    b. Lyell.
    c. Lamarck.
    d. Henslow.

    *a. yes; economist and clergyman who indicated population grows faster than food supply
    b. no; a geologist who proposed the long time required for geologic processes
    c. no; suggested the theory of use and disuse, or the inheritance of acquired characteristics
    d. no; a botanist that got Darwin his job as naturalist aboard the H.M.S. *Beagle*

6. In his writing, Lyell presented arguments for the slow, gradual occurrences of all but which of the following?
    a. erosion
    b. mountain formation
    c. formation of fossils
    d. volcanic activity

    a. incorrect; a slow process
    b. incorrect; a slow process
    *c. correct; did not express an opinion on this idea
    d. incorrect; a slow process

7. Natural selection is due to
    a. differential reproductive rates.
    b. differential survival resulting in change in a population.
    c. competition.
    d. all of the above

    a. yes; a partial answer
    b. yes; a partial answer
    c. yes; a partial answer
    *d. yes; all of the above are correct

8. *Archaeopteryx*
    a. is an example of a "missing link."
    b. was an animal with teeth and a long bony tail.
    c. is a fossil reptile with feathers.
    d. all of the above

    a. yes; a partial answer
    b. yes; a partial answer
    c. yes; a partial answer
    *d. yes; all of the above are correct

9. Darwin was
    a. strongly encouraged to publish his work by his friends because of Wallace's similar conclusions.
    b. the first person to propose a theory of evolution.
    c. one of several people to suggest the concept of natural selection.
    d. quick to publish his ideas in both scientific papers and in a book.

    *a. yes; Darwin's colleagues encouraged him to publish
    b. no; several people had suggested evolution, but Darwin's contribution was to provide a mechanism for it to happen
    c. no; Darwin and Wallace shared this idea
    d. no; Darwin's voyage started in 1831 and his paper was published in 1858

10. The process of evolution occurs in
   a. individuals.
   b. populations.
   c. species.
   d. families.

   a. no; individuals may change over time (e.g., aging), but this is not evolution because gene frequencies do not change
   *b. yes; a group of interbreeding organisms evolve
   c. no; segments of species evolve and may lead to new species
   d. no; this chapter deals with microevolution, which is evolution at the population level or lower; the evolution of higher taxa is known as macroevolution

11. Which of the following sources of variation does NOT result from shuffling existing genes?
   a. gene mutation
   b. crossing over
   c. genetic recombination
   d. independent assortment of chromosomes

   *a. correct; creates new genes, not new combinations
   b. incorrect; breaks linkage relationships and increases genetic variation
   c. incorrect; combines the potential variation of both parents (if one parent produces 8 million genetic combinations, then the combination of both parents would be 65 trillion)
   d. incorrect; there are 2 to the 23rd power (8,000,000+) ways to arrange the chromosomes of humans by independent assortment alone

12. Which of the following conditions would upset a population at genetic equilibrium and allow evolution or change to occur?
   a. random mating
   b. absence of differential survival or mating
   c. migration among populations
   d. lack of mutations

   a. no; this stabilizes and thus prevents change from happening
   b. no; if this occurred, natural selection would not occur
   *c. yes; allows for new genes to be introduced into the population
   d. no; mutation is one of the obvious sources of change in a population

13. If the frequency of expression of a recessive gene in a population were 16 percent, the frequency of the heterozygote carriers would be
   a. 36 percent.
   b. 60 percent.
   c. 40 percent.
   d. 48 percent.

   a. no; the frequency of the homozygous dominant individuals in the population
   b. no; the frequency of the dominant allele in the population
   c. no; the frequency of the recessive allele in the population
   *d. yes; $2pq = 2 \times (60\%)(40\%) = 48\%$

14. To determine the frequency of the different genotypes for a particular allele in a population following the Hardy-Weinberg equilibrium, the first thing that you would need to do would be to determine the value of
    a. p^2, or the homozygous dominant individuals.
    b. q^2, or the homozygous recessive individuals.
    c. $2pq$, or the heterozygous individuals.
    d. p, or the frequency of the dominant allele.

    a. no; unable to distinguish which is homozygous and which is heterozygous by looking at dominant individuals
  *b. yes; all homozygous recessive individuals, and only homozygous recessive individuals, will express the recessive trait, and from this value all other values in the Hardy-Weinberg equations can be calculated
    c. no; unable to distinguish between homozygous dominants and heterozygous forms expressing dominant trait
    d. no; no way to determine this information without doing another step

15. Which of the following would NOT drive a population away from a genetic equilibrium?
    a. random mating in a large population
    b. genetic drift
    c. gene flow
    d. natural selection

  *a. correct; a large population that mates randomly eliminates the influence of chance in changing gene frequencies
    b. incorrect; in a small population, genetic drift can result in change simply by chance
    c. incorrect; migration or the introduction of alleles to, or loss of alleles from, a population could result in change
    d. incorrect; differences in reproductive or survival rates with reference to one or more alleles could result in change in the genetic composition of a population

16. If a population that is in genetic balance has a frequency of 49 percent for the expression of the recessive allele, then the frequency of the dominant allele would be
    a. 30 percent.
    b. 50 percent.
    c. 70 percent.
    d. none of the above

  *a. yes; if $q^2 = 49\%$ and $q = 70\%$, then p equals 30%
    b. no; for this value to be correct, q^2 would have to be 25%
    c. no; for this value to be correct, q^2 would have to be 9%
    d. no; one of the above is correct

17. Most mutations are
    a. harmful.
    b. lethal.
    c. neutral.
    d. beneficial.

    *a. yes; a change in the instructions in a gene will usually result in the formation of a protein with one or more different amino acids, which would result in a different enzyme. Since enzymes are specific, this new enzyme might not work, and therefore the mutation is harmful.
    b. no; many mutations may produce minor changes and the organisms possessing them do not necessarily die from a defective protein; example: sickle-cell hemoglobin
    c. no; there are many types of hemoglobin, some of which are simple molecular variations that do not affect its functioning
    d. no; some mutations may produce conditions that are favorable to a changed environment such as the one suggested by the text in which an enzyme that functioned at a higher temperature is favored if the temperature rises

18. Which of the following will prevent genetic drift from happening?
    a. genetic isolation
    b. random mating
    c. large population
    d. the founder effect or the bottleneck effect

    a. no; would tend to support genetic drift by keeping the population small
    b. no; is a requirement for genetic drift
    *c. yes; would tend to prevent the frequency of an allele from changing drastically or being eliminated from a population
    d. no; both are examples of genetic drift

19. Which of the following inferences can be drawn from the following observations: Organisms produce more offspring than can survive, quantities of resources remain relatively constant, environmental resources limit population growth?
    a. competition
    b. survival of the fittest
    c. biotic potential
    d. Extinction is the ultimate fate of a species.

    *a. yes; there is competition among a growing population for limited resources
    b. no; this happens because the fittest have the best chance in competition
    c. no; this addresses only the first observation
    d. no; a conclusion that may be based on a great number of observations (including those given) but dependent on other observations

20. Which of the following inferences is NOT supported by the observation that organisms exhibit highly variable traits that are inherited from earlier generations?
    a. Over generations populations change and evolve.
    b. There is differential reproduction.
    c. Organisms tend to exceed their natural limit of numbers.
    d. Some heritable traits are more adaptive than others.

    a. incorrect; this inference is supported by the observation
    b. incorrect; this inference is supported by the observation
    *c. correct; there is nothing in the observation to support this inference
    d. incorrect; this inference is supported by the observation

21. Which of the following is responsible for the changing frequencies of the alleles controlling the color of the peppered moths in England?
    a. artificial selection
    b. stabilizing selection
    c. disruptive selection
    d. directional selection

    a. no; humans did not direct the selection of peppered moths as they might with domesticated animals
    b. no; there was an increase in the frequency of one form over the other
    c. no; did not result in bimodal distribution
    *d. yes; the color pattern of the dark form was favored because of environmental changes following the onset of the industrial revolution

22. In sickle-cell anemia,
    a. both homozygous forms have less chance of survival in tropical and subtropical Africa than do heterozygotes.
    b. the different forms represent balanced polymorphism.
    c. one-third of the population in central Africa may be heterozygous for the trait.
    d. all of the above

    a. yes; a partial answer
    b. yes; a partial answer
    c. yes; a partial answer
    *d. yes; all of the above are correct

23. Which type of selection is operating when any particular trait gives an organism competitive advantage over others in selecting a mate and producing offspring?
    a. disruptive selection
    b. directional selection
    c. sexual selection
    d. stabilizing selection

    a. no; results in two different forms such as found in sexual dimorphism
    b. no; results in organisms at one extreme having advantage over the others
    *c. yes; the female selects males on the basis of sexual features
    d. no; refers to the type of selection that eliminates the extremes and reduces variability

24. _____ leads to speciation.
    a. Evolution
    b. Isolation
    c. Divergence
    d. all of the above

    a. yes; a partial answer; if it results in changes in populations sufficient to prevent interbreeding
    b. yes; a partial answer; if sufficient changes occur during isolation to prevent interbreeding
    c. yes; a partial answer; refers to the accumulation of differences in populations
    *d. yes; all of the above are correct

25. Polyploidy
    a. can result in the immediate formation of species.
    b. leads to geographic isolation of a population.
    c. occurs only in animals.
    d. is the end result of natural selection.

*a. yes; prevents interbreeding or results in formation of sterile hybrids, thereby separating the two populations as different species
    b. no; has no specific relationship to geographic distribution
    c. no; less likely to occur in animals but does occur in plants and may persist through asexual reproduction
    d. no; polyploids may or may not be better adapted than diploids, but it is not correct to say that natural selection leads to polyploidy

CHAPTER 15

LIFE'S ORIGINS AND MACROEVOLUTION

1. Factors leading to evolution include all but which one of the following?
    a. mutation
    b. natural selection
    c. genetic equilibrium
    d. reproductive isolation

    a. incorrect; this is the driving force of evolution that provides changes
    b. incorrect; this is the guiding force of evolution that determines which of the variously adapted individuals survive
    *c. correct; when a population reaches genetic equilibrium, it is stable and does not undergo evolution
    d. incorrect; speciation may occur if isolated populations become so different that they are no longer able to interbreed

2. Which of the following represents an area where fossils would be unlikely to form and be preserved?
    a. shallow seas with continuous deposits of sediments
    b. tar pits
    c. swamps and flood plains
    d. rivers, hillsides, sites of rapid erosion

    a. no; fossils are often well preserved under these conditions
    b. no; animals are trapped, as in quicksand, and are preserved by the tar
    c. no; these sites favor preservation, particularly if decomposition does not occur
    *d. yes; areas of disturbance are unlikely to provide a stable situation where material can fossilize or be preserved

3. The most modern of the four major geologic divisions is the _____ Era.
    a. Paleozoic
    b. Mesozoic
    c. Cenozoic
    d. Proterozoic

    a. no; the second oldest era
    b. no; the third oldest era (Age of Reptiles)
    *c. yes; the most recent era (Age of Mammals)
    d. no; the oldest era

4. Vertebrates are all placed in the same phylum because they
    a. all possessed gills as embryos or subadults.
    b. have similar structural features that demonstrate their kinship.
    c. exhibit many homologous structures.
    d. all of the above

    a. yes; a partial answer
    b. yes; a partial answer
    c. yes; a partial answer
    *d. yes; all of the above are correct

5. Organisms sharing analogous structures
   a. have a common ancestor.
   b. evolved from the same prototype form.
   c. exhibit structures that perform the same function even if the two forms are not closely related embryologically.
   d. none of the above

   a. no; statement would be true if homologous structures were considered
   b. no; statement would be true if homologous structures were considered
   *c. yes; by definition analogous structures share the same function; for example, the wing of a bird and the wing of an insect
   d. one of the above is correct

6. Which of the following radioactive isotopes has the shortest half-life and would NOT be used to determine the age of the planet Earth?
   a. carbon 14
   b. rubidium 87
   c. thorium 232
   d. uranium 238

   *a. correct; only 5,730 years
   b. incorrect; 49 billion years
   c. incorrect; 14 billion years
   d. incorrect; 4.5 billion years

7. The speed of radioactive decay may be increased by subjecting the isotope to
   a. heat.
   b. pressure, such as being buried underground.
   c. certain chemical reactions.
   d. none of the above

   a. no; unable to modify the rate of radioactive decay
   b. no; unable to modify the rate of radioactive decay
   c. no; unable to modify the rate of radioactive decay
   *d. yes; none of the above are able to modify the rate of radioactive decay

8. Which of the following is false?
   a. Morphological convergence leads to analogous structures.
   b. A neutral mutation has no measurable effect on the survival and reproduction of the organism that bears it.
   c. The ancestors of the modern horse had five toes, not one.
   d. A molecular clock is based on the number of substantive rather than neutral mutations that occur over time.

   a. incorrect; this statement is true; structures show adaptations to their environment
   b. incorrect; this statement is true; a simple definition of a neutral mutation
   c. incorrect; this statement is true; the fossil lineage shows a reduction in number of toes
   *d. correct; this statement is false; neutral mutations are used rather than substantive mutations, which might modify survival rates and the number of mutations produced (i.e., major mutations might be attended by a number of minor ones and throw off the accuracy of a molecular clock of evolution)

9. Which of the following ingredients was deemed necessary for the origination of life on earth?
    a. free oxygen
    b. water in a liquid form
    c. the absence of sunlight for parts of a day
    d. all of the above

    a. no; free oxygen actually would be antagonistic to the formation of some organic compounds
   *b. yes; liquid water was necessary to form salt solutions and a medium in which life could flourish
    c. no; no need for either light or darkness in the beginning because photosynthesis had not evolved
    d. no; only one of the above is correct

10. The first templates (structural patterns) for protein synthesis were most likely
    a. complex polysaccharides.
    b. nucleic acids.
    c. clay.
    d. inorganic crystals.

    a. no; no evidence to support this
    b. no; these came later
   *c. yes; long chains of proteins could be formed with inherent stability to keep them from breaking apart
    d. no; structural patterns would not permit this

11. Which of the following was NOT one of the four gases used in Stanley Miller's simulation of the synthesis of organic compounds on the early earth?
    a. methane`
    b. ammonia
    c. water vapor
    d. carbon dioxide

    a. incorrect; methane was used
    b. incorrect; ammonia was used
    c. incorrect; water vapor was used
   *d. correct; carbon dioxide was not one of the four gases used

12. Which of the following is the *least* likely mechanism leading to the establishment of membranes around cells?
    a. Fragments of cellulose (the most common organic compound in the world) joined together to form the first membrane.
    b. Lipid molecules self-assembled into small water-filled sacs.
    c. Membranes arose spontaneously and involved both amino acids and lipids.
    d. Chains of amino acids self-assembled into small stable spheres that later added lipids at their surface.

   *a. correct; cellulose was not available at this time
    b. incorrect; one plausible explanation of the origin of membranes
    c. incorrect; one plausible explanation of the origin of membranes
    d. incorrect; one plausible explanation of the origin of membranes

13. The large land mass that started breaking up during the Mesozoic Era and is still moving apart today is
    a. Gondwana.
    b. Pangea.
    c. Eurasia.
    d. Nazca plate.

    a. no; an early land mass that formed part of Pangea
    *b. yes; the large common land mass
    c. no; a tectonic plate that includes much of Europe and Asia
    d. no; a tectonic plate located west of South America in the Pacific Ocean

14. At the beginning of geologic eras, there were
    a. massive extinctions.
    b. catastrophic climatic and geologic events.
    c. periods of recovery, adaptive radiation, and filling of vacant niches and adaptive zones.
    d. periods of stasis with minimal biotic change.

    a. no; marked the closing of a previous era rather than the beginning of a new one
    b. no; marked the closing of a previous era rather than the beginning of a new one
    *c. yes; many vacant niches existed following the massive extinctions, and organisms adapted to new environmental conditions
    d. no; there were periods of intense evolutionary activity

15. Which of the following epochs was NOT part of the tertiary period?
    a. Pleistocene
    b. Eocene
    c. Miocene
    d. Pliocene

    *a. correct; part of the quaternary period
    b. incorrect; part of the tertiary period
    c. incorrect; part of the tertiary period
    d. incorrect; part of the tertiary period

16. Evolutionary access to an adaptive zone may occur
    a. through an extinction that provides a vacancy in that zone.
    b. if the invading organism is able to out-compete the resident species.
    c. with the development of a key innovation.
    d. all of the above

    a. yes; a partial answer
    b. yes; a partial answer
    c. yes; a partial answer
    *d. yes; all of the above are correct

17. The appearance of oxygen in the Proterozoic atmosphere was dependent on the
    a. action of methanogens.
    b. synthesis of organic compounds.
    c. evolution of photosynthetic bacteria.
    d. appearance of heterotrophic organisms.

    a. no; would produce methane
    b. no; would not generate free oxygen
    *c. yes; would produce oxygen as a by-product
    d. no; would consume free oxygen

18. The most recent period of the six periods of the Paleozoic Era was the
    a. Cambrian.
    b. Permian.
    c. Carboniferous.
    d. Devonian.

    a. no; oldest of the six periods
    *b. yes; most recent of the six periods
    c. no; fifth oldest of the six periods
    d. no; fourth oldest of the six periods

19. The fossil fuels were formed during the
    a. Cretaceous.
    b. Cambrian.
    c. Cenozoic.
    d. Carboniferous.

    a. no; part of the Mesozoic
    b. no; too early, first period of the Paleozoic
    c. no; too late, the most recent geologic era
    *d. yes; the term means carbon bearing

20. Which of the following periods was NOT characterized by giant reptiles?
    a. Permian
    b. Triassic
    c. Cretaceous
    d. Jurassic

    *a. correct; large dinosaurs had not yet developed
    b. incorrect; reptiles were dominant forms
    c. incorrect; reptiles were dominant forms
    d. incorrect; reptiles were dominant forms

21. The flowering plants arose and underwent major radiation during the
    a. Permian.
    b. Triassic.
    c. Cretaceous.
    d. Quaternary.

    a. no
    b. no
    *c. yes; over a brief 10-million-year span
    d. no

22. The presence of the element _____ is taken as evidence to support the idea that the earth was struck by an asteroid or a comet.
    a. titanium
    b. iridium
    c. vanadium
    d. cesium

    a. no
    *b. yes
    c. no
    d. no

23. Which of the following includes related orders?
    a. class
    b. phylum
    c. family
    d. genus

    *a. yes; related orders are in the same class
    b. no; phyla are composed of related classes
    c. no; families are composed of related genera
    d. no; genera are composed of related species

CHAPTER 16
HUMAN EVOLUTION

1. The new traits that develop during the evolutionary process that leads to producing a new species
   a. arise *de novo* and appear for the first time when that species first evolves.
   b. are modifications of traits that arose before.
   c. are the results of a process of natural selection from a great number of alternate choices.
   d. are the intermediate steps in the grand design that led to the development of a new species (changes appear not to be random).

   a. no; there are a few new innovations that are seen for the first time in a new species. The majority of the features are copies or modifications of previously existing traits.
   *b. yes
   c. no; natural selection begins when innovations are first produced. Large groups of parts are not waiting around to be assembled into a new species.
   d. no; there is no evidence of an orderly grand design destined to produce a particular new species (changes appear to be random)

2. The mammalian brain is composed of _____ main parts.
   a. two
   b. three
   c. four
   d. five

   a. no
   *b. yes; forebrain, midbrain, hindbrain
   c. no
   d. no

3. The mammalian teeth that resemble the shape of a chisel are the
   a. cuspids or canines.
   b. bicuspids or premolars.
   c. molars.
   d. incisors.

   a. no; dog teeth or fangs used for ripping flesh, biting, piercing
   b. no; flattened teeth providing a platform for grinding food
   c. no; flattened teeth for grinding food, characteristic of herbivores
   *d. yes; used to bite sandwiches or corn on the cob, or for a horse to hold onto grass as it pulls its head away

4. Which of the following groups does NOT include humans?
   a. anthropoids
   b. prosimians
   c. primates
   d. hominoids

   a. incorrect; includes monkeys, apes, and humans
   *b. correct; includes the primitive primates
   c. incorrect; includes all groups listed
   d. incorrect; includes apes, humans, and recent human ancestors

5. Which of the following is the most highly evolved?
   a. prosimians
   b. hominids
   c. anthropoids
   d. hominoids

   a. no; includes the primitive primates
   *b. yes; members of the human lineage
   c. no; includes monkeys
   d. no; includes apes

6. Which of the following is NOT a trend in human evolution?
   a. change in method of locomotion
   b. increase in size and number of teeth
   c. increased use of stereoscopic and color vision and a decline in the use of the sense of smell
   d. enlargement and development of the brain

   a. incorrect; development of hand important in human evolution
   *b. correct; number and size of teeth decreased rather than increased
   c. incorrect; humans began to rely more on sight than smell
   d. incorrect; perhaps the most important trend in human evolution

7. Which of the following features is characteristic of the monkeys, but not the apes?
   a. Monkeys' armbones are longer than their legbones.
   b. Monkeys can swivel their arms above their heads.
   c. Monkeys can run palms down.
   d. Monkeys are biped whereas apes are quadripeds.

   a. no; monkeys' armbones are shorter than their legbones
   b. no; this is a characteristic of the apes
   *c. yes
   d. no; monkeys are quadripeds; humans are the only true biped in the primates

8. The type of diet most characteristic of modern monkeys includes
   a. flesh.
   b. fruits and leaves.
   c. insects.
   d. a combination of foods found in trees.

   a. no; not typical of monkeys
   b. no; included in diet of monkeys, but their diet is more varied
   c. no; characteristic of primitive monkey group
   *d. yes; eat foods available in trees, including insects, leaves, fruits

9. Which of the following was NOT one of the evolutionary trends in primates?
   a. longer life spans
   b. longer span of time between pregnancies
   c. more offspring at a time, increase in litter size
   d. longer period of infant dependency with longer periods of learning

   a. incorrect; life span has increased
   b. incorrect; there is a longer time between pregnancies
   *c. correct; there has been a *decrease* in litter size
   d. incorrect; there is a longer period of dependency and learning

10. The most primitive primates resembled small
    a. monkeys.
    b. rodents.
    c. squirrels.
    d. opossums.

    a. no; monkeys are more advanced primates
    *b. yes
    c. no; even though they were both arboreal (lived in trees)
    d. no; opossums are primitive marsupials, not placental mammals

11. In the evolutionary development of the primitive primates, the fossil evidence indicates that not only did their cranial capacity increase but also they developed
    a. a longer, more pronounced snout.
    b. nocturnal vision.
    c. claws and specialized teeth.
    d. refined grasping movements.

    a. no; snout regressed
    b. no; enhanced daytime vision
    c. no; had these features already
    *d. yes; to enhance their climbing abilities

12. The tree habitat
    a. offered the primitive primate a haven from ground-based predators.
    b. required color vision to see ripened fruit and to judge features in its environment.
    c. required a coordination of muscle and brain to move efficiently.
    d. all of the above

    a. yes; a partial answer
    b. yes; a partial answer
    c. yes; a partial answer
    *d. yes; all of the above are correct

13. The first hominoid appeared _____ years ago.
    a. 38–54 million
    b. 30–35 million
    c. 20–23 million
    d. 6–10 million

    a. no; this was the Eocene epoch, during which the primitive primates developed
    b. no; the tree-dwelling ancestors of the monkeys appeared in this time period
    *c. yes
    d. no; the origin of modern gorillas, chimpanzees, and humans

14. During the evolution of the hominids,
    a. the environment became cooler and drier.
    b. there was an expansion of the tropical rainforest habitat.
    c. there was a decrease in grasslands.
    d. the environment became hotter and wetter.

    *a. yes; perhaps leading to isolation of arboreal populations
    b. no; forests gave way to grasslands
    c. no; grasslands increase under drier conditions
    d. no

15. Which of the following fossil evidences does NOT directly or indirectly support the bipedalism of the hominids?
    a. footprints and tools
    b. muscle insertions in hipbone and structure of hipbone
    c. enlarged cranial capacity
    d. skeletal material of Lucy showing the backbone directly over the hips

    a. incorrect; both would indicate bipedalism
    b. incorrect; the characteristics of the pelvic girdle would support bipedalism
    *c. correct; this feature could develop independent of the type of gait
    d. incorrect; the backbone needs to be over the hindlimbs for upright walking

CHAPTER 17
VIRUSES, BACTERIA, AND PROTISTANS

1. The monerans and protists are alike in that they are essentially
   a. unicellular.
   b. producers.
   c. eukaryotic.
   d. motile.

   *a. yes; protists and bacteria are unicellular
   b. no; the many parasitic and heterotrophic forms are not all producers
   c. no; monerans are prokaryotic
   d. no; motility varies among these organisms and is not an important or diagnostic feature

2. A virus
   a. takes over the control of a host cell and forces it to make more virus particles.
   b. is a naked molecule of nucleic acid.
   c. is a living obligate parasite of certain animals.
   d. is a chemical poison that disrupts the normal metabolic processes of a cell.

   *a. yes; typical of the lytic cycle of viral infection
   b. no; viruses have a protective protein coat or sometimes are encased in a lipid envelope
   c. no; viruses are not alive and may infect a wide range of hosts including bacteria, fungi, and plants
   d. no; could be true of a number of chemical toxins

3. A virus can replicate
   a. while attached to a receptor on the surface of a cell.
   b. only after its DNA/RNA has entered the host cell and started to control the biosynthetic machinery of the cell.
   c. under a wide range of environmental conditions, thus making viruses extremely dangerous pathogens.
   d. only in warm-blooded animals and a few insect vectors.

   a. no; unable to replicate unless it enters a living cell
   *b. yes
   c. no; only under very specific conditions inside a cell
   d. no; may infect and reproduce in a wide variety of host cells

4. Which of the following activities occurs first during the invasion of a cell by a virus?
   a. The DNA or RNA is injected into the cell.
   b. The virus locks onto a specific receptor molecule on the surface of a host cell.
   c. The virus gains control over the cell's metabolic machinery.
   d. Viral nucleic acids are replicated and viral proteins produced.

   a. no; occurs second
   *b. yes; occurs first
   c. no; occurs third
   d. no; occurs fourth

5. Viroids are infective units composed of
   a. DNA fragments.
   b. RNA fragments.
   c. viral proteins.
   d. proteins and nucleic acids.

   a. no; fragments of a gene, not a virus
   *b. yes; cause plant diseases and certain types of cancer
   c. no; not infective by themselves
   d. no; a virus, not a viroid, contains nucleic acid and proteins

6. Which statement is false?
   a. Bacteria lack an organized nucleus.
   b. Bacteria have a plasma membrane but lack membranes to surround the organelles.
   c. Bacteria lack ribosomes.
   d. Bacteria are prokaryotic rather than eukaryotic.

   a. incorrect; this statement is true; they have one long chromosome, but it is not surrounded by nuclear membrane
   b. incorrect; this statement is true; they lack membrane-bound organelles
   *c. correct; this statement is false; they possess ribosomes and use them to produce proteins
   d. incorrect; this statement is true; they are primitive forms of life

7. The majority of bacteria are
   a. photosynthetic autotrophs.
   b. chemosynthetic autotrophs.
   c. pathogens.
   d. heterotrophs.

   a. no; a small number function this way
   b. no; an even smaller number function as chemosynthesizers
   c. no; disease-producing bacteria are a minority
   *d. yes; vast majority are decomposers and derive their food heterotrophically

8. Extracircular pieces of chromosome found in bacteria are called
   a. pili.
   b. peptidoglycans.
   c. flagella.
   d. plasmids.

   a. no; a conjugation tube
   b. no; ingredients in the walls of bacteria
   c. no; organelles used for movement
   *d. yes

9. Which of the following is NOT closely related to the other three?
   a. extreme halophiles
   b. methanogens
   c. Gram-positive bacteria
   d. thermoacidophiles

   a. incorrect; representatives of the archaebacteria
   b. incorrect; representatives of the archaebacteria
   *c. correct; one of the types of eubacteria
   d. incorrect; representatives of the archaebacteria

10. The methanogens are responsible for all but which one of the following?
    a. chemosynthetic production of food
    b. production of swamp gas
    c. production of gas in sewage-treatment facilities
    d. production of gases by cattle and similar organisms

   *a. yes; are not chemosynthetic bacteria
    b. no; decomposition leads to production of methane
    c. no; methane is produced in sewage plants
    d. no; cattle are a major source of methane

11. Bacteriorhodopsin is a bacterial
    a. vitamin.
    b. light-trapping pigment.
    c. food storage product.
    d. metabolic waste product.

    a. no; not a dietary food necessity
   *b. yes
    c. no; food is stored in various compounds
    d. no; numerous waste products are produced by bacteria (including strong toxins) but this
       is not one of them

12. Heterocysts are cells in the cyanobacteria that
    a. fix nitrogen.
    b. anchor the plant.
    c. develop into spores.
    d. develop into gametes.

   *a. yes
    b. no; such cells are called holdfasts
    c. no; such cells are called sporangia
    d. no; such cells are called gametangia

13. Flagellated, photosynthetic protistans that are capable of living heterotrophically are
    a. chrysophytes.
    b. euglenids.
    c. paramecia.
    d. sporozoans.

    a. no; autotrophic only
   *b. yes; able to produce food or exist heterotrophically
    c. no; ciliated protistans unable to photosynthesize
    d. no; incapable of independent movement or autotrophic nutrition

14. The chrysophytes include all but which of the following?
    a. yellow-green algae
    b. golden algae
    c. dinoflagellates
    d. diatoms

    a. incorrect; are chrysophytes
    b. incorrect; are chrysophytes
   *c. correct; a separate group of protistans
    d. incorrect; are chrysophytes

15. Red tides kill fish by
    a. suffocation through the production of excess oxygen.
    b. clogging fish gills with a large number of organisms.
    c. a nerve poison (neurotoxin).
    d. a chemical that paralyzes the large swimming muscles of the fish.

    a. no; not an apparent problem
    b. no; not an apparent problem
    *c. yes
    d. no; not an apparent problem

CHAPTER 18
FUNGI AND PLANTS

1. Fungi can be best described by all of the following EXCEPT
   a. autotrophs.
   b. saprobes.
   c. heterotrophs.
   d. parasites.

   *a. correct; they do produce their own food
   b. incorrect; they do derive their food from dead material
   c. incorrect; they do not produce their own food
   d. incorrect; some fungi derive their food from a living host

2. Which of the following statements is false?
   a. The body of a multicellular fungus is composed of hyphae, some of which extract food from organic matter.
   b. Fungi function in the recycling of elements.
   c. Fungi spores can be produced by either mitosis or meiosis, and these spores can be part of the sexual or asexual life cycle.
   d. Fungi are composed of naked protoplasts separated from each other by a thin pellicle except in those that produce cellulose fruiting bodies such as mushrooms or toadstools.

   a. incorrect; this statement is true
   b. incorrect; this statement is true
   c. incorrect; this statement is true
   *d. correct; this statement is false; fungi have cell walls reinforced with chitin

3. In the generalized life cycle of a fungus, _____ usually are produced by meiosis.
   a. gametes
   b. vegetative bodies
   c. spores
   d. zygotes

   a. no; produced by mitosis from vegetative cells
   b. no; produced by mitosis from other vegetative cells
   *c. yes; meiosis reduces the chromosome number and is involved in spore formation
   d. no; produced by fertilization to generate the diploid phase of the life cycle

4. Which of the following types of fungi have motile spores?
   a. chytrids and water molds
   b. sac fungi
   c. club fungi
   d. imperfect fungi

   *a. yes; these spores can swim to a site where they germinate
   b. no; the yeasts and multicellular sac fungi
   c. no; the mushrooms, smuts, and rusts
   d. no; some of the medically important antibiotic producers and pathogens

5. Which of the following has representatives that do not (or have not been observed to have) sexually reproducing forms?
   a. club fungi
   b. zygospore-forming fungi
   c. chytrids and water molds
   d. fungi imperfecti

   a. no; reproduce both sexually and asexually
   b. no; reproduce both sexually and asexually
   c. no; reproduce both sexually and asexually
   *d. yes; no sexually reproducing forms yet found

6. Gills are structural characteristics of
   a. chytrids or water molds.
   b. mushrooms.
   c. yeasts that cause vaginal and oral infections.
   d. lichens.

   a. no
   *b. yes; structural divisions of the mushroom that produce spores
   c. no
   d. no; a mutualistic association of an alga and a fungus

7. Which of the following are often used to measure air pollution?
   a. lichens
   b. mushrooms
   c. green algae
   d. mosses

   *a. yes; lichens are intolerant of air pollution
   b. no; a mushroom is only the fruiting (reproductive) phase of an organism that is mostly concealed underground
   c. no; often very tolerant species
   d. no; often very tolerant species

8. Sporophytes
   a. are the dominant phase in the life cycle of most terrestrial plants.
   b. are the haploid stage in the plant life cycle.
   c. reproduce sexually.
   d. develop from spores and produce gametes.

   *a. yes; these larger plants can release their spores to the wind for better dissemination
   b. no; develop from the diploid zygote
   c. no; reproduce asexually by spores
   d. no; develop from the zygote and reproduce by spores

9. Which of the following is NOT a vascular plant?
   a. bryophyte
   b. conifer
   c. angiosperm
   d. fern

   *a. correct; no vascular tissues in the nonvascular mosses and liverworts
   b. incorrect; has vascular tissues
   c. incorrect; has vascular tissues
   d. incorrect; has vascular tissues

10. Which of the following is NOT a representative of a group of true algae?
    a. red algae
    b. brown algae
    c. blue-green algae
    d. green algae

    a. incorrect; red algae include the delicate seaweeds
    b. incorrect; brown algae include the giant seaweeds such as the kelps
    *c. correct; these are cyanobacteria and classified as monerans
    d. incorrect; marine, freshwater, and terrestrial algae

11. The sporophyte and gametophyte stages live independently of the following EXCEPT
    a. lycophytes.
    b. bryophytes.
    c. horsetails.
    d. ferns.

    a. incorrect; both sporophyte and gametophyte are independent
    *b. correct; in the bryophytes the sporophyte is dependent on the gametophyte
    c. incorrect; both sporophyte and gametophyte are independent
    d. incorrect; both sporophyte and gametophyte are independent

12. A sorus is a
    a. specialized spore characteristic of some mosses.
    b. structure associated with the seeds of gymnosperms.
    c. group of gametophyte cells capable of breaking off from the present plant and starting a new independent life.
    d. none of the above

    a. no
    b. no
    c. no
    *d. yes; a sorus is a cluster of sporangia found on the leaves of a fern

13. A pine seed contains all but which one of the following?
    a. pollen grain
    b. seed coat
    c. female gametophyte
    d. embryo

    *a. correct; only delivers the male gamete
    b. incorrect; covers the seed
    c. incorrect; contained within the seed
    d. incorrect; contained within the seed

14. Which of the following is a dicot?
    a. grasses
    b. lilies
    c. cacti
    d. orchids

    a. no; a typical monocot
    b. no; a typical monocot
    *c. yes
    d. no; a typical monocot

15. The endosperm
    a. is specialized tissue found only in the male reproductive system.
    b. supplies food for the developing sporophyte.
    c. becomes the young embryo.
    d. is part of the zygote.

    a. no; found surrounding the embryo in the female organ
    *b. yes; produces nourishment for the young embryo
    c. no; not a part that develops into the embryo
    d. no; a separate entity from the zygote

16. Which of the following was NOT one of the major evolutionary trends in the flowering plants?
    a. development of vascular tissue and increased independence from water
    b. shift of dominance from the haploid (gametophyte) generation to the diploid (sporophyte)
    c. reduction in the frequency of occurrence of sexual reproduction
    d. change to the development of two different types of spores

    a. incorrect; one of the important evolutionary developments
    b. incorrect; one of the trends is commonly described as the rise of the sporophyte and the decline of the gametophyte
    *c. correct; sexual reproduction increased with a corresponding decrease in asexual reproduction
    d. incorrect; two different spores called heterospores were produced (megaspores and microspores)

17. Which of the following are the flowering plants?
    a. angiosperms
    b. gymnosperms
    c. bryophytes
    d. lycopods

    *a. yes
    b. no; the conifers
    c. no; the mosses
    d. no; primitive vascular plants

18. Which of the following are no longer dependent on water for reproduction?
    a. angiosperms
    b. bryophytes
    c. conifers
    d. both (a) and (c)

    a. yes; a partial answer; flowering plants do not need water for reproduction
    b. no; mosses, liverworts, and stoneworts
    c. yes; a partial answer; conifers do not need water for reproduction
    *d. yes; both (a) and (c) are correct; both groups use pollen grains and nonmotile microspores

CHAPTER 19
ANIMALS

1. The flatworms belong to the phylum
   a. Cnidaria.
   b. Nematoda.
   c. Annelida.
   d. Platyhelminthes.

   a. no; includes the hydrozoans, jellyfish, corals, and sea anemones
   b. no; includes roundworms, such as hookworms and pinworms
   c. no; includes segmented worms such as earthworms, sandworms, and leeches
   *d. yes; the turbellarians, flukes, and tapeworms

2. The largest phylum second to the Arthropoda is
   a. Nematoda.
   b. Annelida.
   c. Chordata.
   d. Mollusca.

   a. no; 20,000 species
   b. no; 15,000 species
   c. no; 47,000 species
   *d. yes; 110,000 species

3. Which of the following exhibit cephalization?
   a. cnidarians
   b. arthropods
   c. roundworms
   d. sponges

   a. no; no head region
   *b. yes; in the insects the body is divided into the head, thorax, and abdomen
   c. no; no head region
   d. no; no head region

4. The peritoneum is the
   a. first part of the intestinal tract.
   b. lining of the coelomic cavity.
   c. membrane surrounding and protecting the heart.
   d. none of the above

   a. no; this is the duodenum
   *b. yes
   c. no; this is the pericardium
   d. no; one of the above is correct

5. Which of the following phyla is characterized by the presence of a pseudocoelom?
   a. Annelida
   b. Mollusca
   c. Nematoda
   d. Platyhelminthes

   a. no; has a true coelom
   b. no; has a true coelom
   *c. yes; has a pseudocoelom
   d. no; no cavity between gut and body wall

6. Medusae are part of the life cycle of the
   a. annelids.
   b. poriferans.
   c. platyhelminths.
   d. cnidarians.

   a. no
   b. no
   c. no
   *d. yes; a free-floating bell-shaped stage like a jellyfish

7. Which of the following is NOT characteristic of cnidarians?
   a. flame cells
   b. nerve net
   c. nematocysts
   d. mesoglea

   *a. correct; specialized organs involved in excretion in turbellarians
   b. incorrect; pattern of nervous system of cnidarians
   c. incorrect; stinging devices characteristic of cnidarians
   d. incorrect; jellylike layer characteristic of cnidarians

8. Which of the following is NOT primarily parasitic?
   a. flukes
   b. rotifers
   c. tapeworms
   d. leeches

   a. incorrect; a parasitic group of animals
   *b. correct; free-living forms
   c. incorrect; a parasitic group of animals
   d. incorrect; a parasitic group of animals

9. *Trichinella* infection is contracted by
   a. swimming in infected water.
   b. eating undercooked pork.
   c. eating contaminated vegetables.
   d. being bitten by a female mosquito.

   a. no
   *b. yes
   c. no
   d. no

10. Which of the following is a protostome?
    a. annelids
    b. echinoderms
    c. chordates
    d. both (a) and (c)

    *a. yes; a protostome
    b. no; a deuterostome
    c. no; a deuterostome
    d. no; one of the above is correct

11. *Mollusca* literally means
    a. spiny-skinned animal.
    b. shelled animal.
    c. soft body.
    d. none of the above

    a. no; echinoderms
    b. no; mollusks have shells but the name of the phylum refers to something else
    *c. yes
    d. no; one of the above is correct

12. Which phylum does NOT include parasitic forms?
    a. Annelida
    b. Mollusca
    c. Platyhelminthes
    d. Nematoda

    a. no; leeches are parasitic
    *b. yes
    c. no; tapeworms and flukes are parasitic
    d. no; many nematodes are parasites of plants or animals

13. Setae are
    a. the bristles of annelids that aid in locomotion.
    b. excretory organs of annelids.
    c. digestive organs of annelids.
    d. branches of an annelid nervous system.

    *a. yes
    b. no
    c. no
    d. no

14. The exoskeleton
    a. is made of protein and chitin to enable growth.
    b. restricts growth and must be shed if an insect outgrows it.
    c. prevents water loss and provides protection.
    d. all of the above

    a. yes; a partial answer
    b. yes; a partial answer
    c. yes; a partial answer
    *d. yes; all of the above are correct

15. Tracheae are
    a. digestive organs.
    b. respiratory tubes.
    c. appendages.
    d. reproductive structures.

    a. no
    *b. yes
    c. no
    d. no

16. _____ have ten legs (often with claws) and many segments with a covering (the carapace) over some or all of the segments.
    a. Crustaceans
    b. Chelicerates
    c. Insects
    d. Trilobites

    *a. yes
    b. no
    c. no
    d. no

17. If reproductive capacity and habitat exploration are important measures of success, the _____ would rank first.
    a. mollusks
    b. chordates
    c. arthropods
    d. echinoderms

    a. no
    b. no
    *c. yes
    d. no

18. The Malpighian tubules function in
    a. digestion.
    b. excretion.
    c. respiration.
    d. circulation.

    a. no
    *b. yes
    c. no
    d. no

19. Which of the following is NOT an echinoderm?
    a. sea urchin
    b. sea cucumber
    c. sea star
    d. sea anemone

    a. incorrect; is an echinoderm
    b. incorrect; is an echinoderm
    c. incorrect; is an echinoderm
    *d. correct; is a cnidarian

20. Which of the following is found in adult echinoderms?
    a. a water vascular system
    b. bilateral symmetry
    c. a radula
    d. a thorax

    *a. yes; used for locomotion
    b. no; found only in larval echinoderms
    c. no; found in some mollusks
    d. no; a region of many animal bodies with bilateral symmetry

21. Which of the following is NOT characteristic of *all* chordates?
    a. a notochord
    b. a post-anal tail
    c. pharyngeal gill slits
    d. vertebrae

    a. incorrect; found in all chordates
    b. incorrect; found in all chordates
    c. incorrect; found in all chordates
    *d. correct; not found in the invertebrate chordates

22. Which of the following were the immediate ancestors of the land-dwelling vertebrates?
    a. cartilaginous fishes
    b. jawless fishes
    c. lobe-finned fishes
    d. ray-finned fishes

    a. no; more primitive than the bony fishes
    b. no; the most primitive group of fish
    *c. yes; the immediate ancestors of the amphibia
    d. no; they did not give rise to terrestrial forms

23. The part of the brain that underwent a major expansion during the evolution of the vertebrates was the
    a. medula oblongata.
    b. cerebrum.
    c. cerebellum.
    d. reticular formation.

    a. no
    *b. yes
    c. no
    d. no

24. Placoderms were ancient
    a. fishes.
    b. reptiles.
    c. birds.
    d. mammals.

    *a. yes
    b. no
    c. no
    d. no

25. _____ are the most successful type of bony fish today.
    a. Ray-finned fish (teleosts)
    b. Bichirs
    c. Crossopterygians
    d. Lungfishes

    *a. yes; the ray-finned fishes
    b. no
    c. no
    d. no

26. The land egg is typical of all but which of the following?
    a. amphibians
    b. birds
    c. mammals
    d. reptiles

   *a. yes; do not possess an amniotic egg; must place eggs in a watery environment
    b. no; have an amniotic egg
    c. no; some have an amniotic egg; others modify it for internal development
    d. no; some have an amniotic egg

CHAPTER 20
PLANT TISSUES

1. Which of the following is NOT a ground tissue?
   a. parenchyma
   b. xylem
   c. sclerenchyma
   d. collenchyma

   a. incorrect; a ground tissue
   *b. correct; not a ground tissue, but a vascular tissue
   c. incorrect; a ground tissue
   d. incorrect; a ground tissue

2. Which of the following is specialized to conduct food?
   a. xylem
   b. parenchyma
   c. phloem
   d. sclerenchyma

   a. no; specialized to conduct water and minerals
   b. no; unspecialized cells used for various purposes such as food storage
   *c. yes
   d. no; dead strengthening fibers that function in support

3. Which of the following types of cells would be expected to have a thin cell wall surrounding the cell?
   a. parenchyma
   b. xylem
   c. sclerenchyma
   d. collenchyma

   *a. yes
   b. no; has thick cell walls often with pits and recesses and is used as mechanical tissue to support the plant
   c. no; often has very thick wall used in support
   d. no; has irregularly thickened walls

4. Cutin is a waxy substance deposited on the outer surface of _____ cells.
   a. xylem
   b. collenchyma
   c. phloem
   d. epidermal

   a. no; lignin impregnates these cell walls
   b. no; lignin impregnates these cell walls
   c. no; cell walls are not usually filled with any particular substance
   *d. yes; prevents excess water loss from plant surface

5. Secondary growth
   a. is responsible for the increase in the length of a stem.
   b. is the responsibility of lateral meristems.
   c. occurs at the root and stem tips.
   d. is found only in herbaceous annual plants.

   a. no; would be the responsibility of apical meristem
   *b. yes; increases the width (girth) of a plant
   c. no; occurs throughout the plant
   d. no; usually only primary growth is found in herbaceous annuals

6. The point where leaves arise from the stem is the
   a. stoma.
   b. cuticle.
   c. node.
   d. pith.

   a. no; a pore for gas exchange
   b. no; a layer composed of cutin that reduces water loss
   *c. yes
   d. no; central parenchyma in a stem

7. Which of the following is a dicot?
   a. iris
   b. beech tree
   c. orchids
   d. grasses

   a. no; a monocot
   *b. yes; a dicot as are most trees (have a vascular cambium to produce secondary xylem)
   c. no; a monocot
   d. no; a monocot

8. A cotyledon is a
   a. seed leaf.
   b. protective sheath.
   c. segment of the root system.
   d. part of a flower.

   *a. yes; monocots have one seed leaf, dicots have two
   b. no; called the coleoptile
   c. no
   d. no

9. Which of the following tissues is NOT characterized by rapid cell division?
   a. cork cambium
   b. lateral meristem
   c. vascular cambium
   d. periderm

   a. incorrect; a type of embryonic tissue that produces the periderm
   b. incorrect; a group of embryonic cells that produce cells that cause the plant to thicken
   c. incorrect; a group of embryonic cells that produce vascular tissues
   *d. correct; is secondary tissue produced by divisions of the cork cambium; does not divide itself

10. The periderm
    a. replaces the epidermis.
    b. is produced by the cork cambium.
    c. is a protective layer that surrounds older plant tissues (i.e., old stems or roots).
    d. all of the above

    a. yes; a partial answer
    b. yes; a partial answer
    c. yes; a partial answer
    *d. yes; all of the above are correct

11. Which of the following is characteristic of dicots?
    a. one pore or furrow in their pollen grains
    b. a single seed leaf
    c. vascular bundles arranged in a ring surrounding a central pith
    d. parallel veins in their leaves

    a. no; a characteristic of monocots
    b. no; a characteristic of monocots
    *c. yes; a characteristic of dicots
    d. no; a characteristic of monocots

12. The cortex is
    a. a stem of a leaf.
    b. tissue that surrounds the vascular bundles.
    c. ground tissue found outside the ring of vascular tissues.
    d. a portion of a terminal bud.

    a. no; the petiole
    b. no; vascular bundle sheath
    *c. yes; cortex is located between the veins and epidermis
    d. no

13. Companion cells are found in
    a. phloem.
    b. xylem.
    c. cortex.
    d. pith.

    *a. yes; a type of phloem cell that surrounds and supports sieve tubes
    b. no; includes tracheids and vessel elements
    c. no; composed of parenchyma cells
    d. no; composed of parenchyma cells

14. Which of the following does NOT have deciduous leaves?
    a. camellia or holly
    b. hickory tree
    c. maple tree
    d. sweet gum tree

    *a. correct; evergreen, not deciduous
    b. incorrect; sheds its leaves each year
    c. incorrect; sheds its leaves each year
    d. incorrect; sheds its leaves each year

15. Photosynthesis primarily occurs in the _____ of a leaf.
    a. upper epidermis
    b. lower epidermis
    c. mesophyll
    d. all of the above

    a. no; colorless cells with the exception of guard cells surrounding the stoma
    b. no; colorless cells with the exception of guard cells surrounding the stoma
    *c. yes; the majority of the chloroplasts are found in the mesophyll cells
    d. no; only one of the above is correct

16. Lateral roots arise from the
    a. epidermis.
    b. cortex.
    c. endodermis.
    d. pericycle.

    a. no
    b. no
    c. no
    *d. yes

17. Grasses are primarily characterized by
    a. adventitious roots.
    b. fibrous root systems.
    c. taproot systems.
    d. both (a) and (b)

    a. yes; a partial answer; the primary root dies and is replaced by adventitious roots
    b. yes; a partial answer; the adventitious roots form a fibrous root system
    c. no; although a few grasses may have a taproot
    *d. yes; both (a) and (b) are correct

18. Corn, marigolds, and beans are examples of
    a. annuals.
    b. biennials.
    c. perennials.
    d. both (a) and (b)

    *a. yes; live for only one year
    b. no
    c. no
    d. no; only one of the above is correct

19. All of the cells between the vascular cambium and the surface of a woody stem or root collectively make up the
    a. wood.
    b. bark.
    c. cork.
    d. cortex.

    a. no; inside the vascular cambium
    *b. yes
    c. no; only those cells produced by the vascular cambium
    d. no; only cells between vein and epidermis

CHAPTER 21
PLANT NUTRITION AND TRANSPORT

1. The concentration of carbon dioxide in the atmosphere is _____ parts per million.
   a. 35
   b. 350
   c. 3,500
   d. 35,000

   a. no
   *b. yes
   c. no
   d. no

2. Which of the following is NOT one of the three major elements used in compounds that form the structural compounds of plants?
   a. carbon
   b. oxygen
   c. nitrogen
   d. hydrogen

   a. incorrect; is one of the three
   b. incorrect; is one of the three
   *c. correct; is not one of the three; but nitrogen is found in the proteins that plants manufacture
   d. incorrect; is one of the three

3. Chlorosis is
   a. a yellowing of leaves due to a reduction in chlorophyll.
   b. a production of dead spots on leaves.
   c. the thickening and curling of leaves.
   d. the premature browning and shedding of leaves.

   *a. yes
   b. no
   c. no
   d. no

4. Which of the following micronutrients has a role in electron transport and chlorophyll synthesis?
   a. zinc
   b. manganese
   c. chlorine
   d. iron

   a. no; in addition to formation of chlorophyll, zinc is involved in auxin and starch formation
   b. no; does involve chlorophyll, but not electron transport
   c. no; involved in root and shoot growth and in photolysis
   *d. yes; involved in both processes

5. Nitrogen-fixing bacteria
    a. take nitrogen out of the atmosphere and make it available to plants.
    b. are examples of symbiotic organisms.
    c. live in nodules on the roots of legumes.
    d. all of the above

    a. yes; a partial answer
    b. yes; a partial answer
    c. yes; a partial answer
    *d. yes; all of the above are correct

6. The Venus flytrap feeds on insects to gain access to the nutrient _____, which is available in low concentration in its environment.
    a. phosphorus
    b. iron
    c. nitrogen
    d. sulfur

    a. no
    b. no
    *c. yes
    d. no

7. Root hairs are
    a. found on the root cap.
    b. branch roots.
    c. immature roots.
    d. extensions of epidermal cells.

    a. no; this is a protective cap and the root hairs would be destroyed if located here
    b. no; root hairs are too small to be called branch roots
    c. no; root hairs do not develop into roots
    *d. yes; each is an extension of a single epidermal cell

8. Mycorrhizae are
    a. symbiotic fungi that grow on roots.
    b. cytoplasmic extensions of root systems that increase their efficiency.
    c. parasites that cause root kill in certain breeds of trees.
    d. sites where nitrogen fixation occurs.

    *a. yes; increase ability of plants to secure water and minerals
    b. no; mycorrhizae are living fungi
    c. no; not parasites
    d. no; fixation occurs in nodules filled with nitrogen-fixing bacteria

9. The Casparian strip
    a. is a layer of rapidly dividing cambium cells.
    b. is a tangential section of ring porous wood.
    c. prevents water from entering the vascular cylinder.
    d. funnels water destined for the vascular cylinder through the cytoplasm of endodermal cells.

    a. no; not a cellular layer
    b. no; a section of wood
    c. no; does prevent movement of water through itself, but water does reach the vascular cylinder
    *d. yes

10. Loss of water in gaseous form from leaves, stems, and exposed plant parts is called
    a. guttation.
    b. transpiration.
    c. evaporation.
    d. cohesion.

    a. no; the loss of water in a liquid form
    *b. yes; the loss of water from plants in a gaseous state
    c. no; the correct answer is a special type of evaporation (a better answer is available)
    d. no; cohesion is the binding of water molecules to each other

11. The major use of water in a plant (as measured by the amount used in each activity) is
    a. in photosynthesis.
    b. to promote growth.
    c. in transpiration.
    d. to maintain turgor and prevent wilting.

    a. no; only a small portion of water is incorporated into the organic compounds of a plant
    b. no; some small amount is used to supply the 70–90 percent of fresh body weight due to water found in protoplasm
    *c. yes; the amount of water that passes through the plant to supply the water lost through transpiration is astounding
    d. no; essentially the same as answer (b)

12. Transpiration *primarily* occurs through the
    a. stem.
    b. guard cells.
    c. cuticle.
    d. stomata.

    a. no; a small amount of water loss does occur through stomata and lenticels (spaces) in the stem
    b. no; a relatively small amount is lost through these cells that surround the stomata
    c. no; the waxy layer reduces water loss
    *d. yes; water vapors simply move through these openings to the exterior of a leaf

13. The stomata open
    a. when the guard cells are turgid.
    b. when active transport carries potassium out of a cell.
    c. at night when it is dark.
    d. none of the above

    *a. yes; the turgid condition forces the guard cells to open
    b. no; the stoma opens when potassium enters the guard cells
    c. no; the stomata usually close at night but may close at any time under stress
    d. no; one of the above is correct

14. The most universal source of ATP throughout the plant is
    a. anaerobic respiration.
    b. aerobic respiration.
    c. photosynthesis.
    d. cyclic photophosphorylation.

    a. no; not a major source of ATP
    *b. yes; throughout the plant ATP is made available in this way
    c. no; a source of ATP only in plant tissue with chloroplasts
    d. no; not a major source for most plants

15. In most plant cells, carbohydrates are stored as
    a. glucose.
    b. fructose.
    c. sucrose.
    d. starch.

    a. no; the primary form produced in photosynthesis
    b. no; combines with glucose to form sucrose
    c. no; is too mobile to be stored
    *d. yes; insoluble and easy to store

16. The main form of carbohydrates transported throughout a plant is
    a. glucose.
    b. fructose.
    c. sucrose.
    d. starch.

    a. no; this product of photosynthesis is modified before it moves
    b. no; combines with glucose before moving through the plant
    *c. yes; simple soluble molecules and easy to move
    d. no; large insoluble molecules cannot move from cell to cell

17. The honeydew of an aphid is
    a. its main food supply.
    b. the sugary contents of plant cells that are forced through the aphid by a pressure differential.
    c. pure fructose.
    d. none of the above

    a. no; it is excreted from the aphid's anus
    *b. yes; forced through the body of the insect by pressure
    c. no
    d. no; one of the above is correct

18. The sink region of a plant is
    a. the leaves.
    b. any green part of a plant.
    c. any place that needs glucose.
    d. all of the above

    a. no; a source region
    b. no; a source region
    *c. yes; the glucose flows to this part
    d. no; only one of the above is correct

19. Movement of material in the phloem is explained by
    a. gravity.
    b. pressure flow hypothesis.
    c. cohesion theory.
    d. transpiration pull.

    a. no; can move against the force of gravity
    *b. yes; pressure forces material to flow from source to sink region
    c. no; explains transpiration pull
    d. no; explains movement of water to top of plant

CHAPTER 22
PLANT REPRODUCTION AND DEVELOPMENT

1. Plants surpass humans in the capability to
   a. use color for sexual attraction.
   b. reproduce asexually.
   c. use aromas for sexual attraction.
   d. none of the above

     a. no; both use color for this
   *b. yes; humans cannot reproduce asexually
     c. no; both use aromas for this
     d. no; one of the above is correct

2. Sporophytes
   a. are exemplified by a radish plant, a cactus, and an elm tree.
   b. are produced through meiosis.
   c. give rise to cells that reproduce sexually.
   d. produce sexually reproducing gametes.

   *a. yes; these are all sporophytes
     b. no; produced through fertilization
     c. no; produce spores
     d. no; reproduce asexually

3. The name for the complete female part of a flower is the
   a. ovary.
   b. ovule.
   c. carpel.
   d. egg.

     a. no; a hollow chamber containing ovules, part of the female part of a flower
     b. no; a structure containing the female gametophyte
   *c. yes; the female part of the plant
     d. no; the female gamete

4. A part of the carpel where pollination occurs is the
   a. ovary.
   b. ovule.
   c. stigma.
   d. style.

     a. no; contains the ovules to which the pollen tube grows
     b. no; contains the embryo sac
   *c. yes; pollen is deposited here
     d. no; the neck through which the pollen tube grows

5. Imperfect flowers
   a. lack petals.
   b. may be either male or female.
   c. possess both sex organs.
   d. have stamens and carpels but lack petals or sepals.

     a. no; some flowers such as wind-pollinated flowers may lack petals
   *b. yes; they lack one sex, express the other
     c. no
     d. no; lack either stamens or carpels

6. The outermost part of a flower is the
   a. corolla.
   b. stigma.
   c. sepal.
   d. stamen.

   a. no; formed by petals but still has structures outside of it
   b. no; part of the flower where pollination occurs
   *c. yes; the outermost part of a flower
   d. no; the male part inside the corolla

7. Microspores are produced by the
   a. embryo sacs.
   b. anther of the stamen.
   c. ovule.
   d. process of mitosis.

   a. no; the tissue that produces the megaspore
   *b. yes; the part of the stamen that produces pollen grains
   c. no; contains the embryo sac or female gametophyte
   d. no; by meiosis from the diploid microspore mother cells

8. The structure that will eventually develop into a seed is the
   a. ovule.
   b. ovary.
   c. megaspore.
   d. embryo.

   *a. yes; develops into the seed
   b. no; develops into the fruit
   c. no; develops into the female gametophyte or embryo sac
   d. no; is the young sporophyte that is contained in seeds

9. Bees are NOT attracted to flowers of _____ color because they cannot see them.
   a. yellow
   b. blue
   c. ultraviolet
   d. red

   a. incorrect; a common color of bee-pollinated flowers
   b. incorrect; a common color of bee-pollinated flowers
   c. incorrect; bees use this component to see flowers
   *d. correct; bees cannot see this long wavelength of light (just as humans cannot see infrared radiation)

10. Which of the following pollinators would be attracted to large white flowers with strong sweet perfumes and long tubular corollas with large petals?
    a. bees
    b. butterflies
    c. moths
    d. beetles and flies

    a. no; yellow or blue flowers preferred
    b. no; usually day pollinators preferring red, flat, upright flowers
    *c. yes; night fliers find flowers by the large white petals and strong aromas
    d. no; usually strong rancid or fetid odors

11. Which of the following tissues is triploid?
    a. anther
    b. embryo sac
    c. endosperm
    d. sporophyte

    a. no; the tissue is diploid except for the haploid pollen it produces
    b. no; this is the tissue of the female gametophyte and is therefore haploid
    *c. yes; formed by the fusion of the generative tube nucleus with the two sets of female chromosomes found in the polar nuclei, thus producing triploid tissue with three sets of chromosomes
    d. no; the sporophyte is diploid throughout

12. The function of a fruit is
    a. dispersal.
    b. reproduction and protection.
    c. dispersal and reproduction.
    d. dispersal and protection.

    a. no; a fruit is involved in more than just dispersal
    b. no; a fruit is involved in dispersal, not included in this choice
    c. no; reproduction has already occurred
    *d. yes; a fruit performs both of these functions

13. Which of the following are examples of multiple fruits?
    a. pineapple, fig, mulberry
    b. strawberry, blackberry, raspberry
    c. rice, sunflower, maple, wheat
    d. grape, banana, cherry, lemon, orange

    *a. yes; multiple fruits include multiple ovaries plus accessory tissues
    b. no; these are aggregate fruits
    c. no; dry intact fruits
    d. no; fleshy fruits

14. The hypocotyl is
    a. a protective sheath that surrounds the first leaves.
    b. a seed leaf.
    c. the part of the embryo below the cotyledon.
    d. the part of the embryo above the cotyledon.

    a. no; the coleoptile
    b. no; a cotyledon
    *c. yes; the part of the seedling below the cotyledons (hypo = below)
    d. no; the part above the cotyledon that develops into the shoot system is the epicotyl (epi = above)

15. The plant hormone gibberellin
    a. controls flowering.
    b. promotes fruit ripening and abscission of leaves, flowers, and fruits.
    c. promotes closing of stomata and might trigger bud and seed dormancy.
    d. promotes stem elongation, stimulates the breakdown of starch, and might trigger bud dormancy

    a. no; florigen
    b. no; ethylene
    c. no; abscisic acid
    *d. yes; gibberellin

16. The plant hormone cytokinin
    a. promotes cell elongation and is thought to be involved in phototropism and gravitropism.
    b. promotes stem elongation and might control bud and seed dormancy.
    c. promotes cell division, promotes leaf expansion, and retards leaf aging.
    d. promotes fruit ripening and abscission of leaves, flowers, and fruits.

    a. no; auxin
    b. no; gibberellin
    *c. yes; cytokinin
    d. no; ethylene

17. Under which of the following conditions will a coleoptile grow?
    a. when it is decapitated
    b. when a decapitated coleoptile has a plain agar block on top
    c. when a decapitated coleoptile is covered with an agar block on which a coleoptile tip has been resting for some time
    d. when a decapitated coleoptile has light shining on it

    a. no; no source of auxin available
    b. no; no source of auxin available
    *c. yes; auxin from the tip moves to agar blocks and then to coleoptile to stimulate growth
    d. no; no source of auxin available

18. The growth response that enables a tendril to wrap around a support is known as
    a. gravitropism.
    b. phototropism.
    c. thigmotropism.
    d. none of the above

    a. no; the growth response to gravity
    b. no; the growth response to light
    *c. yes; the growth response to touch
    d. no; one of the above is correct

19. Phytochrome far-red wavelengths control
    a. flowering, fruiting, and setting seeds.
    b. germination of seeds and leaf expansion.
    c. stem elongation and branching.
    d. all of the above

    a. yes; a partial answer
    b. yes; a partial answer
    c. yes; a partial answer
    *d. yes; all of the above are correct

20. Long-day plants
    a. actually respond to short dark periods, not long light periods.
    b. will not bloom if the dark period is interrupted by light.
    c. include such plants as cocklebur, chrysanthemum, poinsettia.
    d. all of the above

    *a. yes; more obvious in the short-day plants that will not bloom when the dark period is interrupted
    b. no; this is true of short-day plants, but long-day plants are induced by short dark periods
    c. no; these are all short-day plants blooming in the fall or winter
    d. no; only one of the above is correct

21. The shedding of plant parts is called
    a. photoperiodism.
    b. senescence.
    c. abscission.
    d. dormancy.

    a. no; the response of an organism to duration of light and darkness
    b. no; the aging of a plant that leads to death
    *c. yes; the dropping of plant parts
    d. no; the decline in the physiological activities of a plant in dry seasons or before the onset of cold temperature

22. An ovule contains one
    a. microspore.
    b. megaspore.
    c. pollen grain.
    d. both (a) and (c)

    a. no; a male spore
    *b. yes; contains the megaspores that will develop into the female gametophyte
    c. no; contains the male gamete
    d. no; only one of the above is correct

CHAPTER 23

TISSUES, ORGAN SYSTEMS, AND HOMEOSTASIS

1. Which of the following types of cells is NOT classified as somatic tissue?
    a. nerve cells
    b. muscle cells
    c. germ cells
    d. epithelial cells

    a. incorrect; a type of body cell
    b. incorrect; a type of body cell
    *c. correct; reproductive cells are not body cells
    d. incorrect; a type of body cell

2. Which of the following is NOT secreted by exocrine glands?
    a. hormones
    b. milk
    c. saliva
    d. digestive enzymes

    *a. correct; secreted by endocrine glands
    b. incorrect; secreted by exocrine glands
    c. incorrect; secreted by exocrine glands
    d. incorrect; secreted by exocrine glands

3. Epithelial cells
    a. line body cavities.
    b. line body ducts and tubes.
    c. are found in the skin covering the body.
    d. all of the above and more

    a. yes; a partial answer
    b. yes; a partial answer
    c. yes; a partial answer
    *d. yes; all of the above are correct

4. Tendons
    a. are composed of connective tissue.
    b. connect bone to bone.
    c. are filled with collagen fibers.
    d. both (a) and (c)

    a. yes; a partial answer
    b. no; connects muscle to bone
    c. yes; a partial answer; collagen in the tissue resists being pulled apart under tension
    *d. yes; both (a) and (c) are correct

5. Adipose tissue
    a. serves as an energy reserve.
    b. is a type of epithelial tissue that underlies the skin.
    c. is a muscle tissue specialized to maintain body temperature.
    d. is a specialized tissue found in the brains of college students.

    *a. yes; fat in these cells can be used as an energy source
    b. no; may underlie the skin, but is not epithelial tissue
    c. no; does have an insulating characteristic, but it is not muscle tissue
    d. no; not associated with nervous tissue

6. Cartilage is found
    a. at the ends of many bones.
    b. between vertebrae.
    c. in the external ear and nose.
    d. all of the above

    a. yes; a partial answer
    b. yes; a partial answer
    c. yes; a partial answer
   *d. yes; all of the above are correct

7. Which of the following tissues lines the gut and respiratory tract?
    a. simple squamous
    b. simple columnar
    c. simple cuboidal
    d. stratified squamous

    a. no; lines walls of blood vessels and air sacs
   *b. yes
    c. no; lines kidney tubules and ducts of some glands
    d. no; lines mouth and throat and outer surface of skin

8. Which of the following tissues stores mineral salts?
    a. muscle
    b. bone
    c. epithelial
    d. adipose

    a. no; minerals are found here in connection with muscle action but not "stored"
   *b. yes
    c. no
    d. no

9. Blood is included under which of the following tissue types?
    a. epithelial
    b. muscle
    c. connective
    d. nervous

    a. no
    b. no
   *c. yes; it is considered a "fluid" connective tissue
    d. no

10. Which of the following types of muscle cells is (are) striated and branched?
    a. smooth
    b. skeletal
    c. cardiac
    d. both (b) and (c)

    a. no; neither striated nor branched
    b. no; striated, but unbranched
   *c. yes; striated and branched
    d. no; both (b) and (c) are striated, but only one type of cell is branched

11. Which organ system has the following functions: protection from injury, excretion, temperature control, reception of external stimuli, and defense against microbes?
    a. urinary system
    b. lymphatic system
    c. skeletal system
    d. integumentary system

    a. no; of those functions listed, involved only in excretion
    b. no; of those functions listed, involved only in defense
    c. no; of those functions listed, involved only in protection
    *d. yes; carries out those functions listed

12. *Homeostasis* refers to the ability of an organism to
    a. rid its body of wastes.
    b. maintain a relatively constant internal environment.
    c. maintain a limited range of body temperature.
    d. control the pH of the body fluids within a narrow range.

    a. yes; but a more complete answer is available
    *b. yes; the most complete and therefore the best answer
    c. yes; but a more complete answer is available
    d. yes; but a more complete answer is available

13. Homeostatic mechanisms in an organism
    a. regulate changes that occur within certain limits.
    b. prevent any change from occurring and maintain a set point.
    c. encourage changes in response to changes in external environment.
    d. encourage changes in response to changes in internal environment.

    *a. yes; prevent excess changes and maintain a relatively small range of internal conditions
    b. no; allow some change within limits and tend to bring conditions back toward a set point
    c. no; external changes (e.g., increased temperature) may provoke actions that lead to changes (e.g., response of sweating)
    d. no; encourage the reduction or limitation of changes in response to internal changes.

14. Which of the following involves a positive feedback mechanism?
    a. childbirth
    b. temperature control
    c. control of blood volume
    d. gas content of blood

    *a. yes; as oxytocin induces stronger contractions, more oxytocin is released
    b. no; as sweating or shivering brings temperature back toward normal, signals reduce the amount of sweating or shivering
    c. no; as the blood volume drops, the kidneys reduce the volume of urine
    d. no; as oxygen level in the bloodstream decreases, the rate of respiration increases

15. Negative feedback means
    a. there is no activity occurring in response to an internal change.
    b. that as the amount of one substance or action increases there is a decrease in the amount of another substance or action.
    c. that physiological responses such as occur in sexual stimulation are increased.
    d. there is no nervous control over the physiological process involved.

    a. no; negative feedback does result in some type of reaction or response
    *b. yes; for example, as the level of thyroid hormones increases in the bloodstream, the secretion of thyrotropin hormones from the pituitary gland decreases
    c. no; an example of positive feedback control
    d. no; the nervous system could be involved in receiving the stimulus and integrating the response

16. _____ are voluntary and striated.
    a. Smooth muscles
    b. Skeletal muscles
    c. Smooth muscles and skeletal muscles
    d. Skeletal muscles and cardiac muscles

    a. no; involuntary and nonstriated
    *b. yes
    c. no; smooth muscle is involuntary and nonstriated
    d. no; cardiac muscle is involuntary

CHAPTER 24

PROTECTION, SUPPORT, AND MOVEMENT

1. Which of the following is NOT derived from the skin?
   a. hair and nails
   b. endocrine glands
   c. oil glands
   d. sweat glands

   a. incorrect; derived from the skin
   *b. correct; not derived from the skin
   c. incorrect; derived from the skin
   d. incorrect; derived from the skin

2. *Integumentary* means
   a. integral.
   b. protective.
   c. covering.
   d. incumbent.

   a. no
   b. no
   *c. yes
   d. no

3. The skin produces vitamin
   a. A.
   b. E.
   c. C.
   d. D.

   a. no
   b. no
   c. no
   *d. yes

4. Vitamin D is needed for _____ metabolism.
   a. potassium
   b. iron
   c. calcium
   d. phosphorus

   a. no
   b. no
   *c. yes
   d. no

5. The dermis
   a. anchors the epidermis to the rest of the body.
   b. is composed primarily of epithelial tissue.
   c. is composed primarily of dead cells.
   d. none of the above

   a. no; hypodermis attaches to the dermis and provides this
   b. no; composed of dense connective tissue
   c. no; epidermis is primarily dead because of keratinization in the midepidermis
   *d. yes; none of the above is correct

466

6. The pigment(s) responsible for skin color is (are)
    a. carotene.
    b. melanin.
    c. hemoglobin.
    d. all of the above

    a. yes; a partial answer; abundant pigment in skin of most Asians/Orientals
    b. yes; a partial answer; the pigment responsible for tanning
    c. yes; a partial answer; the pigment found in capillaries that gives a pink cast to some skin
    *d. yes; all of the above are correct

7. Ultraviolet light
    a. ages the skin by destroying the elastin fibers, causing wrinkles and leathery appearance.
    b. could activate the herpes simplex virus and suppress the immune system.
    c. might activate proto-oncogenes and produce skin cancer.
    d. all of the above

    a. yes; a partial answer
    b. yes; a partial answer
    c. yes; a partial answer
    *d. yes; all of the above are correct

8. The aging of the skin is increased by all but which of the following?
    a. cigarette smoke
    b. ultraviolet radiation
    c. prolonged exposure to cold winds
    d. exposure to infrared radiation

    a. incorrect; deepens wrinkles
    b. incorrect; reduces secretion of skin oil
    c. incorrect
    *d. correct; no known effect

9. The tissue responsible for the production of red blood cells is
    a. other red blood cells.
    b. subcutaneous tissues.
    c. bone marrow.
    d. cartilaginous tissue at ends of long bones.

    a. no; do not have a nucleus and cannot divide
    b. no
    *c. yes
    d. no; responsible for growth of the bones

10. A bone hardens as _____ salts are added to it.
    a. calcium
    b. iron
    c. phosphorus
    d. potassium

    *a. yes
    b. no
    c. no
    d. no

11. The appendicular skeleton includes the
    a. pelvic girdle.
    b. vertebral column.
    c. sternum.
    d. cranium or skull.

    *a. yes
    b. no; part of the axial skeleton
    c. no; part of the axial skeleton
    d. no; part of the axial skeleton

12. The most frequently broken bone is the
    a. ribs.
    b. hip.
    c. collarbone.
    d. ulna.

    a. no
    b. no
    *c. yes
    d. no

13. Which of the following is the smallest unit?
    a. myofibril
    b. muscle fiber
    c. actin
    d. skeletal muscle

    a. no; composed of actin and myosin fibers
    b. no; composed of myofibril
    *c. yes
    d. no; composed of muscle fiber

14. Which of the following statements about anabolic steroids is NOT true?
    a. They are variants of testosterone manufactured by pharmaceutical companies.
    b. They are useful in treating anemia and muscle-wasting disease.
    c. They are safe methods used to increase the size and strength and performance of athletes.
    d. They may be useful to prevent atrophy of muscles that are immobilized after surgery.

    a. incorrect; this statement is true
    b. incorrect; this statement is true
    *c. correct; this statement is false
    d. incorrect; this statement is true

15. According to the sliding-filament theory,
    a. actin and myosin filaments slide by each other.
    b. one sarcomere glides by another.
    c. the dark portions of the striations shorten and the light portions lengthen.
    d. the myofilaments swell, resulting in the thickening of the entire muscle fiber.

    *a. yes; actin slides over myosin by forming cross-bridges
    b. no; the sarcomere is the basic unit of contractions
    c. no; this does not happen
    d. no; this happens but does not account for contraction

16. Which of the following statements is true?
    a. The head is on the actin and the binding site on the myosin.
    b. The head is on the myosin and the binding site on the myosin.
    c. The head is on the myosin and the binding site on the actin.
    d. The head is on the actin and the binding site on the actin.

    a. no
    b. no
    *c. yes
    d. no

17. In muscle contraction, ATP is necessary
    a. to allow the heads to release from the binding sites.
    b. to allow the heads to bind to the binding sites.
    c. to prevent the formation of lactic acid that results in fatigue.
    d. none of the above

    *a. yes; if not available, the muscles will become rigid as in rigor mortis
    b. no; allows cross-bridging to occur, but ATP must also be present to release the heads
       from the binding sites to allow ratchet action to move heads to new binding sites
    c. no; ATP will be produced under either aerobic or anaerobic respiration
    d. no; one of the above is correct

18. The cellular organelles that are especially abundant in muscle cells are
    a. mitochondria.
    b. Golgi apparatuses.
    c. ribosomes.
    d. centrioles.

    *a. yes; the organelle associated with ATP production
    b. no; muscle cells are not particularly involved in secretion
    c. no; not a type of cell that produces many proteins
    d. no; cells normally have only one centriole until they start mitosis; muscle cells do not
       divide often

19. The ion stored in the sarcoplasmic reticulum associated with muscle contraction is
    a. phosphorus.
    b. manganese.
    c. calcium.
    d. potassium.

    a. no
    b. no
    *c. yes; the calcium ions bind to sites on actin and allow cross-bridges to form
    d. no

20. Which of the following organ systems is NOT credited with controlling the body's shape
    and superficial features?
    a. skeletal system
    b. integumentary system
    c. digestive system
    d. muscular system

    a. incorrect; controls body framework and overall shape
    b. incorrect; forms a sac that contains the body organs
    *c. correct; an internal set of organs that generally does not influence body shape
    d. incorrect; muscles provide most of the bulk and weight of the body

CHAPTER 25
DIGESTION AND HUMAN NUTRITION

1. In addition to digestion, the digestive system is characterized by
   a. movement.
   b. secretion.
   c. absorption.
   d. all of the above

   a. yes; a partial answer; to allow mixing and passage of food through the system
   b. yes; a partial answer; secretion of digestive enzymes
   c. yes; a partial answer; to make food available to the rest of the body
   *d. yes; all of the above are correct

2. Which of the following are classified as ruminant animals?
   a. parasitic flatworms
   b. birds
   c. cattle
   d. humans

   a. no; have an incomplete digestive system
   b. no; have a standard complete digestive tract
   *c. yes; have four stomachlike chambers
   d. no; have a standard complete digestive tract

3. Peristalsis
   a. refers to the contraction of smooth muscles in the digestive tract.
   b. is independent of neural or hormonal control.
   c. involves chewing food in the mouth.
   d. refers only to the contraction of the sphincter that allows food to enter and leave the stomach.

   *a. yes; functions to increase contact of food with enzymes
   b. no; requires stimulation from both
   c. no; called mastication
   d. no; involves smooth muscles throughout the digestive tract

4. Saliva
   a. contains no digestive enzymes, only mucus.
   b. initiates the digestion of starch.
   c. initiates the digestion of fats.
   d. initiates the digestion of proteins.

   a. no; amylase is present
   *b. yes; salivary amylase begins the digestion of starch
   c. no; no fat-digesting enzymes available in saliva
   d. no; no protein-digesting enzymes available in saliva

5. Bile is produced by the
   a. gallbladder.
   b. liver.
   c. large intestine.
   d. pancreas.

   a. no; bile is stored in the gallbladder
   *b. yes; produced by the liver and then stored in the gallbladder
   c. no
   d. no; secretes pancreatic juice, not bile

6. Protein digestion begins in the
   a. mouth.
   b. stomach.
   c. small intestine.
   d. esophagus.

   a. no; polysaccharide digestion (starch specifically) starts here
   *b. yes; protein digestion begins in the acid environment
   c. no; most of digestion is completed here
   d. no; no digestion occurs here; simply a connection between mouth and stomach

7. The speed at which food moves through the stomach is influenced by
   a. the size of the meal just eaten.
   b. hormones.
   c. fear, depression, and emotional condition.
   d. all of the above

   a. yes; a partial answer
   b. yes; a partial answer
   c. yes; a partial answer
   *d. yes; all of the above are correct

8. Which of the following statements is false?
   a. The epiglottis covers the trachea when you swallow.
   b. The pharynx and esophagus are not involved in digestion.
   c. The stomach often begins its secretion before food is put in the mouth.
   d. Gastrin is an enzyme that digests proteins.

   a. incorrect; the statement is true
   b. incorrect; the statement is true
   c. incorrect; the statement is true
   *d. correct; the statement is false; gastrin is a hormone, not an enzyme

9. Gastric juice includes all but
   a. hydrochloric acid.
   b. gastrin.
   c. pepsinogen.
   d. mucus.

   a. incorrect; part of gastric juice
   *b. correct; this hormone is secreted into the blood in response to the presence of gastric juice
   c. incorrect; part of gastric juice
   d. incorrect; part of gastric juice

10. Bicarbonate is secreted by the
    a. small intestine.
    b. gallbladder.
    c. pancreas.
    d. stomach.

    a. no; although it is the site of bicarbonate action
    b. no
    *c. yes
    d. no

11. Bile contains all but which of the following?
    a. digestive enzymes
    b. bile salts and pigments
    c. cholesterol
    d. lecithin (a phospholipid)

    *a. correct; contains no digestive enzymes
    b. incorrect; bile salts aid in the emulsification (making small droplets) and digestion of fats in the small intestine
    c. incorrect; one of the ways cholesterol is removed from the body
    d. incorrect

12. Villi are structures found in the
    a. esophagus.
    b. stomach.
    c. small intestine.
    d. large intestine.

    a. no
    b. no
    *c. yes; to increase the surface area available for absorption
    d. no

13. Which of the following is NOT a final product of digestion in the small intestine?
    a. fatty acids and monoglycerides
    b. disaccharides
    c. amino acids
    d. glucose, fructose, and other monosaccharides

    a. incorrect; produced in the breakdown of fats and lipids
    *b. correct; produced by action of the disaccharidases but broken down further to monosaccharides
    c. incorrect; produced in the breakdown of proteins
    d. incorrect; final product of polysaccharide digestion

14. The lymphatic vessels will absorb and transport
    a. triglycerides and fats.
    b. nucleotides and their components.
    c. monosaccharides.
    d. amino acids.

    *a. yes; carried by lymph vessels that eventually drain into general circulation
    b. no; carried by capillaries and veins that eventually drain the intestines
    c. no; carried by capillaries and veins that eventually drain the intestines
    d. no; carried by capillaries and veins that eventually drain the intestines

15. Which of the following enzymes does NOT digest proteins or long chains of amino acids?
    a. pepsin
    b. carboxypeptidase
    c. trypsin and chymotrypsin
    d. lipase

    a. incorrect; digests proteins in the stomach
    b. incorrect; digests peptide fragments in the small intestine
    c. incorrect; digests proteins and polypeptides in the small intestine
    *d. correct; digests triglycerides in the small intestine

16. The human appendix is located
    a. on the left side of the body.
    b. at the end of the small intestine, beginning of large intestine.
    c. at the beginning of the small intestine.
    d. both (a) and (b)

    a. no; on the right side of the body
    *b. yes; at the beginning of the large intestine
    c. no; at the beginning of the large intestine
    d. no; not on the left side

17. Which of the following is false?
    a. We may be able to prevent appendicitis and colon cancer by our diet.
    b. Our diets are too high in bulk or fiber.
    c. Diet may affect the incidence of kidney stones, breast cancer, and circulatory disorders.
    d. Body weight varies because of differences in physical activity, basic rate of metabolism, age, sex, hormonal activity, and emotional state.

    a. incorrect; this statement is true
    *b. correct; this statement is false; our diets are generally deficient in fiber
    c. incorrect; this statement is true
    d. incorrect; this statement is true

18. A person's ideal weight is based on
    a. height.
    b. frame or bone size.
    c. sex.
    d. all of the above

    a. yes; a partial answer
    b. yes; a partial answer
    c. yes; a partial answer
    *d. yes; all of the above are correct

19. The body's main source of energy is
    a. fat.
    b. protein.
    c. simple carbohydrates.
    d. complex carbohydrates.

    a. no; fats contribute energy but are not a major source
    b. no; very minor contribution to energy yield
    c. no; simple sugars are not a large component of most diets
    *d. yes

20. Which of the following statements is (are) true?
    a. Eight of the twenty amino acids can be synthesized by the human body.
    b. Proteins should be the second most common food in the diet after carbohydrates.
    c. Plant proteins are often incomplete, and animals provide complete proteins.
    d. both (b) and (c) are true

    a. incorrect; this statement is false; eight essential amino acids must be supplied in the diet; twelve are synthesized by the body
    b. incorrect; this statement is false; fats should amount to about 30 percent of the total diet
    *c. correct; this statement is true
    d. incorrect; only one of the above answers is correct

21. Which of the following is a fat-soluble vitamin?
    a. A (retinol)
    b. B$_1$ (thiamine)
    c. C (ascorbic acid)
    d. all of the above

    *a. yes; a fat-soluble vitamin
    b. no; a water-soluble vitamin
    c. no; a water-soluble vitamin
    d. no; only one is a fat-soluble vitamin

22. Which mineral is used in thyroid hormone formation?
    a. iron
    b. zinc
    c. iodine
    d. potassium

    a. no; used in hemoglobin and cytochrome formation
    b. no; digestive hormone ingredient; sperm formation
    *c. yes; thyroid hormone formation
    d. no; used in muscle and nerve function, pH balance, and protein synthesis

23. If the body's supply of glucose decreases, blood levels of glucose are maintained by
    a. glycerol breaking down into glucose.
    b. proteins breaking down and amino acids being converted to glucose.
    c. fats breaking down to form fatty acids and glycerol being converted to glucose.
    d. all of the above

    a. yes; a partial answer; a source of glucose
    b. yes; a partial answer; a source of glucose
    c. yes; a partial answer; a source of glucose
    *d. yes; all of the above

CHAPTER 26
CIRCULATION

1. Which of the following is an animal that does NOT have an open circulatory system?
   a. grasshopper
   b. octopus
   c. cat
   d. scorpion

   a. incorrect; has an open system
   b. incorrect; has an open system
   *c. correct; has a closed system
   d. incorrect; has an open system

2. In a bumblebee, the blood returns to the heart by the
   a. veins.
   b. sinuses.
   c. ostia.
   d. capillaries.

   a. no; does not have veins
   b. no; there may be spaces, but this is not the way that blood returns to the heart
   *c. yes; openings into the heart
   d. no; does not have capillaries

3. The amount of blood found in an average adult male is about
   a. 5 pints.
   b. 5 liters.
   c. 10 liters.
   d. 5 gallons.

   a. no
   *b. yes; or, in English measure, about 5 quarts
   c. no
   d. no

4. Hemoglobin transports
   a. oxygen.
   b. carbon dioxide.
   c. glucose.
   d. both (a) and (b)

   a. yes; a partial answer
   b. yes; a partial answer
   c. no; glucose is dissolved in blood plasma
   *d. yes; both (a) and (b) are correct

5. The most common cells in the blood are
   a. red blood cells.
   b. lymphocytes.
   c. leukocytes.
   d. platelets.

   *a. yes; 4,500,000–5,500,000/microliter
   b. no; 1,000–2,700/microliter
   c. no; 4,275–10,620/microliter
   d. no; 250,000–300,000/microliter

6. Red blood cells arise from
   a. other red blood cells.
   b. cells in the red bone marrow.
   c. white blood cells.
   d. cells in the yellow bone marrow.

   a. no; they do not have a nucleus
   *b. yes
   c. no; may produce more white blood cells
   d. no; yellow marrow enters into fat metabolism but is converted to red marrow under conditions of severe anemia

7. _____ are the most common type of leukocytes.
   a. Neutrophils
   b. Basophils
   c. Monocytes
   d. Eosinophils

   *a. yes; 3,000–6,750/microliter
   b. no; 25–90/microliter
   c. no; 150–720/microliter
   d. no; 100–360/microliter

8. Megakaryocytes produce
   a. erythrocytes.
   b. leukocytes.
   c. platelets.
   d. all of the above

   a. no
   b. no
   *c. yes
   d. no; one of the above is correct

9. Which of the following is false?
   a. Both the systemic and pulmonary circuits begin with arteries.
   b. A given volume of blood making the systemic circuit often goes through two or more capillary beds.
   c. The pulmonary circuit leaves the right side of the heart and returns to the left side.
   d. The blood in the systemic circuit is high in oxygen at the beginning and high in carbon dioxide at its end.

   a. incorrect; the statement is true
   *b. correct; the statement is false
   c. incorrect; the statement is true
   d. incorrect; the statement is true

10. The initiation of heart contraction begins at the
    a. semilunar valve.
    b. atrioventricular node.
    c. atrioventricular valve.
    d. sinoatrial node.

    a. no; a valve at the exit from ventricles, not a site for excitation
    b. no; the second activating site
    c. no; a valve between the atrium and ventricle, not a site for excitation
    *d. yes; the initiator of heart contractions

11. The highest blood pressure outside the heart is found in the
    a. aorta.
    b. femoral arterioles.
    c. capillary beds.
    d. vena cava.

    *a. yes; highest blood pressure found closest to the heart
    b. no; blood pressure drops the farther away from the heart it is measured
    c. no; blood pressure drops the farther away from the heart it is measured
    d. no; blood pressure drops the farther away from the heart it is measured

12. The inner lining of an artery or a vein is called the
    a. endothelium.
    b. basement membrane.
    c. layer of elastic fibers.
    d. smooth muscle layer.

    *a. yes
    b. no
    c. no
    d. no

13. A sphygmomanometer measures
    a. blood pH.
    b. blood volume.
    c. blood pressure.
    d. all of the above and other factors as well

    a. no
    b. no
    *c. yes
    d. no; only one of the above is correct

14. The systole occurs when the
    a. ventricle relaxes.
    b. ventricle contracts.
    c. atrium contracts.
    d. atrium relaxes.

    a. no; the diastole occurs at this time
    *b. yes; the time of maximum blood pressure
    c. no; the pressure from the atrium does not escape to the ventricle
    d. no; the pressure from the atrium does not escape to the ventricle

15. Veins differ from arteries in that they
    a. are reservoirs for blood and contain more blood than arteries do.
    b. lack valves that are found in arteries.
    c. have higher blood pressure to contend with than arteries do.
    d. have a layer of smooth muscles that arteries lack.

    *a. yes; veins hold 50 to 60 percent of the blood
    b. no; veins have valves, arteries do not
    c. no; arteries have higher blood pressure
    d. no; both have smooth muscles

16. Smoking
    a. increases blood pressure and carbon monoxide concentration in blood.
    b. causes the adrenal gland to secrete adrenalin, which is a powerful vasoconstrictor.
    c. causes a more rapid pulse rate.
    d. all of the above

    a. yes; a partial answer
    b. yes; a partial answer
    c. yes; a partial answer
    *d. yes; all of the above are correct

17. Which of the following is false?
    a. Balloon angioplasty is used to counteract plaque.
    b. Low-density lipoprotein is the good form of lipoprotein.
    c. Bradycardia is a healthy condition.
    d. Proteins carry cholesterol in the bloodstream.

    a. incorrect; this statement is true; balloons break loose or collapse plaque inside the walls of blood vessels
    *b. correct; this statement is false; LDL is bad (HDL is good) because it seems to transport cholesterol
    c. incorrect; this statement is true; many athletes have bradycardia or slow pulse rate
    d. incorrect; this statement is true; HDL refers to high-density lipoprotein that transports cholesterol

18. Which of the following is the first step in hemostasis?
    a. contraction leading to drawing ruptured blood vessels together
    b. clumping of platelets
    c. spasm of blood vessel
    d. coagulation of blood

    a. no; occurs fourth or last
    b. no; occurs second
    *c. yes; occurs first
    d. no; occurs third

19. The universal donor belongs to blood type
    a. A.
    b. B.
    c. AB.
    d. O.

    a. no; type A (antigen A) donor's blood would clump with recipient's type O (antibodies A and B) and B (antibody B)
    b. no; type B (antigen B) donor's blood would clump with recipient's type O (antibodies A and B) and A (antibody A)
    c. no; type AB (antigens A and B) donor's blood would clump with recipient's type O (antibodies A and B), A (antibody A), and B (antibody B)
    *d. yes; type O has no antigens that would respond to antibodies in any type of blood

20. A person with blood type _____ can tolerate a transfusion from all blood types.
    a. A
    b. B
    c. AB
    d. O

    a. no; has antibody B that will react with incoming blood
    b. no; has antibody A that will react with incoming blood
    *c. yes; has no antibodies that will react with incoming blood
    d. no; has antibodies A and B that will react with incoming blood

21. The situation leading to erythroblastosis fetalis involves
    a. Rh-positive mother, Rh-positive child.
    b. Rh-positive mother, Rh-negative child.
    c. Rh-negative mother, Rh-negative child.
    d. Rh-negative mother, Rh-positive child.

    a. no; mother does not become sensitized to produce positive antibodies
    b. no; mother does not become sensitized to produce positive antibodies
    c. no; child does not have positive blood to clump
    *d. yes; mother can be sensitized and produce positive antibodies that could affect the positive child

22. Which of the following is NOT considered a lymphoid organ?
    a. liver
    b. thymus
    c. tonsil
    d. spleen

    *a. correct; not a tissue that produces infection-fighting cells
    b. incorrect; an example of a lymphoid organ
    c. incorrect; an example of a lymphoid organ
    d. incorrect; an example of a lymphoid organ

CHAPTER 27
IMMUNITY

1. Edward Jenner developed the first vaccination in
   a. 1746.
   b. 1796.
   c. 1846.
   d. 1896.

   a. no; too early
   *b. yes
   c. no; too late
   d. no; too late

2. Which of the following is NOT a phagocytic cell?
   a. neutrophil
   b. basophil
   c. eosinophil
   d. monocyte

   a. incorrect
   *b. correct
   c. incorrect
   d. incorrect

3. The complement system is composed of
   a. circulating plasma proteins.
   b. native antibodies.
   c. introduced antigens.
   d. phagocytic cells.

   *a. yes
   b. no; antibodies are formed in response to exposure to antigen except in ABO blood typing
   c. no; introduced antigens come from outside the body
   d. no; the complement is not cellular

4. Which of the following is false?
   a. Gradients in complement proteins attract phagocytes to an area.
   b. Complement proteins help kill pathogens by promoting lysis.
   c. Complement proteins act antagonistically to phagocytes and antibodies.
   d. both (a) and (b)

   a. incorrect; this statement is true
   b. incorrect; this statement is true
   *c. correct; this statement is false
   d. incorrect; only one of the above answers is false

5. The chemical associated with rendering the capillaries "leaky" for the purpose of promoting the inflammatory response is which of these?
   a. antihistamine
   b. histamine
   c. histone
   d. immunoglobulins

   a. no; counteracts histamine
   *b. yes
   c. no; used as a core in nucleosomes, DNA is wound around this protein
   d. no; antibodies

6. Inflammation
    a. causes a localized increase in temperature, increasing the rate of reactions.
    b. results in the blood vessels near the infection site becoming "leaky."
    c. causes local swelling.
    d. all of the above

    a. yes; a partial answer
    b. yes; a partial answer
    c. yes; a partial answer
    *d. yes; all of the above are correct

7. _____ cells are responsible for producing antibodies.
    a. Macrophage
    b. Helper T
    c. B
    d. none of the above

    a. no; are phagocytic cells
    b. no; stimulate rapid divisions of B cells and killer T cells
    *c. yes; produce antibodies
    d. no; one of the above is correct

8. Which of the following is NOT an antigen and does NOT contain antigens?
    a. "self" proteins
    b. viruses and bacteria
    c. bee venom
    d. cells used in organ transplants

    *a. correct; these contain the correct MHC markers, not antigens
    b. incorrect; the antigens found on these pathogens trigger the immune response
    c. incorrect; a common antigen
    d. incorrect; contains antigens; therefore, immunosuppressant drugs are used in conjunction with these procedures

9. Which of the following would NOT elicit an immune response?
    a. self MHC marker only
    b. any macromolecule recognized as foreign
    c. antigen plus self MHC marker
    d. damaged or mutant MHC marker

    *a. correct; will not trigger the immune response
    b. incorrect; will trigger the immune response
    c. incorrect; will trigger the immune response
    d. incorrect; will trigger the immune response

10. Helper T cells secrete
    a. histamines.
    b. interleukin-1.
    c. lymphokine.
    d. interferon.

    a. no; secreted by basophils and mast cells
    b. no; secreted by macrophages
    *c. yes; secreted by helper T cells
    d. no; secreted by cells infected with a virus

11. A virgin B cell
    a. has membrane-bound antibodies and has not made contact with an antigen.
    b. is an antibody-secreting descendant of an activated B cell.
    c. is one of a clonal population of B cells set aside during a primary immune response.
    d. modulates or turns off the immune response.

    *a. yes
    b. no; a plasma cell
    c. no; a memory cell that is responsible for the rapid secondary response
    d. no; a suppressor T cell

12. An antibody is a receptor molecule shaped like the letter
    a. E.
    b. K.
    c. W.
    d. Y.

    a. no
    b. no
    c. no
    *d. yes; with two antigen-binding sites

13. Killer T cells start developing in the bone marrow and then move to the
    a. spleen.
    b. thymus.
    c. liver.
    d. lymph nodes.

    a. no
    *b. yes
    c. no
    d. no

14. Which of the following are the most efficient antibody factories?
    a. virgin B cells
    b. cloned B cells
    c. plasma cells
    d. memory cells

    a. no; have not contacted an antigen so they do not yet produce antibodies
    b. no; some produce antibodies and others divide to form more B cells
    *c. yes; 2,000 antibodies produced each second
    d. no; responsible for response to secondary invasion

15. Cancer cells may be destroyed by
    a. killer T cells.
    b. natural killer T cells.
    c. helper T cells.
    d. both (a) and (b)

    a. yes; a partial answer
    b. yes; a partial answer
    c. no; master switch of immune system that turns on the production of killer T cells and
       B cells
    *d. yes; both (a) and (b) are correct

16. Which of the following is considered to be the main switch to control the immune system?
    a. memory cells
    b. helper T cells
    c. killer T cells
    d. B cells

    a. no; not effective in the primary infection (have not been formed yet)
    *b. yes; major switch that turns on the production of killer T cells
    c. no; control only the cell-mediated immune response
    d. no; control only the antibody-mediated immune response

17. One of the newest treatments for cancer is
    a. surgery.
    b. radiation.
    c. chemotherapy.
    d. immune therapy.

    a. no; the oldest approach
    b. no; an old approach
    c. no; an old approach
    *d. yes; specifically designed way of attacking cancer cells with monoclonal antibodies

18. Monoclonal antibodies can be used to
    a. determine if cancer is present in an individual.
    b. determine where the cancer is located.
    c. indicate the size of a cancer.
    d. all of the above

    a. yes; a partial answer
    b. yes; a partial answer
    c. yes; a partial answer
    *d. yes; all of the above are correct

19. Antibody diversity
    a. is the result of the action of memory cells.
    b. occurs because the plasma cells produce many different kinds of antibody once they have been turned on.
    c. occurs because of DNA recombinations that occur in the development of B cells in the bone marrow.
    d. both (a) and (c)

    a. no; memory cells produce only one specific type of immune response
    b. no; clones of B cells called plasma cells produce the same kinds of antibodies
    *c. yes
    d. no; only one of the above answers is correct

20. The primary immune response is _____ than the secondary immune response.
    a. slower
    b. of longer duration
    c. more intense
    d. both (b) and (c) are correct

    *a. yes; it takes longer to produce defensive clones
    b. no; the secondary response lasts longer
    c. no; the secondary response is stronger because of the fast response of memory cells
    d. no; only one of the above answers is correct

21. The *purpose* of a vaccination is to provoke the production of
    a. killer and natural killer T cells.
    b. B cells.
    c. phagocytes.
    d. memory cells.

    a. no; an incidental effect
    b. no; an incidental effect
    c. no; an incidental effect
    *d. yes; the purpose of vaccinations is to prepare the body to rapidly marshall the immune system defenses the next time the antigen is encountered—this is exactly what memory cells do

22. Passive immunity
    a. fails to develop any response on the part of the body's immune system.
    b. utilizes antibodies from other sources to combat an exposure to a pathogen.
    c. is not lasting but is often an effective way to prevent a disease from striking a person.
    d. all of the above

    a. yes; a partial answer
    b. yes; a partial answer
    c. yes; a partial answer
    *d. yes; all of the above are correct

23. Allergies
    a. are supernormal or simple secondary immune responses to a normally harmless substance.
    b. are entirely environmental and have no genetic component.
    c. result in the production of all types of immunoglobulins except IgE antibodies.
    d. all of the above

    *a. yes
    b. no; tendency toward allergy is inherited, but allergies are strongly tied to the environment
    c. no; allergies elicit IgE antibodies
    d. no; only one of the above is correct

24. AIDS attacks the _____ cells of the immune system.
    a. killer T
    b. helper T
    c. suppressor T
    d. B

    a. no
    *b. yes
    c. no
    d. no

25. The AIDS virus
    a. is a retrovirus containing RNA.
    b. does not elicit antibodies because it attacks and destroys the immune system.
    c. will have its RNA converted into DNA by the enzyme reverse transcriptase and then inserted into host chromosomes.
    d. both (a) and (c)

    a. yes; a partial answer
    b. no; antibodies to several HIV proteins are formed
    c. yes; a partial answer
    *d. yes; both (a) and (c) are correct

26. Early symptoms of AIDS include all but which of the following?
    a. weight loss and night sweats
    b. Kaposi's sarcoma and a protozoan pneumonia
    c. brown or blue-violet spots on the legs and flu-like symptoms of fatigue and malaise
    d. body rash and itching, low grade fever, and hair loss

    a. incorrect; common symptoms
    b. incorrect; common symptoms
    c. incorrect; common symptoms
    *d. correct; these are not symptoms of AIDS

CHAPTER 28
RESPIRATION

1. Which of the following animals do NOT depend on integumentary exchange?
   a. earthworms
   b. humans
   c. flatworms
   d. nematodes

   a. incorrect; depend on diffusion through integument to supply body with oxygen
   *b. correct; too large to depend on integumentary exchange; have lungs for gas exchange
   c. incorrect; depend on diffusion through integument to supply body with oxygen
   d. incorrect; depend on diffusion through integument to supply body with oxygen

2. Which of the following is false?
   a. Flatworms are small enough not to require a circulatory system.
   b. Humans would be unable to survive on the low concentrations of oxygen dissolved in water.
   c. In most large animals, the diffusion of oxygen at the body surface is fast enough to sustain the respiratory needs.
   d. Oxygen must dissolve in some fluid before it is able to move from the external environment to the interior of an organism.

   a. incorrect; this statement is true
   b. incorrect; this statement is true
   *c. correct; this statement is false
   d. incorrect; this statement is true

3. External gills are characteristic of
   a. some amphibians.
   b. some fishes.
   c. some insects.
   d. both (a) and (c)

   a. yes; a partial answer
   b. no; fish gills are covered by a flap of skin, the operculum
   c. yes; a partial answer
   *d. yes; both (a) and (c) are correct

4. A spiracle associated with a trachea
   a. allows the level of carbon dioxide to build up.
   b. makes the gases flow in only one direction.
   c. prevents excessive water loss through evaporation.
   d. increases the efficiency of the respiratory system.

   a. no; does not affect carbon dioxide concentration to any great extent
   b. no; oxygen may enter and carbon dioxide may leave the trachea
   *c. yes; prevents excessive evaporation
   d. no

5. Bird respiratory systems are characterized by
   a. tracheae.
   b. air sacs.
   c. gas exchange occurring in both inhale and exhale cycles.
   d. both (b) and (c)

   a. no
   b. yes; a partial answer
   c. yes; a partial answer
   *d. yes; both (b) and (c) are correct

6. Before entering the pharynx, air is
   a. filtered.
   b. moistened.
   c. warmed.
   d. all of the above

   a. yes; a partial answer
   b. yes; a partial answer
   c. yes; a partial answer
   *d. yes; all of the above are correct

7. The epiglottis partially covers the
   a. esophagus.
   b. food passage to prevent air from getting into the digestive tract.
   c. air passage to the larynx.
   d. both (a) and (b)

   a. no; if this happened, food would not enter the digestive tract
   b. no; not a problem for most eaters (except newborn infants that need to burp after taking a bottle)
   *c. yes; to prevent food from entering the lungs
   d. no; only one of the above answers is correct

8. The tube leading to each individual lung is the
   a. trachea.
   b. larynx.
   c. pharynx.
   d. bronchus.

   a. no; leads to the two bronchi
   b. no; the voice box
   c. no; the throat
   *d. yes; the bronchi lead to the lungs

9. The large muscle that separates the lungs from the abdominal cavity is the
   a. alveolus.
   b. bronchus.
   c. pleura.
   d. diaphragm.

   a. no; the air sac where gas exchange occurs
   b. no; the large tubes leading to the lungs
   c. no; the membrane surrounding the lungs
   *d. yes; its contraction increases space inside the lungs

10. The goal of the Heimlich maneuver is to
    a. forceably raise the diaphragm.
    b. increase the space available in the lungs.
    c. expand the volume in the chest cavity.
    d. none of the above

    *a. yes; and it is hoped that the reduction in space will force any blockage out of the respiratory passage
    b. no; this would force the blocking object into the lungs
    c. no; actually want to increase internal pressure on the lungs to expel foreign item
    d. no; one of the above is correct

11. When the diaphragm contracts,
    a. it moves upward.
    b. it moves downward.
    c. the other muscles lower and reduce the size of the pleural cavity.
    d. both (a) and (c)

    a. no
    *b. yes; it moves downward into the abdominal cavity
    c. no; must raise and move the rib cage outward
    d. no; only one of the above answers is correct

12. The movement of oxygen across the lungs to the capillaries involves
    a. active transport.
    b. bulk flow.
    c. osmosis.
    d. diffusion.

    a. no; no extra energy needs to be expended
    b. no
    c. no; does not involve movement of water
    *d. yes; simple diffusion is enough to account for the movement of oxygen

13. The majority of the carbon dioxide in the blood is carried
    a. by the hemoglobin molecule.
    b. as a dissolved gas in the blood plasma.
    c. by the bicarbonate ion.
    d. in changing proportions depending on metabolic conditions.

    a. no; some carried by hemoglobin, but oxyhemoglobin is more common
    b. no; only some carried as a dissolved gas
    *c. yes; the majority carried in bicarbonate ions
    d. no; the amount may change, but not greatly enough to change proportions

14. The majority of the oxygen in the blood is carried
    a. by the hemoglobin molecule.
    b. as a dissolved gas in the blood plasma.
    c. by the bicarbonate ion.
    d. in changing proportions depending on metabolic conditions.

    *a. yes; majority of oxygen carried by oxyhemoglobin
    b. no; about one molecule in seventy
    c. no; not involved in oxygen transport
    d. no; not a major factor

15. Which acid is associated with the movement of carbon dioxide?
    a. acetic acid
    b. hydrochloric acid
    c. carbonic acid
    d. citric acid

    a. no
    b. no
    *c. yes; formed when carbon dioxide combines with water
    d. no

16. In emphysema, the
    a. bronchioles become clogged.
    b. alveoli become enlarged.
    c. alveoli fill with fluid.
    d. spaces around the alveoli become filled with fluid.

    a. no; a number of conditions could produce this
    *b. yes
    c. no; characteristic of some pneumonias
    d. no; characteristic of pleurisy

17. Hypoxia occurs
    a. at high altitudes.
    b. when carbon monoxide competes with oxygen for the hemoglobin molecule.
    c. during hyperventilation before compensation for lack of oxygen has been reached.
    d. all of the above

    a. yes; a partial answer
    b. yes; a partial answer
    c. yes; a partial answer
    *d. yes; all of the above are correct; under all of these conditions there is a shortage of oxygen in the bloodstream

CHAPTER 29
WATER-SOLUTE BALANCE

1. Water is lost from the body through
   a. urine.
   b. sweat plus evaporation.
   c. feces.
   d. all of the above

   a. yes; a partial answer; water is dissolved in urine (may be diluted or concentrated)
   b. yes; a partial answer; sweat contains water
   c. yes; a partial answer; some water is lost with normal elimination, the more liquid lost the looser is the stool
   *d. yes; all of the above are correct

2. Which of the following is an example of unnoticed water loss?
   a. urination
   b. respiration
   c. sweating
   d. defecation

   a. no; an obvious form of liquid loss
   *b. yes; lost as a gas and therefore not noticed
   c. no; liquid forms on the skin and is noticeable
   d. no; not as noticeable as some other ways because most water is absorbed by the large intestine

3. Which of the following is NOT considered to be a metabolic waste?
   a. water
   b. ammonia
   c. urea
   d. uric acid

   *a. correct; a by-product of metabolism but since it can be used again is not considered a waste substance
   b. incorrect; a waste product in primitive forms
   c. incorrect; a waste product in humans
   d. incorrect; a waste product in birds and reptiles

4. Urea is formed in
   a. all cells of the body as a waste product of metabolism.
   b. liver cells.
   c. the kidney.
   d. all of the above

   a. no; nitrogen wastes are formed in all cells of the body, but urea is not formed in them
   *b. yes; two ammonia molecules are joined together in the liver to form urea
   c. no; urea is concentrated by the kidney
   d. no; only one of the above is correct

5. Urine is first formed in the
   a. nephron.
   b. urethra.
   c. ureter.
   d. urinary bladder.

   *a. yes; the site where urine is collected
   b. no; the last place where urine is found in the body
   c. no; the tube between the kidney and the bladder
   d. no; the place where urine is stored

6. The external portion of the kidney is called the
   a. cortex.
   b. medulla.
   c. pelvis.
   d. none of the above

   *a. yes; the outer layer of the kidney
   b. no; the internal part of the kidney
   c. no; the part of the kidney that drains into the ureter
   d. no; one of the above is correct

7. Filtration starts in the
   a. loop of Henle.
   b. glomerulus.
   c. proximal tubule.
   d. distal tubule.

   a. no
   *b. yes; filtration occurs in the glomerular capillaries surrounded by the Bowman's capsule
   c. no
   d. no

8. Water, nutrients, and salts are selectively returned to the blood by
   a. filtration.
   b. excretion.
   c. reabsorption.
   d. secretion.

   a. no
   b. no
   *c. yes
   d. no

9. The movement of excess hydrogen and potassium ions from the capillaries to the tubular parts of the nephrons is known as
   a. filtration.
   b. secretion.
   c. reabsorption.
   d. excretion.

   a. no
   *b. yes
   c. no
   d. no

10. Which of the following is removed from the blood during filtration?
   a. water
   b. proteins
   c. blood cells
   d. large solutes

   *a. yes; removed from the blood and goes into the Bowman's capsule
   b. no; too large to be removed during filtration
   c. no; cells remain behind in the blood
   d. no; too large to be removed during filtration

11. Which of the following is reabsorbed in greatest quantity?
   a. glucose
   b. water
   c. sodium ions
   d. urea

   *a. yes; glucose does not usually occur in the urine unless diabetes or some other abnormality is involved
   b. no; the amount of water is controlled by the volume of urine
   c. no; some are lost, may affect blood volume
   d. no; the function of the kidney is to eliminate urea in the urine, but the organ is not completely efficient so that some is reabsorbed

12. Water is conserved by the kidney under the influence of ADH because this hormone makes
   a. the end regions of the distal tubules and collecting ducts more permeable to water.
   b. the end regions of the distal tubules and collecting ducts less permeable to water.
   c. the loop of Henle more permeable to minerals thereby increasing water uptake.
   d. none of the above

   *a. yes; more water is absorbed from the urine, making it more concentrated
   b. no; if this were to happen, more water would be lost through copious flow of urine
   c. no; this would increase the flow of urine
   d. no; one of the above is correct

13. Thirst is controlled by the
   a. thyroid gland.
   b. parathyroid.
   c. hypothalamus.
   d. cerebrum.

   a. no
   b. no
   *c. yes; the saiety center where major drives are located
   d. no

14. Of the following minerals, which is found in greatest quantity in the interstitial fluid?
   a. calcium
   b. phosphorus
   c. sodium
   d. magnesium

   a. no
   b. no
   *c. yes
   d. no

15. Renin is a(n)
    a. hormone that controls kidney function.
    b. enzyme that prods the adrenal cortex to secrete aldosterone.
    c. enzyme that digests steroids such as cholesterol and aldosterone.
    d. activator for the enzyme aldosterone.

    a. no; not a hormone
    *b. yes; triggers aldosterone secretion
    c. no; does not digest aldosterone
    d. no; not a coenzyme

16. High salt concentration in the diet may
    a. lead to increased water retention.
    b. lead to hypertension.
    c. cause increased urine flow.
    d. both (a) and (b)

    a. yes; a partial answer
    b. yes; a partial answer
    c. no; does not occur
    *d. yes; both (a) and (b) are correct

17. Secretion refers to the movement of
    a. water out of the tubules.
    b. ions and other substances out of the tubules.
    c. ions and other substances into the tubules from the peritubular capillaries (capillaries around the tubules).
    d. water into the proximal and distal tubules.

    a. no; would result in retention of water
    b. no; would result in retention of ions
    *c. yes; movement of material into the nephron for later excretion
    d. no; would result in a more copious flow of urine

18. The body controls pH by
    a. kidney excretion.
    b. respiration.
    c. buffer systems.
    d. all of the above

    a. yes; a partial answer
    b. yes; a partial answer
    c. yes; a partial answer
    *d. yes; all of the above are correct

19. Peritoneal dialysis
    a. is characterized by an external membrane that is used to remove toxic wastes.
    b. involves the flow of blood from an artery through a kidney machine.
    c. places a fluid with proper concentration in the abdominal cavity and then drains it.
    d. is another name for hemodialysis.

    a. no; characteristic of hemodialysis
    b. no; characteristic of hemodialysis
    *c. yes; the peritoneum serves as the dialysis membrane
    d. no; peritoneal dialysis is the other choice in dialysis

CHAPTER 30
NEURAL CONTROL AND THE SENSES

1. Which of the following types of neurons is (are) connected to effectors?
   a. sensory neurons
   b. interneurons
   c. motor neurons
   d. all of the above

   a. no; connected to the sense organs
   b. no; nerves within the central nervous system
   *c. yes; nerves connected to the effectors such as muscles and glands
   d. no; only one of the above is correct

2. The _____ is nearest to the site where stimuli are normally received.
   a. axon
   b. dendrite
   c. cell body
   d. both (a) and (b)

   a. no; the output zone
   *b. yes; the common input zone
   c. no; not a stimulus receptor zone
   d. no; only one of the above is correct

3. Which statement is false?
   a. The interior of a neuron tends to be more negative than the exterior.
   b. A sudden reversal in the polarity of charge across the plasma membrane of a neuron is called an action potential and results in the formation of a nerve impulse.
   c. Some membrane proteins are always open while others open and close and serve as gates for various substances.
   d. When a neuron is "at rest," most of the channels for sodium are open and some of the potassium channels are closed.

   a. incorrect; this statement is true; this is a result of the movement of ions
   b. incorrect; this statement is true, and an action potential is the wave of depolarization that passes down the membrane
   c. incorrect; this statement is true
   *d. correct; this statement is false; the sodium channels are closed

4. When a neuron is at rest,
   a. sodium "leaks" out of its channels.
   b. as sodium "leaks" out of the neuron's interior it becomes negatively charged.
   c. there is no net movement of potassium across the membrane.
   d. the potassium channels are closed and some of the sodium channels are open.

   a. no; the statement is true about potassium
   b. no; the neuron's interior becomes negative because of the movement of potassium—the sodium channels are closed
   *c. yes; the difference in concentration is maintained until an action potential disturbs it
   d. no; the sodium channels are closed while some of the potassium channels are open, others are closed

5. An action potential
   a. is triggered by a voltage disturbance of a minimal level called a threshold.
   b. will move down the neuron whenever any stimulus that exceeds the threshold limit is applied.
   c. causes the sodium channels to open in an accelerating way as in a positive feedback mechanism.
   d. all of the above

   a. yes; a partial answer
   b. yes; a partial answer
   c. yes; a partial answer
   *d. yes; all of the above are correct

6. After an action potential passes, the
   a. sodium gates are open.
   b. potassium gates are shut.
   c. original voltage difference across the membrane is restored by the sodium-potassium pump.
   d. all of the above

   a. no; the sodium gates are shut
   b. no; the potassium gates are open
   *c. yes
   d. no; only one of the above is correct

7. During the refractory period,
   a. a neuron cannot respond to stimulation.
   b. it takes a stronger stimulus to overcome the threshold.
   c. the sodium-potassium pump fails to operate.
   d. the neuron can be triggered to respond by minimal stimuli as long as they exceed the threshold.

   *a. yes; the neuron is insensitive to stimulation
   b. no; it does not make any difference how strong the stimulus is, the neuron will not respond
   c. no; the pump is operating to restore the resting potential so the neuron can fire again
   d. no; this statement about a neuron is true at any time except during the refractory period

8. The significance of the sheath surrounding some neurons is that it is
   a. composed of fat cells.
   b. composed of Schwann cells that completely isolate the neuron.
   c. able to transmit impulses faster because they jump from node to node.
   d. a method to overcome the limitation or response of nerves imposed by the threshold effect.

   a. no; the statement is true, but not significant by itself
   b. no; there are gaps in the coverings at the nodes
   *c. yes; the significant feature is the speed of transmission
   d. no; the limitation is still there

9. Action potentials
    a. simply travel directly from one neuron to the next because neurons overlap each other.
    b. are able to move from one neuron to another via chemical transmitter substances released at the synapse.
    c. travel across synapses that occur only between two neurons.
    d. are propagated by simple diffusion of chemical transmitter substances across the synapse.

    a. no; there is no physical connection between neurons; a physical gap called the synaptic cleft exists
    *b. yes
    c. no; may occur between a neuron and an effector (muscle or gland)
    d. no; not fast enough; involves active transport

10. Synaptic integration
    a. is the moment-by-moment combining of excitatory and inhibitory signals acting on adjacent membrane regions of a neuron.
    b. involves the release of acetylcholine into the synaptic cleft.
    c. involves the transmission of impulses to the brain and central nervous system.
    d. is the response characteristic of myelinated neural fibers.

    *a. yes; by definition
    b. no; only one aspect, that dealing with the transmission of information from the presynaptic fiber
    c. no; also involves nerve transmission among neurons throughout the body
    d. no; not restricted to myelinated fibers

11. At any chemical synapse,
    a. the postsynaptic cell releases neurotransmitter molecules.
    b. the signal given may have an excitatory or inhibitory effect on the postsynaptic cell.
    c. the outcome of a chemical signal at a synapse depends on which presynaptic cell releases the neurotransmitters.
    d. excitatory and inhibitory signals operate independent of the threshold effect.

    a. no; neurotransmitters are released by the presynaptic neurons
    *b. yes
    c. no; the result depends on which postsynaptic neurons are activated
    d. no; the excitatory signal can decrease the stimulus needed, and the inhibitory signal can increase the stimulus needed

12. Through synaptic integration, signals arriving at any given neuron can be
    a. dampened.
    b. reinforced.
    c. suppressed or sent on.
    d. all of the above

    a. yes; a partial answer
    b. yes; a partial answer
    c. yes; a partial answer
    *d. yes; all of the above are correct

13. A reflex arc consists of
    a. motor neurons.
    b. sensory neurons.
    c. the brain.
    d. both (a) and (b)

    a. yes; a partial answer
    b. yes; a partial answer
    c. no; not part of a reflex arc
    *d. yes; both (a) and (b) are required, but the brain is not involved in the reflex response to a stimulus

14. The nerves that supply the skeletal muscles are more specifically part of the
    a. somatic nervous system.
    b. central nervous system.
    c. autonomic nervous system.
    d. sympathetic nervous system.

    *a. yes; the most specific response
    b. no; includes spinal cord and brain
    c. no; includes parasympathetic and sympathetic nervous systems
    d. no; a division of the autonomic nervous system

15. Nerves that supply the glands and smooth muscles are part of the _____ system.
    a. autonomic
    b. somatic
    c. peripheral
    d. afferent

    *a. yes; supplies glands and smooth muscles
    b. no; supplies skeletal muscles
    c. no; nerves to and from brain and spinal cord
    d. no; carries sensory messages to CNS

16. Signals from _____ nerves tend to slow down "housekeeping" chores and speed up parts of the body that would be involved in the "fight-flight" response.
    a. peripheral
    b. somatic
    c. parasympathetic
    d. sympathetic

    a. no; nerves to and from the central nervous system, which does include some of these nerves
    b. no; nerves to skeletal muscles
    c. no; antagonistic to the sympathetic system
    *d. yes; slows down housekeeping, speeds up defense

17. The parasympathetic nervous system
    a. originates in the thoracic-lumbar region of the spinal column.
    b. stimulates peristalsis.
    c. contracts sphincters.
    d. none of the above

    a. no; originates in the cranial and sacral vertebrae
    *b. yes; increases the digestive process
    c. no; relaxes the sphincter
    d. no; one of the above is correct

18. Which of the following statements is false?
    a. The white matter of the spinal cord contains the ascending and descending tracts to and from the brain.
    b. The gray matter of the spinal cord deals with reflex actions.
    c. "Biofeedback" refers to conscious efforts to enhance or dampen autonomic and physiological responses.
    d. The gray matter is composed of nerves surrounded by myelin sheaths.

    a. incorrect; this statement is true
    b. incorrect; this statement is true
    c. incorrect; this statement is true
    *d. correct; this statement is false; the myelin sheath is found in the white matter

19. The hindbrain includes all but which one of the following?
    a. pons
    b. medulla oblongata
    c. tectum
    d. cerebellum

    a. incorrect; part of the hindbrain
    b. incorrect; part of the hindbrain
    *c. correct; part of the midbrain
    d. incorrect; part of the hindbrain

20. The emotional part of the brain is the
    a. cerebellum.
    b. pons.
    c. limbic system.
    d. reticular activating system.

    a. no; center for coordination
    b. no; bridge for nerve tracks between brain centers
    *c. yes; includes regions called the thalamus, hypothalamus, amygdala, and hippocampus
    d. no; region of the brain controlling levels of consciousness

21. Which of the following is NOT a substance occurring naturally in the body?
    a. serotonin
    b. dopamine
    c. norepinephrine
    d. dexedrine

    a. incorrect; occurs in the body
    b. incorrect; occurs in the body
    c. incorrect; occurs in the body
    *d. correct; an artificial stimulant

22. Which of the following is a natural internal analgesic produced by humans in response to stress?
    a. endorphin
    b. enkephalin
    c. serotonin
    d. both (a) and (b)

    a. yes; a partial answer
    b. yes; a partial answer
    c. no; induces sleep
    *d. yes; both (a) and (b) are correct

23. The reason we perceive different sensations from identical action potentials is that
    a. some parts of the brain can interpret incoming signals only in certain limited ways.
    b. there is a difference in frequency of action potentials.
    c. there are differences in the number of action potentials.
    d. all of the above

    a. yes; a partial answer
    b. yes; a partial answer
    c. yes; a partial answer
    *d. yes; all of the above are correct

24. Pheromones are detected by
    a. photoreceptors.
    b. chemoreceptors.
    c. thermoreceptors.
    d. mechanoreceptors.

    a. no; response to light energy
    *b. yes; response to taste or smell
    c. no; response to temperature or infrared
    d. no; no response to touch

25. Hair cells are part of the sense receptor for
    a. sight.
    b. taste.
    c. olfaction.
    d. none of the above

    a. no
    b. no
    c. no
    *d. yes; none of the above is correct; hair cells are found in mechanoreceptors (sense of hearing, motion, and balance)

26. The outer coat of the vertebrate eye is the
    a. choroid.
    b. retina.
    c. sclera.
    d. none of the above

    a. no; the dark pigmented material in the middle layers
    b. no; the inner visceral tissue
    *c. yes; the outer coat
    d. no; one of the above is correct

CHAPTER 31
ENDOCRINE CONTROL

1. The first hormone to be discovered was one secreted by the
   a. anterior pituitary gland.
   b. pancreas.
   c. thyroid.
   d. adrenal cortex.

   a. no
   *b. yes; secretin
   c. no
   d. no

2. Bayliss and Starling discovered the hormone secretin by
   a. severing the nerves leading to the small intestine.
   b. testing cells lining the small intestine.
   c. isolating the small intestine from its normal blood supply.
   d. both (a) and (b)

   a. yes; a partial answer
   b. yes; a partial answer
   c. no; it is not possible to isolate the organs from their blood supply and expect them to continue functioning
   *d. yes; both (a) and (b) are correct

3. The "master" endocrine gland is the
   a. pituitary.
   b. thyroid.
   c. adrenal.
   d. pancreas.

   *a. yes; secretes the greatest variety of hormones, and they control the other glands
   b. no; controls metabolic rate primarily
   c. no; produces several hormones but is still not considered "master"
   d. no; produces three hormones

4. Signaling molecules include
   a. transmitting substances.
   b. local signaling molecules.
   c. pheromones.
   d. all of the above

   a. yes; a partial answer
   b. yes; a partial answer
   c. yes; a partial answer
   *d. yes; all of the above are correct

5. The posterior lobe of the pituitary gland secretes
   a. prolactin.
   b. somatotropin.
   c. oxytocin.
   d. luteinizing hormone.

   a. no; an anterior pituitary secretion
   b. no; an anterior pituitary secretion
   *c. yes; a posterior pituitary secretion
   d. no; an anterior pituitary secretion

6. The releasing hormones of the pituitary would eventually lead to stimulation of all but which one of the following?
   a. gonads (sex organs)
   b. adrenal medulla
   c. thyroid gland
   d. adrenal cortex

   a. incorrect; leads to effects via luteinizing and follicle-stimulating hormones
   *b. correct
   c. incorrect; leads to effects via thyrotropin-stimulating hormones
   d. incorrect; leads to effects via corticotropin-stimulating hormones

7. Which of the following is NOT one of the organs affected by hormones secreted by the posterior pituitary?
   a. adrenal gland
   b. breast
   c. kidney
   d. uterus

   *a. correct; the adrenal gland is not affected by hormones from the posterior pituitary
   b. incorrect; is one of the affected organs; oxytocin stimulates milk release from the breast
   c. incorrect; is one of the affected organs; the antidiuretic hormone controls water retention in the kidney
   d. incorrect; is one of the affected organs; oxytocin controls contraction of the uterine wall in labor

8. Lack of _____ in early childhood results in pituitary dwarfism.
   a. oxytocin
   b. somatotropin
   c. prolactin
   d. luteinizing hormone

   a. no
   *b. yes
   c. no
   d. no

9. Acromegaly is a disease resulting from excessive secretion of the
   a. pituitary gland.
   b. pancreas.
   c. thyroid gland.
   d. parathyroid gland.

   *a. yes
   b. no
   c. no
   d. no

10. The _____ gland is the site where white blood cells grow and differentiate.
    a. adrenal
    b. parathyroid
    c. thyroid
    d. thymus

    a. no
    b. no
    c. no
    *d. yes

11. Melatonin is secreted by the
    a. pineal body.
    b. pancreas.
    c. parathyroid gland.
    d. placenta.

    *a. yes
    b. no
    c. no
    d. no

12. The adrenal medulla secretes
    a. cortisol.
    b. corticotropin.
    c. epinephrine.
    d. thyroxine.

    a. no; secreted by the adrenal cortex
    b. no; secreted by the pituitary
    *c. yes; secreted by the adrenal medulla
    d. no; secreted by the thyroid gland

13. The adrenal medulla
    a. secretes hormones that increase blood pressure.
    b. secretes hormones that dilate the air passages in the lungs.
    c. secretes hormones that trigger the sympathetic nervous system.
    d. all of the above

    a. yes; a partial answer
    b. yes; a partial answer
    c. yes; a partial answer
    *d. yes; all of the above are correct

14. The thyroid gland
    a. controls basic metabolic rate.
    b. stimulates the sympathetic nervous system.
    c. influences secondary sexual characteristics.
    d. all of the above

    *a. yes
    b. no; the adrenal medulla does this
    c. no; the adrenal cortex and gonads do this
    d. no; only one of the above is correct

15. The following symptoms (overweight, sluggishness, dry skin, and intolerance of cold) are characteristic of an insufficient secretion from the
    a. thyroid.
    b. pancreas.
    c. adrenal cortex.
    d. adrenal medulla.

    *a. yes
    b. no
    c. no
    d. no

16. Thyroid hormones require the element
    a. sodium.
    b. iodine.
    c. chlorine.
    d. cobalt.

    a. no
    *b. yes
    c. no
    d. no

17. The _____ secretes its hormone when the level of calcium in the blood drops.
    a. thyroid gland
    b. thymus gland
    c. parathyroid gland
    d. pancreas

    a. no
    b. no
    *c. yes
    d. no

18. The lack of vitamin D leads to
    a. scurvy.
    b. night blindness.
    c. rickets.
    d. goiter.

    a. no; lack of vitamin C
    b. no; lack of vitamin A
    *c. yes
    d. no; lack of thyroid hormone due to lack of iodine

19. Glucagon
    a. raises the glucose level in the bloodstream.
    b. raises the level of calcium and phosphorus in the blood.
    c. regulates growth rate.
    d. controls basic metabolic rate.

    *a. yes; causes glycogen to be broken down into glucose
    b. no; the parathyroid gland does this
    c. no; the pituitary gland does this
    d. no; the thyroid gland does this

20. Glucagon is secreted by _____ cells of the pancreas.
    a. alpha
    b. beta
    c. gamma
    d. delta

    *a. yes
    b. no; secrete insulin
    c. no; no such cells involved in hormone production
    d. no; secrete somatostatin

21. Ketones are
    a. normal products of the breakdown of fats.
    b. produced in diabetes mellitus.
    c. secreted by the pineal gland.
    d. both (a) and (b)

    a. yes; a partial answer
    b. yes; a partial answer
    c. no
    *d. yes; (a) and (b) are correct

22. Type I diabetes
    a. is characterized by normal or near normal levels of insulin in the blood.
    b. is the less common, but the more serious, form of diabetes.
    c. is called adult onset diabetes.
    d. all of the above

    a. no; characteristic of type II diabetes
    *b. yes; characteristic of type I diabetes
    c. no; characteristic of type II diabetes
    d. no; only one of the above is correct

23. The pineal gland is primarily influenced by
    a. other hormones.
    b. nerves.
    c. internal chemical changes.
    d. the environment.

    a. no
    b. no
    c. no
    *d. yes; responds to the photoperiod

24. In testicular feminization syndrome,
    a. the individual has functional testes but develops phenotypically as a female.
    b. the individual fails to produce testosterone.
    c. the secondary sexual characteristics are male even though he is sterile with defective testes.
    d. both (a) and (b) are correct

    *a. yes
    b. no; testosterone is produced, but the defective receptor prevents its uptake by the target cell
    c. no; phenotypically a female even though the testes are normal
    d. no; only one of the above is correct

25. Second messengers are
    a. ancillaries that trigger a response in target cells.
    b. characteristic of steroid hormones.
    c. exemplified by cyclic adenosine monophosphate.
    d. both (a) and (c)

    a. yes; a partial answer
    b. no; characteristic of nonsteroid hormones
    c. yes; a partial answer
    *d. yes; both (a) and (c) are correct

26. The antidiuretic hormone is produced by the
    a. kidneys.
    b. adrenal medulla.
    c. adrenal cortex.
    d. none of the above

    a. no
    b. no
    c. no
    *d. yes; none of the above is correct; in this instance, ADH is secreted by the posterior pituitary

CHAPTER 32

REPRODUCTION AND DEVELOPMENT

1. The chief value of sexual reproduction is
   a. its efficiency.
   b. the number of offspring produced.
   c. the variation found among the offspring.
   d. the conservation of the energy needed for reproduction.

   a. no; asexual reproduction is more efficient
   b. no; asexual reproduction often produces more offspring than does sexual reproduction
   *c. yes
   d. no; more energy is released in sexually reproducing forms

2. In cleavage,
   a. the two daughter cells represent the same total volume as the cell that produced them.
   b. a zygote is converted into a blastula.
   c. the daughter cells do not increase in size.
   d. all of the above

   a. yes; a partial answer
   b. yes; a partial answer
   c. yes; a partial answer
   *d. yes; all of the above are correct

3. The mesoderm gives rise to all but which of the following?
   a. circulatory system
   b. digestive system
   c. skeletal system
   d. reproductive and excretory systems

   a. incorrect; produced by the mesoderm
   *b. correct; produced by the endoderm
   c. incorrect; produced by the mesoderm
   d. incorrect; produced by the mesoderm

4. Which of the following is responsible for the development of the nervous system and brain?
   a. ectoderm
   b. endoderm
   c. mesoderm
   d. gastroderm

   *a. yes
   b. no; produces the digestive tract
   c. no; produces most of the adult tissues of the body
   d. no; not one of the germ layers of the embryo

5. The germ layers form during
   a. gastrulation.
   b. cleavage.
   c. organ formation.
   d. growth and tissue specialization.

   *a. yes
   b. no; too early
   c. no; too late
   d. no; too late

6. Morphogenesis
   a. leads to the development of form and structure of the embryo.
   b. results from cell migration and recognition of surface characteristics of neighboring cells.
   c. is exemplified by cell death.
   d. all of the above

   a. yes; a partial answer
   b. yes; a partial answer
   c. yes; a partial answer
   *d. yes; all of the above are correct

7. Seminal fluid is produced by the
   a. prostate gland.
   b. bulbourethral glands.
   c. seminal vesicles.
   d. all of the above

   a. yes; a partial answer
   b. yes; a partial answer
   c. yes; a partial answer
   *d. yes; all of the above are correct

8. The development and maturation of sperm take place in the
   a. seminiferous tubules.
   b. vas deferens.
   c. epididymis.
   d. urethra.

   a. no; site where sperm are first formed
   b. no; tube leading to urethra for sperm delivery
   *c. yes; stored here for development and maturation
   d. no; the common urogenital duct leaving the body

9. Fertilization most commonly occurs in the
   a. vagina.
   b. oviduct.
   c. uterus.
   d. ovary.

   a. no
   *b. yes
   c. no
   d. no

10. Oocytes are stored in the
   a. follicles.
   b. oviducts.
   c. uterus.
   d. cervix.

   *a. yes
   b. no
   c. no
   d. no

11. Which of the following is NOT part of the vulva?
    a. labia minora
    b. labia majora
    c. clitoris
    d. uterus

    a. incorrect; part of the external genitalia
    b. incorrect; part of the external genitalia
    c. incorrect; part of the external genitalia
    *d. correct; part of the internal female reproductive organs

12. After ovulation the follicle becomes transformed into the
    a. primary oocyte.
    b. endometrium.
    c. corpus luteum.
    d. cervix.

    a. no; the egg that is released is a primary oocyte
    b. no; the lining of the uterus
    *c. yes
    d. no; the neck of the uterus

13. The surge of _____ in the blood triggers ovulation.
    a. progesterone
    b. estrogen
    c. follicle-stimulating hormone
    d. luteinizing hormone

    a. no
    b. no
    c. no
    *d. yes

14. In endometriosis,
    a. endometrial tissue anywhere in the body reacts to estrogen.
    b. sterility may result.
    c. displaced cells can grow resulting in pain during urination, menstruation, and/or sexual intercourse.
    d. all of the above

    a. yes; a partial answer
    b. yes; a partial answer
    c. yes; a partial answer
    *d. all of the above are correct

15. Which of the following is most critical to the completion of meiosis II in the female reproductive cycle?
    a. puberty
    b. ovulation
    c. menstruation
    d. fertilization

    a. no; a beginning of reproductive maturity
    b. no; in ovulation eggs are released from the follicle in meiosis I
    c. no; in menstruation the endometrial lining is sloughed along with the unfertilized egg
    *d. yes; meiosis is completed only after fertilization by a sperm occurs

16. The newly conceived offspring implants on the uterine wall as a
    a. zygote.
    b. morula.
    c. blastocyst.
    d. fetus.

    a. no; the fertilized egg; too early
    b. no; a solid ball of cells; too immature to implant
    *c. yes
    d. no; an embryo recognizable as human; occurs much later

17. In eggs with a shell suitable for deposition on land, the _____ stores waste.
    a. allantois
    b. amnion
    c. chorion
    d. yolk sac

    *a. yes
    b. no
    c. no
    d. no

18. Which of the following is a fluid-filled sac?
    a. allantois
    b. amnion
    c. chorion
    d. yolk sac

    a. no
    *b. yes; may be sampled to determine some gene characteristics of the embryo
    c. no
    d. no

19. Which of the following membranes is most closely associated with the placenta?
    a. allantois
    b. amnion
    c. chorion
    d. yolk sac

    a. no
    b. no
    *c. yes; fuses with the endometrial lining of the uterus to form the placenta
    d. no

20. A soft fuzzy hair that covers the embryo is called
    a. lanugo.
    b. zona pellucida.
    c. thalidomide.
    d. estrus.

    *a. yes
    b. no; the membrane surrounding an unfertilized egg
    c. no; a chemical teratogen that disturbs limb-bud formation
    d. no; the reproductive cycle of female mammals

21. Which of the following methods of contraception is the most successful?
    a. contraceptive pill
    b. spermatocides
    c. douche
    d. withdrawal

    *a. yes; nearly 100 percent effective
    b. no; 75 percent effective without other devices such as IUD or condom
    c. no; the textbook says that it is next to useless
    d. no; seminal fluid released prior to ejaculation could contain sperm

22. The most commonly reported sexually transmitted disease in the United States is
    a. AIDS.
    b. gonorrhea.
    c. syphilis.
    d. herpes.

    a. no
    *b. yes; 1,000,000 cases reported/year
    c. no; only 30,000 cases reported/year
    d. no; less than 500,000 cases reported/year

CHAPTER 33
POPULATION ECOLOGY

1. The study of the interaction of organisms with one another and their environment is
    a. evolution.
    b. physiology.
    c. morphology.
    d. none of the above

    a. no; evolution is the change in organisms over time
    b. no; physiology is the study of functions
    c. no; morphology is the study of structures
    *d. yes; none of the above is correct; this is called ecology

2. The place where an organism lives is called its
    a. niche.
    b. habitat.
    c. community.
    d. ecosystem.

    a. no; what an organism does in the environment
    *b. yes; where the organism could be found
    c. no; a group of interacting populations
    d. no; the functional unit in nature consisting of both biotic and abiotic factors

3. The most common distribution pattern of a population is
    a. random.
    b. uniform.
    c. clumped.
    d. dispersed.

    a. no; if the resources the population uses are uniformly dispersed, the population distribution may be random
    b. no; occurs under artificial conditions such as a farm
    *c. yes; because resources are often clumped
    d. no; individuals tend to congregate because of resource availability

4. Zero population growth occurs when
    a. immigration and emigration are equal.
    b. the biotic potential is reached.
    c. natality and mortality are equal.
    d. both (a) and (c)

    a. yes; a partial answer
    b. no; would probably result in rapid growth
    c. yes; a partial answer
    *d. yes; both (a) and (c) are correct

5. The graph of exponential growth is a(n) _____ curve.
    a. J-shaped
    b. L-shaped
    c. M-shaped
    d. S-shaped

    *a. yes
    b. no
    c. no
    d. no

6. To experience exponential growth, a population must
   a. increase.
   b. increase at a constant rate.
   c. not have immigration or emigration.
   d. have a birth rate higher than its death rate.

   a. no; population will grow, but not necessarily exponentially
   *b. yes; will produce a J-shaped curve of exponential growth
   c. no; both factors may affect population growth, but only if population growth occurs at a steady rate will it grow exponentially
   d. no; this condition will result in growth, but not necessarily exponential growth

7. The biotic potential of a population
   a. refers to its maximum reproductive rate.
   b. could theoretically be achieved under ideal conditions for a limited time.
   c. is influenced by the age at which reproduction starts and the number of offspring that are produced.
   d. all of the above

   a. yes; a partial answer
   b. yes; a partial answer
   c. yes; a partial answer
   *d. yes; all of the above are correct

8. A population may not reach its full biotic potential because
   a. some limiting factor is present.
   b. predation, pollution, or competition may influence survival and/or reproduction.
   c. environmental resistance prevents the population from reaching its carrying capacity.
   d. all of the above

   a. yes; a partial answer
   b. yes; a partial answer
   c. yes; a partial answer
   *d. yes; all of the above are correct

9. Which of the following is constant?
   a. reproductive potential
   b. carrying capacity
   c. environmental resistance
   d. none of the above

   a. no; many factors affect reproductive rates
   b. no; the number of individuals that can be sustained in a given area varies from time to time depending on environmental conditions
   c. no; the interaction of all of the limiting factors would be expected to vary over time
   *d. yes; none of the above are constant

10. Which of the following is NOT a density-dependent factor controlling population growth?
   a. predation
   b. parasitism
   c. competition
   d. drought

   a. incorrect; is a density-dependent factor; a larger number of predators will reduce a population and if the number of predators drops, the pressure on the prey population will relax
   b. incorrect; is a density-dependent factor; the more organisms are forced together by a large population the greater the chance that parasitism will occur
   c. incorrect; is a density-dependent factor; the denser the population the greater the competition among organisms
   *d. correct; the number of organisms in a population does not affect the intensity of a drought

11. The bubonic plague is transmitted by
   a. fleas.
   b. flies.
   c. mosquitoes.
   d. cockroaches.

   *a. yes; living on infected rodents
   b. no
   c. no
   d. no

12. A type III survivorship curve is characteristic of all but which of the following?
   a. marine invertebrates
   b. songbirds or lizards
   c. most insects
   d. plants

   a. incorrect; large number of deaths immediately after hatching and then chance of death is low throughout life
   *b. correct; songbirds and lizards have about an equal chance of dying throughout their entire life
   c. incorrect; large mortality early in life
   d. incorrect; large mortality early in life

13. Which of the following is the closest approximation of current birth rates?
   a. 10,000/hour
   b. 1,700,000/week
   c. 90,000,000/year
   d. all of the above

   a. yes; a partial answer
   b. yes; a partial answer
   c. yes; a partial answer
   *d. yes; all of the above represent approximately the same amount

14. Which of the following led to dramatic increases in human population?
    a. domestication of plants and animals
    b. the end of the bubonic plague
    c. the start of the industrial revolution
    d. agriculturally based urban societies
    e. all of the above except (b)

    a. yes; a partial answer
    b. no; a temporary drop of 25 million people
    c. yes; a partial answer
    d. yes; a partial answer
    *e. yes; all of the above except (b) are correct

15. The current exponential growth
    a. will double the world's population in about 15 years.
    b. will add 1 billion new people in about 25 years.
    c. is not sustainable.
    d. all of the above

    a. no; it will take about 40 years
    b. no; it may take less than 10 years
    *c. yes
    d. no; only one of the above is correct

16. Which of the following is NOT a country characterized by large numbers of immigrants?
    a. Australia
    b. United States
    c. Canada
    d. Japan

    a. incorrect; many immigrants
    b. incorrect; many immigrants
    c. incorrect; many immigrants
    *d. correct; few immigrants

17. The greatest annual population growth occurs in
    a. Africa.
    b. South America.
    c. Europe.
    d. Asia.

    *a. yes; greatest
    b. no; second greatest growth
    c. no; least growth
    d. no; intermediate growth

18. Population growth rate is greatest during the
    a. preindustrial stage.
    b. transitional stage.
    c. industrial stage.
    d. postindustrial stage.

    a. no; high birth and death rates with little population growth
    *b. no; high birth rates and low death rates with much population growth
    c. yes; both birth and death rates decline
    d. no; zero population growth is reached

19. Mexico would be classified as a country belonging to the
    a. preindustrial stage.
    b. transitional stage.
    c. industrial stage.
    d. postindustrial stage.

    a. no; underdeveloped countries belong to this stage
    *b. yes
    c. no; not that far advanced
    d. no; not that far advanced

20. If family planning programs were fully successful,
    a. the replacement level in less developed countries would be 2.5/woman.
    b. the replacement level in more developed countries would be 2.1/woman.
    c. it would take 60 years for zero population growth to occur.
    d. all of the above

    a. yes; a partial answer
    b. yes; a partial answer
    c. yes; a partial answer
    *d. yes; all of the above are correct

21. An age-structure population graph of a rapidly growing country
    a. resembles a pyramid with a broad base rather than a diagram with all age classes about the same dimensions.
    b. shows a disproportionate number of males.
    c. shows a relatively small number of people in prereproduction categories and a major increase in the number of those in the reproductive category.
    d. all of the above

    *a. yes
    b. no
    c. no
    d. no; only one of the above is correct

CHAPTER 34
COMMUNITY INTERACTIONS

1. In the rain forests of New Guinea, there are nine different species of pigeons because there are at least nine different _____ in the rain forests.
   a. habitats
   b. nesting sites
   c. niches
   d. fruits or food sources

   a. no; habitats control number of organisms, not number of different species
   b. no; these control amount of reproduction and density of population
   *c. yes; each species has its own distinct niche
   d. no; although fruits and food sources would control population size, and pigeons could feed on more than one food, a better answer is available

2. Along a streambank, a tree squirrel occupies a(n) _____ habitat.
   a. aquatic
   b. arboreal
   c. aerial
   d. disturbed

   a. no; refers to water, such as the organisms in the stream
   *b. yes; arboreal refers to tree, which is where the squirrel lives
   c. no; refers to air (e.g., birds)
   d. no; humans live in disturbed habitats, squirrels in a natural habitat

3. From a community standpoint, diversity refers to the number of different
   a. genotypes.
   b. individuals.
   c. habitats.
   d. species.

   a. no; most likely would be referred to as genetic diversity to avoid confusion
   b. no; most likely would be referred to by the term *density*
   c. no; diversity is a biological feature, not a physical feature, of a community
   *d. yes

4. In a commensal relationship,
   a. both species benefit.
   b. one species gains while the second loses.
   c. one species gains while the second is essentially unaffected.
   d. both species are negatively affected.

   a. no; mutualism
   b. no; parasitism or predation
   *c. yes; by definition
   d. no; competition

5. If the yucca moth were to become extinct, then
   a. some other insect would fill its niche.
   b. the yucca plant would become extinct.
   c. the seeds of the yucca plant would develop without interference from the moth.
   d. nothing else would happen—there simply would be one less species on earth.

   a. no; candidates are not immediately available; it is unlikely that enough time would be available for another insect to fill the niche
   *b. yes; no way for pollination to occur, therefore reproduction could not be accomplished
   c. no; if the yucca moth were extinct, there would be no seeds
   d. no; the yucca plant depends on the yucca moth for its survival

6. The decline in the hare population is caused by
   a. an increase in the number of lynx.
   b. a lack of food for the lynx/hare populations.
   c. stresses to the hares from feeding on toxic plants coupled with increased predation by lynx.
   d. changes in physical factors that are completely independent of biotic considerations.

   a. no; not the critical factor
   b. no; not the critical factor
   *c. yes; toxic plants allow lynx predation to reduce the population size of the hares
   d. no; sometimes may reduce both populations but would not give the typical repeated oscillation pattern

7. The interaction of predator and prey is an example of
   a. disruptive selection.
   b. coevolution.
   c. stabilizing selection.
   d. directional selection.

   a. no; disruptive selection results in two forms of a species such as occurs in sexual dimorphism
   *b. yes; the interaction between species A and species B results in changes in each, resulting in evolution of both
   c. no; stabilizing selection results in reduced variability
   d. no; directional selection involves changes in one population, not an interaction between both populations

8. Which of the following is NOT an example of coevolution?
   a. development of sexual dimorphism in a species
   b. interaction of pollinator and flower
   c. development of parasitism
   d. development of mimicry

   *a. correct; may result from disruptive or differential selection
   b. incorrect; both interact to result in coevolution of both organisms
   c. incorrect; another example of coevolution in which the longer the two are together the less severe is the reaction between them
   d. incorrect; in coevolution, the more noxious the model the more successful the mimic

9. From an evolutionary perspective, the longer a parasite has been associated with a particular host species
    a. the greater number of offspring it will produce.
    b. the more likely it is that the host will develop a defense against the parasite and severe reactions will develop in the host as soon as the parasite enters the host.
    c. the less likely it is that the host will develop any symptoms that indicate the presence of the parasite.
    d. No relationship can be drawn, as the interactions between parasites and hosts are too variable to enable generalizations.

    a. no; there is no relationship between length of host/parasite association and the number of offspring; number of offspring is more likely to be related to the difficulty of the parasite in completing its life cycle
    b. no; it would be a disadvantage to the parasite if the host reacted adversely to its presence
    *c. yes; through coevolution, the longer the two species are together the less likely that symptoms will develop when the host is infected
    d. no; the longer the association the less violent the interaction

10. A brightly colored organism is likely to be
    a. toxic, dangerous, or bad tasting.
    b. a slow-moving, defenseless form.
    c. found in habitats such as caves where its color would not be noticed.
    d. a form of aggressive coloration typical of many predators.

    *a. yes; a predator quickly learns to associate the prey's warning color pattern with negative results, thereby increasing survival chances
    b. no; these defenseless forms would quickly become extinct under unrestricted predation pressure
    c. no; in such habitats, the colors would go unnoticed and not be effective (cave forms are often drab in color, for example)
    d. no; warning coloration is a defense, not an offense; most predators are cryptic (hidden) so they may get close to their prey

11. The reason that water hyacinths became a pest in the Southeast in the twentieth century was
    a. the introduction of the manatee, which destroyed the hyacinth's competitors.
    b. the completion of the intercoastal waterway, which gave the hyacinth access to the entire Southeast.
    c. the lack of any native competitors to keep the hyacinth in check once it was introduced into this country.
    d. the development of many man-made impoundments that provided a new habitat, which enabled hyacinths to flourish.

    a. no; the manatee is actually one animal that reduces the hyacinth population
    b. no; no correlation whatsoever
    *c. yes; typical of exotics that have no natural controls once they become established
    d. no; water hyacinths can become established in any waterway

12. In a community of annual plants, mallow plants
    a. grew where their shallow fibrous roots could extract moisture quickly.
    b. became established early in deep soil where their taproots were effective.
    c. were found in shady areas away from excess heat and drying sunlight.
    d. grew only in areas where the soil was continually wet.

    a. no; mallow plants have a taproot
    *b. yes; the structure of the root system allowed them to dominate areas where early moisture allowed the taproot to become established
    c. no; no information that would support the idea that light was a critical factor controlling distribution or survival
    d. no; not supported by the information given; smartweed was characteristic of the wet areas

13. Parasitoids
    a. are true parasites.
    b. are nonliving viruses that infect and kill their host.
    c. are parasites that are restricted to human hosts.
    d. can be an effective biotic control for some types of pests.

    a. no; they are insect larvae that usually kill their hosts, whereas parasites seldom kill their hosts
    b. no; parasitoids are not viruses, but insect larvae
    c. no; parasitoids seldom infect humans
    *d. yes; more effective than pesticides and pests do not develop resistance to them

14. Which of the following is NOT characteristic of camouflage?
    a. irregular color pattern that masks the shape or characteristics of an organism
    b. patterns that startle or give warning such as a large eyespot
    c. color patterns that resemble the area where the organism is found
    d. modifications in behavior that enable an organism to remain undetected

    a. incorrect; typical camouflage such as patterns painted on warships
    *b. correct; an example of warning coloration
    c. incorrect; typical of well-known animals such as chameleons, anoles, and bottom fish that change to resemble their background
    d. incorrect; behavior has to be modified or camouflage will not be successful; for example, an insect that resembles a twig must be motionless or it will be eaten

15. Pioneer species are characterized by all but which of the following? They are
    a. small plants with numerous seeds that are easily dispersed.
    b. often symbiotic with nitrogen-fixing soil microbes.
    c. perennial plants that can store energy to gain advantage in competition early in the growing season.
    d. small low-growing plants that often start from scratch at the beginning of the growing season.

    a. incorrect; characteristic of pioneers; need to be able to reach areas where succession is beginning
    b. incorrect; characteristic of pioneers; there is little or no nitrogen in a bare area where succession starts
    *c. correct; not characteristic of pioneers, but of later stages in succession; these features would enable these plants to outcompete early successional species in a mature community
    d. incorrect; characteristic of pioneers; typical of plants in early successional stages

16. If you pinched the straw of a friend sharing a small milkshake with you, you would be exhibiting
    a. competitive exclusion.
    b. interference competition.
    c. exploitation competition.
    d. interspecific competition.

    a. no; both are able to get to the resource—neither will die out from the action
    *b. yes; pinching the straw interferes with your friend getting the milkshake
    c. no; does not deny the resource to competitors
    d. no; humans are members of the same species

CHAPTER 35
ECOSYSTEMS

1. An ecosystem is a
   a. complex of organisms and their physical environment.
   b. group of interacting organisms sharing the same habitat.
   c. group of interbreeding organisms sharing the same gene pool.
   d. group of interacting physical factors found in an environment surrounding a community.

   *a. yes; by definition
   b. no; a community
   c. no; a species
   d. no; leaves out the biotic component and not broad enough

2. Which of the following groups gets energy from partly decomposed organic material?
   a. decomposers
   b. detritivores
   c. parasites
   d. omnivores

   a. no; extract energy from the remains or products of organisms
   *b. yes
   c. no; the food source for parasites is definitely living
   d. no; this group feeds on anything

3. Which of the following includes earthworms, crabs, and nematodes?
   a. decomposers
   b. detritivores
   c. parasites
   d. omnivores

   a. no; fungi and bacteria
   *b. yes; extract energy from partially decomposed material
   c. no; include tapeworms, flukes, and ectoparasites
   d. no; include humans, primates, and some birds

4. Which group secures nutrients and energy for the ecosystem?
   a. producers
   b. decomposers
   c. consumers
   d. detritivores

   *a. yes; plants store food energy through photosynthesis and supply minerals
   b. no; function in the cycling of elements but don't supply food
   c. no; use both nutrients and energy, but don't supply food
   d. no; use fragments and partially decomposed material

5. Which of the following is true?
   a. Ecosystems are closed systems.
   b. Nutrient input equals nutrient output in all ecosystems.
   c. Ecosystems are self-sustaining.
   d. Energy output from an ecosystem occurs as low-grade energy (heat).

   a. no; energy is externally supplied
   b. no; for example, eutrophic lakes have an excess input of nutrients
   c. no; require input of energy
   *d. yes

6. Primary producers
   a. are the members of the ecosystem closest to the energy source.
   b. include photosynthetic autotrophs.
   c. form the base of any food chain or pyramid.
   d. all of the above

   a. yes; a partial answer
   b. yes; a partial answer
   c. yes; a partial answer
   *d. yes; all of the above are correct

7. The stem of the word *trophic* means
   a. turn.
   b. level or group.
   c. food.
   d. none of the above

   a. no; tropism means a growth toward or away from a stimulus, but it does not have the "h" of troph-
   b. no; a word used with trophic
   *c. yes
   d. no; one of the above is correct

8. Net primary productivity is controlled by
   a. gross primary productivity.
   b. the rate of autotrophic respiration.
   c. the activity of consumers and decomposers.
   d. all of the above

   a. yes; a partial answer; gross primary productivity determines the amount of energy fixed
   b. yes; a partial answer; the rate of autotrophic respiration reduces the amount of energy that can be stored
   c. yes; a partial answer; the feeding of consumers and decomposers determines the amount of energy available to be stored
   *d. yes; all of the above are correct

9. Gross primary productivity is controlled by
   a. the activity of living organisms other than plants.
   b. the amount of sunlight received.
   c. other physical environmental factors.
   d. both (b) and (c)

   a. no; other organisms may affect net primary productivity but not gross (which is controlled by the plant)
   b. yes; a partial answer; the energy source determines how much is available for photosynthesis
   c. yes; a partial answer; other physical factors such as rainfall and temperature could affect the rate of photosynthesis
   *d. yes; both (b) and (c) are correct

10. Which of the following is true?
    a. Heat loss represents a one-way flow of energy out of an ecosystem.
    b. In grazing food webs, the energy flows from plants through decomposers and detritivores.
    c. In detrital food webs, energy flows from plants to herbivores and then to carnivores.
    d. all of the above

    *a. correct; this statement is true; there is no way to capture this loss
    b. incorrect; this statement is false; refers to detrital food web
    c. incorrect; this statement is false; refers to grazing food webs
    d. incorrect; only one of the above is true

11. The most accurate representation of the trophic structure of an ecosystem is a pyramid
    a. with four trophic levels.
    b. of numbers.
    c. of biomass.
    d. of energy.

    a. no; the number of trophic levels varies for different ecosystems
    b. no; this pyramid could be inverted if large trees were considered
    c. no; this pyramid could be inverted if large trees were considered
    *d. yes; indicates the amount of energy available in each trophic level

12. In discussing energy flow, energy inputs are measured in terms of energy per unit of
    a. weight.
    b. time.
    c. land.
    d. both (b) and (c)

    a. no; amount of energy varies from one organism to another depending on factors such as type of tissue and metabolic rate
    b. yes; a partial answer
    c. yes; a partial answer
    *d. yes; for example, kilocalories per square meter per year

13. About _____ percent of the energy available at one trophic level is transferred to the next.
    a. 1–5
    b. 6–16
    c. 17–23
    d. 25 or more

    a. no; too little
    *b. yes
    c. no; too much
    d. no; too much

14. In nutrient cycling in an ecosystem,
    a. the nutrients being recycled are organic compounds such as fats, carbohydrates, and so on.
    b. the amount of nutrient being recycled is usually less than the amount entering or leaving an ecosystem in a year's time.
    c. environmental inputs include rainfall, snowfall, sedimentation, metabolism, and the physical and chemical weathering of rocks.
    d. the nutrients being recycled are controlled primarily by the producers and consumers found in the ecosystem.

    a. no; nutrients are mineral ions
    b. no; the opposite of this statement is true
    *c. yes
    d. no; controlled primarily by the decomposers and detritivores

15. Carbon dioxide enters the atmosphere from
    a. volcanic eruptions.
    b. respiration.
    c. combustion.
    d. all of the above

    a. yes; a partial answer
    b. yes; a partial answer
    c. yes; a partial answer
    *d. yes; all of the above are correct

16. The nutrient that influences the growth of land plants that is in shortest supply is
    a. carbon.
    b. nitrogen.
    c. phosphorus.
    d. potassium.

    a. no
    *b. yes
    c. no
    d. no

17. Nitrogen is lost to the atmosphere during
    a. ammonification.
    b. nitrification.
    c. denitrification.
    d. nitrogen fixation.

    a. no; nitrogen compounds broken down into ammonia
    b. no; ammonia converted into nitrite or nitrate
    *c. yes; nitrate converted into nitrogen gas that may be lost
    d. no; nitrogen gas converted into ammonia

18. Nitrogen scarcity may be attributed to
    a. denitrification.
    b. leaching from soil.
    c. waterlogging of the soil, which causes decomposers to convert fixed nitrogen to nitrogen gas.
    d. all of the above

    a. yes; a partial answer
    b. yes; a partial answer
    c. yes; a partial answer
    *d. yes; all of the above are correct

19. Plants that are symbiotic participants in nitrogen fixation with nitrogen bacteria belong to the _____ family.
    a. mint
    b. rose
    c. legume
    d. all of the above

    a. no
    b. no
    *c. yes; only legumes seem to have this ability
    d. no; only one of the above is correct

20. DDT
    a. is insoluble in water and soluble in fat.
    b. builds up in concentration as it moves through a food chain.
    c. is a target-specific insecticide.
    d. both (a) and (b)

    a. yes; a partial answer
    b. yes; a partial answer; this is known as biological magnification
    c. no; not target specific and may affect any organism that comes in contact with it
    *d. yes; both (a) and (b) are correct

21. The use of DDT in Borneo
    a. enabled humans to swap malaria for sylvatic plague.
    b. benefited the small lizards living in the village.
    c. was resolved by bringing in more of the native cats to the villages.
    d. killed the caterpillars that lived on the thatched huts of the villagers.

    *a. yes
    b. no; the lizards were killed
    c. no; parachuting cats worked to control the rats
    d. no; DDT killed the wasps that kept the thatch-eating caterpillars under control

CHAPTER 36
THE BIOSPHERE

1. Climate is influenced by
   a. topography and distribution of land and water.
   b. variations in the amount of incoming solar radiation.
   c. the earth's daily rotation and its yearly path around the sun.
   d. all of the above

   a. yes; a partial answer
   b. yes; a partial answer
   c. yes; a partial answer
   *d. yes; all of the above are correct

2. The global air circulation that influences weather occurs in the
   a. troposphere.
   b. stratosphere.
   c. ionosphere.
   d. mesosphere.

   *a. yes; name means "turning sphere"; the movement of atmosphere in this layer is responsible for our weather
   b. no; some circulation and mixing do occur here but do not produce major effects on weather
   c. no; variations here may affect communications, but generally not the weather
   d. no; movement here does not affect the weather

3. Deserts occur at about 30 degrees north and south of the equator because
   a. of the prevailing easterly and westerly winds.
   b. of the subsidence (falling) of dry air that had risen over the tropics.
   c. a belt of high temperature persists in these two regions of the world.
   d. none of the above

   a. no; the east-west movement of air is not the major contributing factor
   *b. yes; the global circulation pattern brings dry air down to the earth's surface at these latitudes
   c. no; the lack of moisture, not the high temperature, produces the deserts
   d. no; one of the above is correct

4. The Northern Hemisphere is warmer in the summertime for all but which of the following reasons?
   a. The angle at which the light strikes the earth is more direct during the summer.
   b. The amount of atmosphere that the light must travel through is less in the summer.
   c. The length of the day is longer.
   d. The sun is closer to the earth.

   a. incorrect; the more direct or perpendicular the sun the warmer the temperature; thus the sun warms up at noon, but highest temperatures occur later in the day
   b. incorrect; the light is more direct so there is less atmosphere to absorb the energy
   c. incorrect; the longer the sun is up the more energy strikes the earth and can be absorbed
   *d. correct; even though the text does not point this out, the sun is actually closer to the earth in the wintertime, but the difference is negligible

5. Warm ocean currents are found on the
   a. western coast of the United States.
   b. western coast of Africa.
   c. eastern coast of the United States.
   d. western coast of South America.

   a. no; a cold current, the California current
   b. no; a cold current, the Benguela current
   *c. yes; the Gulf Stream
   d. no; a cold current, the Humboldt

6. Which of the following statements is true?
   a. The rain shadow appears on the leeward side of the mountain.
   b. The vegetation at the top of the mountain is likely to consist of drought-adapted plants.
   c. Drought is characteristic of the windward side of the mountain.
   d. all of the above

   *a. correct; this statement is true; the descending air warms and can hold more moisture so
      that rain is less likely
   b. incorrect; this statement is false; orographic precipitation provides water; as the wet air
      rises it cools and releases water
   c. incorrect; this statement is false; the windward side is the side of the mountain closest to
      the water source (even though there may be water on the leeward side of the mountain,
      the prevailing winds would carry it away from the mountain)
   d. incorrect; only one of the above is correct

7. Short, stunted plant species tend to be found in
   a. cold, dry latitudes at high elevations.
   b. lowlands with moderate temperature and moisture.
   c. tropical areas.
   d. wetlands with warm temperatures.

   *a. yes; this type of plant would be expected to be found in such a habitat
   b. no; more likely intermediate-sized plants
   c. no; usually characterized by luxuriant growth
   d. no; usually characterized by luxuriant growth

8. Which of the following statements is true?
   a. Clay soils are often characterized by excessive leaching.
   b. Clay soils have rapid percolation.
   c. Loam is a mixture of sand, silt, clay, and humus.
   d. The soil of tropical rain forests is characterized by a rich nutrient load.

   a. incorrect; this statement is false; more likely to be waterlogged
   b. incorrect; this statement is false; characteristic of sandy loose soils
   *c. correct; this statement is true
   d. incorrect; this statement is false; very low nutrient content because rainwater promotes
      much leaching

9. The biome characterized by spectacularly flowering annuals and perennials, prickly pear, ocotillo, mesquite, and creosote bush is the
    a. desert.
    b. dry shrubland and woodlands.
    c. prairie.
    d. deciduous forest

   *a. yes
    b. no; characterized by chaparral
    c. no; characterized by grasses
    d. no; characterized by trees that shed their leaves

10. The biome characterized by winter rains and fire during dry periods is the
    a. shortgrass prairie.
    b. chaparral.
    c. desert.
    d. deciduous forest.

    a. no
   *b. yes
    c. no
    d. no

11. Most tallgrass prairies
    a. have scattered trees.
    b. were destroyed by the Dust Bowl.
    c. have been converted to farmland.
    d. exhibit a monsoon climate.

    a. no; scattered trees occur in wet, tropical grasslands; there may be trees along streambanks
    b. no; Dust Bowl occurred in the shortgrass prairie
   *c. yes
    d. no; characteristic of tropical grasslands

12. Evergreen broadleaf forests occur in all but which of the following locations?
    a. South and Central America
    b. Australia
    c. Africa
    d. East Indies and Malay Archipelago

    a. incorrect; found here
   *b. correct; not found in Australia
    c. incorrect; found here
    d. incorrect; found here

13. The biome characterized by bromeliads, vines, mosses, lichens, orchids, and aerial plants is the
    a. desert.
    b. tropical rain forest.
    c. temperate deciduous forest.
    d. savanna.

    a. no; requires drought-resistant plants
   *b. yes; covers the upper strata of the "jungle"
    c. no; not warm enough or moist enough to support such plants
    d. no; a grassland with scattered trees

14. The biome that occupies much of southern and mid Canada is the
    a. temperate deciduous forest.
    b. tundra.
    c. evergreen coniferous forest.
    d. chaparral.

    a. no; broad-leaved trees do not grow as well in the snow as conifers do
    b. no; found in the northern part of Canada
    *c. yes
    d. no; in North America, found primarily in California

15. The tundra is
    a. characterized by evergreen trees.
    b. dominated by spruce and fir.
    c. found above the Arctic Circle and above the treeline of high mountains.
    d. one of the most productive biomes.

    a. no; trees occurring in the tundra are dwarf spruce and willow (*tundra* means treeless plain)
    b. no; dominant plants are lichens
    *c. yes; the arctic and alpine tundra, respectively
    d. no; very low productivity due to poor growing conditions

16. The lake zone close to shore is the
    a. limnetic.
    b. profundal.
    c. thermocline.
    d. none of the above

    a. no; open sunlit areas beyond the littoral zone
    b. no; the deep portion of the lake where it is too dark for photosynthesis to occur
    c. no; the zone of temperature change in a thermally stratified lake
    *d. yes; none of the above is correct; the lake zone close to shore is the littoral zone

17. Overturns occur in a lake during which season?
    a. spring
    b. summer
    c. winter
    d. both (b) and (c)

    *a. yes; when the lake warms up to 4°C, the water on the bottom exchanges places with water on top (also occurs in the fall)
    b. no; a thermocline has been established
    c. no; no change until sufficient heat has been added
    d. no; only one of the above is correct

18. Eutrophication
    a. is characterized by a dense bloom of algae.
    b. occurs naturally as lakes age.
    c. can result from pollution of water with sewage or wastes containing nitrogen and/or phosphorus.
    d. all of the above

    a. yes; a partial answer
    b. yes; a partial answer
    c. yes; a partial answer
    *d. yes; all of the above are correct

19. An estuary
    a. is part fresh water and part marine.
    b. is an area of low productivity and is of little value.
    c. often contains *Spartina,* a salt-tolerant marsh grass that is the base of detrital food webs.
    d. both (a) and (c)

    a. yes; a partial answer; the mixing place for fresh water from rivers with salt water from oceans
    b. no; highly productive area, often the area that forms the cradle and bread basket for marine life
    c. yes; a partial answer; often *Spartina* forms large marshes in the estuaries
    *d. yes; both (a) and (c) are correct

20. Diversity is greatest in the
    a. upper littoral zone of a rocky shore.
    b. mid-littoral zone of a rocky shore.
    c. lower littoral zone of a rocky shore.
    d. all of the above; no variation in life is found in the three zones

    a. no; environment is harsh and many animals die of desiccation or become baked by the sun
    b. no
    *c. yes; most protected zone and exposed only at the lowest tide
    d. no; only one of the above is correct

21. The relatively shallow waters overlying the continental shelf form the
    a. neritic zone.
    b. pelagic province.
    c. oceanic zone.
    d. benthic province.

    *a. yes
    b. no; includes the entire volume of ocean water
    c. no; the water over the ocean basins
    d. no; all sediments and rocky formations of the ocean bottom

22. In the neritic and oceanic zones, the photosynthetic organisms form a suspended pasture of food that provides food directly for
    a. fish.
    b. zooplankton.
    c. detritivores.
    d. carnivores.

    a. no
    *b. yes; zooplankton represent the trophic level next to the phytoplankton
    c. no; usually these are found on the ocean floor
    d. no; feed on herbivores, the zooplankton in this case

23. The producers in the hydrothermal vent community
    a. use sunlight as their primary energy source.
    b. use energy from chemical reactions involving hydrogen sulfide.
    c. lack any significant carnivorous predators.
    d. are similar to species found in the phytoplankton at the surface.

    a. no; too deep and dark to depend on this energy source
    *b. yes
    c. no; carnivores in this community include clams, mussels, tubeworms
    d. no; these are chemosynthetic forms, whereas the surface forms are photosynthetic

24. Upwelling
    a. occurs in the oceans along the margins of continents as a result of wind patterns.
    b. brings colder, nutrient-rich water to the surface.
    c. supports a rich phytoplankton population that in turn supports a rich fish population.
    d. all of the above

    a. yes; a partial answer
    b. yes; a partial answer
    c. yes; a partial answer
    *d. yes; all of the above are correct

CHAPTER 37

HUMAN IMPACT ON THE BIOSPHERE

1. Which of the following is NOT one of the major factors responsible for the growth of the human population?
   a. agricultural revolution
   b. industrial revolution
   c. medical revolution
   d. green revolution

   a. incorrect; the development of agriculture led to the first major expansion of the human population
   b. incorrect; the industrial revolution provided the energy to increase agricultural production
   c. incorrect; the ability to reduce mortality rates led to exponential growth of the human population
   *d. correct; the green revolution has not led to major increases in human population

2. Which of the following continents is characterized by the least population growth and little increase in individual resource consumption in the last couple of decades?
   a. North America
   b. Africa
   c. Asia
   d. South America

   *a. yes; rate of population growth and resource consumption had already stabilized at a high level
   b. no; high rate of population growth and resource consumption
   c. no; high rate of population growth and resource consumption
   d. no; high rate of population growth and resource consumption

3. The problems discussed in this chapter will be resolved
   a. only by stabilizing population.
   b. by realizing that reversing current damaging trends outweighs the personal benefits of ignoring them.
   c. only through individual efforts and sacrifices, not by group activity.
   d. very quickly, once education makes enough people realize the magnitude of the problem.

   a. no; not necessarily the solution because some affluent societies expend many more resources than do the LDCs (less developed countries)
   *b. yes; a philosophical change in viewpoint is necessary to resolve the problems
   c. no; only if enough individuals are involved; much more likely to accomplish goals by appealing to groups, leading to changes in popular opinion and individual support
   d. no; it's not enough to make people aware of the problem; they must be motivated to change their habits

4. The most general definition of pollutants includes the concept that pollutants are
   a. substances with which ecosystems have no prior experience.
   b. any artificial substances released into the ecosystem.
   c. fat-soluble chemicals that build up in food chains.
   d. inorganic chemicals such as toxic heavy metals.

   *a. yes; there has not been sufficient time for ecosystems to develop a way to degrade or destroy these substances
   b. no; some artificial substances such as inorganic fertilizers can cycle through an ecosystem
   c. no; this is characteristic of chlorinated hydrocarbons such as DDT
   d. no; although these are often pollutants, this definition is too limited

5. Which of the following is NOT an organic pollutant?
   a. methane
   b. peroxyacyl nitrate
   c. benzene
   d. chlorofluorocarbon

   a. incorrect; an organic hydrocarbon
   *b. correct; does not contain carbon
   c. incorrect; a six-carbon hydrocarbon that is usually one of the first compounds considered in an organic chemistry course
   d. incorrect; an organic compound

6. The major cause for photochemical smog is
   a. nitrous oxides from cars and trucks.
   b. carbon monoxide and carbon dioxide from combustion.
   c. sulfur dioxide from coal-fired power plants.
   d. chlorofluorocarbons.

   *a. yes; react with sunlight and hydrocarbons to form photochemical smog
   b. no; do not react with sunlight to form photochemical smog
   c. no; involved more in acid deposition than in photochemical smog
   d. no; involved in ozone destruction

7. The 1952 air pollution disaster that killed 4,000 people occurred in
   a. Pittsburgh.
   b. London.
   c. Chicago.
   d. New York.

   a. no
   *b. yes; caused by industrial smog (use of high-sulfur coal)
   c. no
   d. no

8. Which of the following is true about acid deposition?
   a. It is produced by coal-fired power plants, industrial plants, and metal smelters.
   b. It reaches the ground only when the sulfur and nitrous oxides combine with water in the atmosphere to form acid rain.
   c. It is equally damaging regardless of where it occurs.
   d. It affects only living organisms.

   *a. correct; this statement is true; these are the major sources
   b. incorrect; this statement is false; dry acid deposition is common
   c. incorrect; this statement is false; some areas are very sensitive, whereas others have alkaline soils that will help buffer the damaging effects
   d. incorrect; this statement is false; a common cause in the destruction of statues, metals, mortar, rubber, plastic, and nylon stockings

9. Acid rain is a major problem in the _____ part of North America.
   a. northwestern
   b. southwestern
   c. northeastern
   d. southeastern

   a. no
   b. no
   *c. yes; because of the concentration of industries and prevailing winds
   d. no

10. Chlorofluorocarbons are released from
    a. aerosol propellants.
    b. coolants in refrigeration and air conditioning units.
    c. the process involved in the formation of Styrofoam and packaging material.
    d. all of the above

    a. yes; a partial answer
    b. yes; a partial answer
    c. yes; a partial answer
    *d. yes; all of the above are correct

11. In primary sewage treatment,
    a. sludge is filtered from the water and is treated with chlorine.
    b. microbial populations break down organic matter.
    c. waste water is trickled through gravel or aerated.
    d. reverse osmosis, stripping nitrogen from ammonia, and use of ultrasonic energy vibration may be involved.

    *a. yes; primary treatment
    b. no; secondary treatment
    c. no; secondary treatment
    d. no; tertiary treatment

12. The major component of solid waste is
    a. plastic.
    b. garbage.
    c. paper products.
    d. glass.

    a. no
    b. no
    *c. yes; over 50 percent of solid waste
    d. no

13. Modern agriculture employs massive use of
    a. pesticides.
    b. fossil fuels.
    c. fertilizers.
    d. all of the above

    a. yes; a partial answer
    b. yes; a partial answer
    c. yes; a partial answer
    *d. yes; all of the above are correct

14. Tropical rain forests are characterized by all but which one of the following?
    a. rich source of nutrients in the understory
    b. slash-and-burn agriculture
    c. the richest and most diverse flora and fauna in the world
    d. an extremely rapid rate of extinction

    *a. correct; not characteristic of tropical rain forests; very little nutrients available anywhere in this ecosystem
    b. incorrect; this is a characteristic; efforts to provide more food lead to cutting and burning the ecosystem
    c. incorrect; this is a characteristic; there are more species here than in the rest of the world
    d. incorrect; this is a characteristic; more and more species become extinct each day as the ecosystem is exploited

CHAPTER 38
ANIMAL BEHAVIOR

1. Animal behavior involves the
   a. nervous system.
   b. skeletal-muscular system.
   c. endocrine system.
   d. all of the above

   a. yes; a partial answer
   b. yes; a partial answer
   c. yes; a partial answer
   *d. yes; all of the above are correct

2. Which of the following is false?
   a. Behavior differences may be controlled by one gene.
   b. There is a genetic component to behavior.
   c. For a bird to learn its song, it must hear the song during development.
   d. Hormones affect the internal environment of an organism but do not have an effect on its behavior.

   a. incorrect; this statement is true; textbook gives the example of sparrow songs that could be affected by one gene
   b. incorrect; this statement is true; to be able to respond to certain signals, organisms must be capable of recognizing signals
   c. incorrect; this statement is true; in the textbook example, the white-crowned birds were unable to sing their songs because they did not hear them during development
   *d. correct; this statement is false; hormones are responsible for sexual maturation and animals are not aware of sex signals until they mature

3. Melatonin
   a. is secreted by the parathyroid gland.
   b. suppresses the growth and function of the gonads.
   c. increase and the lack of sunlight in the winter trigger the migration of birds.
   d. levels increase in the spring and initiate sexual reproduction.

   a. no; secreted by the pineal gland
   *b. yes; for reproduction to occur, the levels of melatonin must drop
   c. no; migration is not controlled in this manner
   d. no; melatonin levels drop in the spring, allowing gonads to develop

4. The ability (not the trigger) of the male bird to sing is controlled by
   a. melatonin.
   b. estrogen.
   c. testosterone.
   d. insulin.

   a. no; sexual maturity
   *b. yes; for the development of brain and sound system
   c. no; testosterone is a triggering mechanism
   d. no; does not have any responsibility in singing

5. Which of the following is false?
    a. Humans do not exhibit instinctive behavior.
    b. Male stickleback fish attack red objects.
    c. Young cuckoo birds will push other eggs out of a nest.
    d. Human infants will smile at any mask with dark eyespots.

    *a. correct; this statement is false because humans do exhibit instinctive behavior
    b. incorrect; this statement is true; male sticklebacks are red
    c. incorrect; this statement is true; cuckoos lay eggs in other birds' nests and the young cuckoos simply get rid of potential competition by eliminating eggs
    d. incorrect; this statement is true; an example of human instinctive behavior

6. Which of the following is false?
    a. Genetics determines which behavior patterns are possible.
    b. Dogs can learn to associate a bell with food.
    c. There is a limit to the ability of lower animals to learn; for example, earthworms are unable to learn to run a maze.
    d. Chimpanzees are able to learn by insight.

    a. incorrect; this statement is true; genetics imposes limits on the type of behavior an organism can exhibit
    b. incorrect; this statement is true; Pavlov's classical example of conditioned learning
    *c. correct; the statement is true, but the example is false because worms can learn to run a maze
    d. incorrect; this statement is true; a chimpanzee can build a structure to reach a reward

7. Imprinting involves
    a. failure to respond to unimportant stimuli; for example, a dog learns to ignore its master banging his pipe as he cleans it.
    b. young birds adopting large moving objects as their parents.
    c. reflex actions.
    d. development of an internal clock.

    a. no; this is known as habituation
    *b. yes; the object may be another species; or young birds may even imprint on humans
    c. no; imprinting is learned, not reflex, behavior
    d. no; the internal clock is independent of imprinting

8. Altruistic behavior is best defined as
    a. innate behavior.
    b. selfish behavior.
    c. self-sacrificing behavior.
    d. learned behavior.

    a. no; though some altruistic behavior may be innate
    b. no
    *c. yes; similar to the golden rule
    d. no; perhaps partially learned, partially instinctive

9. Newborn garter snakes from the interior of California
    a. preferred banana slugs to tadpoles.
    b. rejected banana slugs because they tasted similar to leeches.
    c. were the offspring of snakes that were not killed by eating leeches.
    d. both (b) and (c).

    a. no; those from the coastal area preferred banana slugs
    b. yes; a partial answer
    c. yes; a partial answer
    *d. yes; both (b) and (c) are correct

10. A heron stands motionless and holds its wings outstretched because
    a. this tends to hide the heron from the prey it feeds on.
    b. this enables the heron to see the prey better.
    c. the shadow produced in this way attracts prey.
    d. both (a) and (c)

    a. no; actually, this behavior should make the bird *more* visible
    b. no; may increase visibility, but this is not the reason for the behavior
    *c. yes; the behavior causes prey to accommodate
    d. no; only one of the above is correct

11. For birds, singing
    a. is a way for a male to attract a female.
    b. is a method of establishing a territory.
    c. reduces the number of conflicts between male birds.
    d. all of the above

    a. yes; a partial answer
    b. yes; a partial answer
    c. yes; a partial answer
    *d. yes; all of the above are correct

12. Which of the following species does NOT produce female defense behavior?
    a. lions
    b. elks
    c. red-winged blackbirds
    d. sage grouse

    a. incorrect; exhibit clustering behavior
    b. incorrect; exhibit clustering behavior
    c. incorrect; exhibit clustering behavior
    *d. correct; no harem involved

13. Nasute termites of Australia defend themselves with
    a. large jaw pinchers.
    b. strands of glue.
    c. noxious odors.
    d. retractable stingers.

    a. no
    *b. yes
    c. no
    d. no

14. Fireflies indicate sexual readiness by using
    a. flashes of light.
    b. chemical pheromones.
    c. acoustical signals.
    d. all of the above

    *a. yes
    b. no; not used by fireflies
    c. no; do not use sounds to communicate
    d. no; only one of the above is correct

15. Which of the following organisms are strongly cued by tactile signals?
    a. majority of birds
    b. honeybees
    c. bats
    d. wolves

    a. no
    *b. yes
    c. no
    d. no

16. Altruism leads to
    a. natural selection.
    b. kin selection.
    c. disruptive selection.
    d. none of the above

    a. no; natural selection may favor altruism, but altruism does not necessarily lead to natural selection (the less alert may be saved by altruistic behavior)
    *b. yes; altruistic behavior may save close relatives thereby allowing related genes to be passed on to the next generation
    c. no; there is no specific altruistic behavior that would result in developing disruptive selection
    d. no; one of the above is correct

17. Which of the following does NOT commit suicide in defending other members of its species?
    a. soldier termites
    b. bees
    c. spiders
    d. ants

    a. incorrect; commit suicide in defending others
    b. incorrect; commit suicide in defending others
    *c. correct; mostly nonsocial and do not defend other spiders
    d. incorrect; commit suicide in defending others

18. In insects
    a. suicidal behavior is adaptive.
    b. sterility is adaptive.
    c. close relatives benefit from kin selection.
    d. all of the above

    a. yes; a partial answer
    b. yes; a partial answer
    c. yes; a partial answer
    *d. yes; all of the above are correct